WORCESTER PORCELAIN
The Klepser Collection

WORCESTER PORCELAIN

The Klepser Collection

Simon Spero

Foreword by Henry Sandon

The Minneapolis Institute of Arts
in association with
Lund Humphries Publishers
London

Copyright © 1984 by The Minneapolis Institute of Arts
Photographs copyright © 1984 by Paul Macapia
All rights reserved

First edition 1984
Published by
Lund Humphries Publishers Ltd
26 Litchfield Street London WC2H 9NJ
and
The Minneapolis Institute of Arts
2400 Third Avenue South
Minneapolis, MN 55404

Trade orders to Lund Humphries Publishers

ISBN 0 85331 486 1

Catalogue photographs by Paul Macapia,
photographer, Seattle Art Museum

Designed by Graham Johnson

Made and printed in Great Britain
by Balding + Mansell Limited, Wisbech, Cambridgeshire

Contents

Acknowledgements

Over the years The Minneapolis Institute of Arts has assembled an important collection of decorative arts: English, American, and Italian silver, French and Italian furniture, a number of period rooms. Although its ceramics holdings include an extraordinary collection of French faïence and some excellent examples of Sèvres, the collection as a whole remains uneven, with little representation of the English factories in particular. The possibility of cataloguing and exhibiting the Klepser collection of Worcester porcelain, therefore, was met with enthusiasm by the staff of the Institute and the Board of the Minneapolis Society of Fine Arts.

I first visited Priscilla and Kenneth Klepser in the summer of 1979. The rarities of early Worcester porcelain assembled in their apartment were remarkable, particularly the wares of the 1750s, so often overlooked by collectors who are enticed by the refinement of the coloured grounds of the 1760s and 1770s. Kenneth Klepser was equally impressive. His description of the development of the collection revealed a methodical, determined, patient enthusiasm that I soon realised mirrored his personality as a whole. Having begun by collecting blue and white wares, he later expanded the scope of his interests to include the coloured grounds (notably the so-called 'named services') and finally concentrated on the pieces produced in the 1750s. This focus and progression distinguished him as a collector. In mastering the study of Worcester porcelain he came to view the early years of growth and experiment at the factory as essential in understanding his chosen field of interest. As I read portions of his correspondence with the English dealer T. Leonard Crow, his acquisitions came to life in a way that I knew would be of interest to other collectors. I hoped that eventually I would have an opportunity of working closely with Kenneth Klepser to produce a catalogue of his collection, but his 1981 death precluded that. This book has become a posthumous tribute to him.

There are many people who have helped The Minneapolis Institute of Arts in this endeavour. Joseph and Elizabeth Handley first introduced me to the Klepsers and their porcelain collection, and they have continued to be loyal supporters of the project as the years progressed. This catalogue would not have been possible without their help. The cooperation of Arnold Jolles and the registraral staff of the Seattle Art Museum under Gail Joice has been invaluable in realising the project. I want also to give a special thanks to Julie Emerson, Seattle's Assistant Curator of Decorative Arts, for her constant advice in organising the exhibition. The special care Seattle's photographer, Paul Macapia, has given to the project has resulted in the excellent images of the publication. Louise Lincoln has carefully and thoughtfully edited the catalogue for The Minneapolis Institute of Arts and she, along with John Taylor and the staff of Lund Humphries Publishers, are responsible for its successful completion. Henry Sandon has very kindly written a foreword to the catalogue and I thank him for making his perceptions in the field of Worcester porcelain available to us. Simon Spero has been involved in the project in innumerable ways and his scrupulous cataloguing of the Klepser objects has significantly advanced scholarship in the field. I have enjoyed working with him closely and I am

6

grateful for the intelligence, enthusiasm and the unfailing seriousness he has given to all aspects of this catalogue and its production.

No publication of Kenneth Klepser's collection would have been possible without the support of Priscilla Klepser, who permitted her own activities as poet and writer to be continually interrupted by the mechanics of the catalogue and exhibition process. She allowed these inconveniences to honour the achievement of her husband, and her guidance and loyalty throughout the endeavour have been of immeasurable value. It is only through her intelligence, patience, and support that this catalogue has been so successfully realised.

Michael Conforti
Bell Memorial Curator of Decorative Arts and Sculpture
The Minneapolis Institute of Arts

In writing this catalogue, I have been very fortunate in the advice, support and encouragement of many friends, collectors and business colleagues. I would like to offer especial thanks to Joseph Handley, whose enthusiasm and humanity were responsible for initiating this enterprise and who has been a constant source of encouragement. I speak for Kenneth and Priscilla Klepser, as well as myself, in saying that no one could wish for a truer and more steadfast friend. I would also like to thank Paul Macapia for his patience and for his outstanding photographs, Peter Macapia who did the printing for the monochrome plates, Anton Gabszewicz who has been so generous with his time and his advice in reading the proofs of this book, and the production team at Lund Humphries of John Taylor, Graham Johnson and Charlotte Burri who have been so easy and helpful to work with.

Michael Conforti has had the daunting task of coordinating the production of this catalogue, written in London and illustrated in Seattle, six thousand miles away. His support, advice and not least, his sense of humour, have been invaluable. I would like to express my thanks to Henry Sandon who wrote the foreword to this catalogue with his customary efficiency, vitality and perception. Nigel Cooke has generously made available to me all his information about the dated pieces of blue and white Worcester and his contribution to this catalogue can be seen in the list in Appendix B. I would also like to thank A.J. Smith for his friendship and advice which I value greatly.

Others who have helped in many ways are:
Mrs Betty Balcom, Mr Percy Crow, Miss Aileen Dawson of the British Museum, Mrs Julie Emerson, Mr Harry Frost of the Dyson Perrins Museum, Mrs Anne George, Dr Paul Riley, Dr Bernard Watney, Mr Robert Williams and Mr Anthony Wood.

Throughout every stage in the planning and writing of this catalogue, Priscilla Klepser has given freely of her time and her wisdom and it has been much appreciated. I am also much indebted to the late Kenneth Klepses and offer the hope that this book is all that he would have wished it to be.

Lastly, I would offer my thanks to my family, to my wife Diane who has worked hard for the making of this book, to my son Christopher who has been very understanding and my daughter Miranda who was born during the writing of it.

Simon Spero

7

Foreword by Henry Sandon

When I was asked to write the foreword to a catalogue of the Klepser collection my mind flew across the width of the Atlantic and the breadth of the United States to see again that little corner of Worcestershire in Seattle, the apartment of Kenneth and Priscilla Klepser. To say that my wife and myself were overwhelmed by our visit to the Klepsers would not be an exaggeration – not so much by the collection of early Worcester porcelain (although, as this catalogue demonstrates, it was of impressive quality) but by the incredible aura of joy that pervaded the place. It was not a large nor flashy apartment but had a simple charm and as we sat there regaled with the nicest cup of tea that we had been presented with in America and ate sandwiches that could not have been bettered in the finest London hotel, I pondered on the three things that in my opinion impel the true collector of Worcester porcelain: the excitement of the building up of the collection, the pleasure to be had in living with it, and the joy in being able to share it with others.

What delight it was to talk to them about their collection. Each piece had a fascinating story behind it, and to see Kenneth pick up a creamjug and enthuse about the shape or the decoration was to realise the love that was there. The gorgeously coloured wares and the 'named services' were justly prized by the Klepsers but just as much loved were the fantastic little pieces of the earliest Bristol/Worcester period that filled the five shelves of a wall cabinet, which will remain in my mind's eye for evermore. The Klepsers were very proud of these and it was fascinating to realise that they had been bought at a time when such simple pieces were out of favour. Really only Dyson Perrins was actively pursuing such things at that time; to read the letters from Leonard Crow, the dear old Tewkesbury antique dealer, was to realise how much of a Solomon he must have been in order to share out these rare but not expensive items between Klepser and Perrins. Crow suggested that his method was to offer the damaged pieces to Perrins, who did not mind a bit of damage to get the piece he wanted, and the perfect ones to Klepser, who prized perfection.

Perfection really does seem the correct description for Worcester porcelain of the eighteenth century. While most porcelain factories show an experimental phase in their earliest days, producing wares with faults and problems that in some instances were never overcome, the Worcester Porcelain Company got off the ground in 1751 in the full flood of perfection. Their experimental period had occurred at the earlier factory of Miller and Lund in Bristol and in a still earlier factory in London, at Limehouse, as we know from a statement by Bishop Richard Pococke. In a letter to his mother, dated 2 November 1750, he refers to a visit to the Bristol manufactory as 'lately established here by one of the principal manufacturers at Limehouse which failed'. He went on to say that 'they have two sorts of ware, one called Stone China which has a yellow cast, both in the ware and in the glazing, that I suppose is made of Pipe-clay and calcin'd Flint. The other they call Old China, this is whiter and I suppose this made of the calcin'd flint and the Soapy rock at Lizard Point which 'tis known they use; this is painted blue . . . they make very beautiful white sauce boats adorned with reliefs of festoons, which sell for sixteen shillings a pair'.

We do not know much about the wares produced at Limehouse; in fact, no pieces have been identified with certainty as yet. We are on firmer ground with regard to the Bristol establishment of Miller and Lund and a few handfuls of pieces marked with the moulded word 'Bristol' or 'Bristoll' are known. The very special ingredient of 'Soapy rock' mentioned by Bishop Pococke, mined at the Lizard in Cornwall, gave this porcelain an edge over other English soft paste porcelains in that it did not craze nor crack with the use of hot liquids, and the founders of the Worcester enterprise appreciated its potential.

On 16 May 1751 a twenty-one-year lease of Warmstry House, a large mansion in the centre of Worcester near the Cathedral, with gardens running down to the River Severn, was granted to Richard Holdship, a glover of the city. Two weeks later, on 4 June, articles were drawn up for 'carrying on the Worcester Tonquin Manufacture', the original title of the firm that was to become known as the Worcester Porcelain Company. Fifteen partners subscribed various sums of money, but the subscriptions of Dr John Wall, a physician, and William Davis, an apothecary, were to be paid out of the total 'as a reward' for passing over the secrets of the discovery of the special body, which suggests that the formula was invented by the two of them. In 1752 the Bristol factory was acquired 'lock stock and barrel' by the Worcester Porcelain Company, including the lease on the soapstone quarry, and Worcester was well and truly under way.

Over the last seventeen years I have been able to carry out a series of controlled archaeological excavations of the factory site of the Worcester Porcelain Company and the information that has come from the ground has been of the utmost use in providing information on what was made and the methods of manufacture. In the first year or so of production it would appear that Worcester continued the Bristol method of manufacture and firing: a very low biscuit firing followed by a higher glost firing. Although this is really a hard paste sequence, the formula of soapstone, ball clay and sand and the relatively low temperature used did not produce a hard paste body. In consequence the blue decoration tended to be very hazy, giving the appearance of being out of focus which has long been held to be one of the characteristics of Lund's Bristol. A considerable quantity of wasters of this type were found in the lowest levels of the Worcester site, however, proving that the new factory's earliest wares are very difficult to tell from those of Bristol; we even found a part of a glazed sauceboat bearing the last two letters of the moulded word 'Bristol', but this was possibly a Bristol-made piece intended for onglaze decoration at Worcester. It is likely that no onglaze decoration was done at Bristol.

Within a year or so Worcester had changed to the method of firing that was to see it through until the end of the eighteenth century: a high biscuit and a low glost firing, with the cobalt oxide put onto the biscuit, an intermediate firing to fix the colour and fire away the medium used, then the piece glazed and fired again. If there was to be no underglaze blue decoration, this intermediate firing was not necessary and the piece would be fired firstly to the biscuit, secondly for glost, which fused the glaze on the surface and then the metallic oxides were applied to the surface of the glaze and subsequently they fused into the glaze in one or more further lower temperature firings.

The earliest shapes were very much in the form of silver vessels with chinoiserie decoration – beautiful soft-coloured depictions of flowers, birds and pseudo-Chinese figures, so well represented in the Klepser collection. These early wares are superb in potting and decoration and have an unconscious humour that causes the viewer to glow with delight and explains their present-day popularity.

From about 1755, a subtle change seems to come about, a growing sophistication, perhaps best put in terms of professionalism. The company became a business, patterns became established to suit the selling of the wares through a London showroom so that re-ordering might produce an exactly matching piece. Shapes became simpler, decoration became sleeker and the introduction of the printing process, at first onglaze in a smoky brown colour and then in black, followed by underglaze in blue, moved the factory still closer to being a business. This is not to say that the more professional wares are not as good as the earlier ones; in fact, in many ways they are finer – better potted and fired, better decorated, but they had lost an element of naïve charm that characterised the simpler early pieces.

Because of the great advantage of lack of cracking of the ware the concentration was on the useful. At first an enormous amount of teaware and hollow-ware was produced and less large flatware, but by the late 1760s dessert services and a small amount of ornamental porcelain were in production. Some white ware – undecorated glazed pieces – was acquired by London decorators, such as James Giles, who painted them to the somewhat exotic and gaudy demands of the London trade. Factory decoration emulated this, inspired by the exotic ground colours produced at Sèvres, in particular with the production of superb blue scale grounds which Worcester made all its own. It should be realised that such decoration was not only extremely difficult to do well but was very time-consuming as well.

A few figure subjects have been proved by finding wasters and models on the factory site, such figures as Cupid at Vulcan's Forge, Gardener and Companion, Sportsman and Companion and a pair of Turks all now being undoubtedly Worcester.

By the middle 1770s, the times had become very difficult for Worcester. Dr Wall, who had retired in 1774, died in 1776 and the factory was continued by William Davis until 1783, when it was acquired by Thomas Flight, the London agent.

Competition with the porcelain factory at Caughley in Shropshire and with cheaper creamware bodies led Worcester to cheapen their production with a move into the field of printed wares of a bright blue colour. In 1792 the Flight family was joined by Martin Barr and the factory was called Flight and Barr until 1804, when it became Barr Flight and Barr, changing its title yet again to Flight Barr and Barr in 1813. The firm had gained its first Royal Warrant in 1789 and the quality had improved to a new high in the nineteenth century, but financial problems led Flight Barr and Barr in 1840 to merge with the breakaway factory of Chamberlain, which had been founded in about 1786 in the Diglis area. The new firm was termed Chamberlain and Company, in 1852 Kerr and Binns and in 1862 the present title of the Worcester Royal Porcelain Company was adopted.

Although the Klepser collection comprises only porcelain of the first 30 years or so, the long history of this great factory is something to look back on with pride. The pieces in this catalogue will speak to all who look at them not only of their own beauty and craftsmanship, but also of the skill in the forming of such a collection, which can be just as much a work of art as the creating of a fine piece of porcelain.

Preface by Simon Spero

A collection is a reflection of one man's taste; but his attitude towards it is a mirror for his character.

There are many reasons why collections are formed. Lord Eccles in his book *On Collecting* suggests that the four principal motives for collecting are 'prestige, making money, furnishing a house, and the purely personal'. Nonetheless, many collections are rooted in more intellectual concerns. Some have been inspired by the challenge of original research. In such cases the acquisition of objects is primarily for the purpose of identification and categorisation, rather than aesthetic merit alone. This academic approach embraces the considerable satisfaction to be derived from expanding the boundaries of knowledge.

An equally exacting challenge is that presented by the formation of a collection devoted to one aspect of a subject, and its gradual refinement to a required standard of excellence. The criterion for this is quality allied to rarity, and the rarer the object the greater the challenge. The attraction of such a challenge for a businessman accustomed to overcoming obstacles is immediately apparent.

Kenneth Klepser was a successful and much respected businessman, but the impulse which motivated his collecting of Worcester porcelain was completely unconnected with its financial value or investment potential. It was not that he was unaware of the value of his collection; he was just not interested in this aspect of collecting. Once he had purchased a piece of porcelain, it became as much a part of his home as his books and gramophone records; its financial value was no longer of relevance. His porcelain was there to be studied, to be cherished and to be a continuous source of pleasure.

As his collection gradually evolved into one of the finest of its type, his feelings towards it remained unchanged. When he showed visitors or fellow collectors around his apartment, it was in a spirit of a shared enjoyment and an interchange of ideas. His delight was a measure of the enthusiasm and scholarship with which he approached collecting, and the modesty with which he viewed what he had achieved. He was a man without ostentation.

The earliest pieces of Worcester were a source of especial pleasure to Mr and Mrs Klepser and some forty of the smaller pieces were displayed in a shallow wall cabinet in their kitchen so that they could see and enjoy them each morning as they sat at breakfast. Nothing could better enshrine their attitude towards their collection. Their porcelain was part of their home and behind almost every piece was a story, a treasured memory, and therein lay its value.

Kenneth Klepser was born in Hiawatha, Kansas, in 1896 of Italian-German descent. He graduated from the University of Michigan with a degree in law, practising in Nebraska before moving west, first to Everett and then to Seattle. There, in the difficult days of the Depression, he built up an ailing Title Insurance company, of which he became president, into one of the most thriving companies of its kind in the North West. He began collecting Worcester porcelain in the early 1940s and his collection was formed principally during the following twenty years.

He was a man of wide and diverse interests which included politics (in which he took an active part), sport, music, art, the theatre and literature. His imposing and extensive library bears witness to his love of reading and his eclectic tastes. Beautifully bound volumes of Hardy, Dickens, Swift and Chaucer stand alongside Proust, Ibsen, Pushkin and Plato. His wife Priscilla shared all these interests and many of their happiest moments together were spent reading aloud to one another.

They shared as well a passion for foreign travel, and during the 1940s and 1950s travelled extensively, not only in Europe but also in Africa, the Near East, India, and South America. Indeed it was seldom in conversation with him that one could mention any country which he had not visited. He greatly relished the difficulties, the primitive accommodation and even the dangers which at that time attended travel in some of the more remote countries which he had determined to see. Many near disasters attended these journeys, but such incidents served only to make them more exciting and memorable. It was fascinating to listen to him, in later years, recounting some of these experiences, vividly recalled with the dry humour and impish wit which so characterised the man. Every trip was meticulously planned beforehand and the itinerary was largely determined by the many travel books in which he immersed himself before each expedition.

I only knew Kenneth Klepser in his reflective and mellow old age, but even then I caught many glimpses in our conversations of the energy, the enthusiasm, and the curiosity which stimulated the varied interests of his life and of the kindness and compassion which so illuminated it.

Mr Klepser's interest in porcelain began, as so often, by a chance encounter and, as has been the case with other collectors, it was his wife who initiated the first move. Mrs Klepser was shopping one morning in the old established Seattle department store of Frederick and Nelson which, like many others of its type at that time, had an excellent antiques department. Whilst looking casually around she noticed on a mantelpiece seven small creamjugs. She was immediately drawn to them and later that day enthusiastically described them to her husband, who lost no time in going to see the little pitchers which had so excited his wife's interest, and, being the man he was, promptly bought all seven.

This was the beginning of their love for porcelain, and it was the point of embarkation for what was to be an absorbing voyage of discovery. Mr Klepser now set about with his accustomed energy, buying the books on ceramics which were eventually to become a comprehensive library on the subject; a collection in itself. He became a student of porcelain and was soon buying pieces whenever the opportunity arose. He concentrated on early English porcelain but in the indiscriminate manner of a traveller who has discovered a new path, but cannot yet discern its direction.

Soon, however, from his study of books and from his own observations, he came to the conclusion that it was Worcester which afforded the variety, quality and range in which he could specialise. Having made this decision, he addressed himself in earnest to the new challenge which was to become his main interest during the last thirty-five years of his life.

At this time, in the mid 1940s, the collecting of English porcelain was a somewhat different pastime than it is today. There were relatively few collectors either in England or North America and the principal problem facing them was not so much finding pieces to buy, but selecting from the plentiful supply on the market. In the field of Worcester porcelain, all but the rarest and finest pieces were readily available.

However, this is not to say that Mr Klepser had entered a field which was free of competition. Unknown to him such formidable collectors as Rissik Marshall, Selwyn Parkinson, Severne MacKenna and Anthony Tuke were active at this time, as well as the legendary Dyson Perrins. All were potential rivals and had created a strong demand for the finest Worcester and, in particular, for the coloured grounds. Indeed it was the colourful shapes and decorative motifs of the 1760s and 1770s which were the main focus of attention for Worcester collectors at the time. Mr Klepser was soon to become one of the first collectors to turn his attention to the beautiful forms of the early 1750s which are nowadays so greatly esteemed. Living in Seattle, in the far North West of the United States, Mr Klepser was to a large extent isolated from the antique shops and auction houses which are the chief sources of porcelain for the American collector. He purchased a number of pieces on his periodic trips to the East Coast but he was principally dependent upon the advice, expertise and guidance of several specialist dealers in England. It was through the exchange of cables and letters with these dealers and the subsequent dispatching of parcels, that the bulk of his collection was acquired.

He also received catalogues of the main auctions of English porcelain held in London and, through his dealer friends, obtained pieces from many of the important collections that were dispersed at the time. During the period when he was buying most actively, between the middle 1940s and the middle 1960s, celebrated collections came upon the market, including those of Darcy Taylor, Esperance, Lady Heilbron, Geoffrey Hart, Reverend Sharp, Frank Arnold, Simon Goldblatt, Selwyn Parkinson and in 1953 a section of the Rissik Marshall Collection. From all of these he made significant purchases.

Shortly after the end of the war, the fine collection of porcelain formed by Frederick Walter Carter between 1900 and 1923 was offered for sale at the Collectors' Room of Marshall Field's department store. This event happily coincided with a visit by Mr Klepser to Chicago. The pieces purchased on this occasion formed a valuable contribution to what was at that time a collection in its infancy.

But, in the autumn of 1944, he had a stroke of good fortune which was to have a profound influence on his collecting and lead to an extraordinary and uniquely rewarding friendship with an antiques dealer in England.

He had seen an advertisement in an antiques magazine for a piece of Worcester which interested him. He wrote off to the dealer, Mr T. Leonard Crow of Tewkesbury in Gloucestershire, to ask for further details. This was the start of a business correspondence which was to blossom into a friendship lasting for sixteen years, until Mr Crow's death in 1960. Sadly, only Mr Crow's letters have survived, but they reveal a fascinating glimpse into the collecting world of that time, into the attitudes, both social and political, held by a certain strata of society and of a unique friendship forged by the common interest in porcelain of two energetic and inquiring minds. From an early point in their business relationship, Mr and Mrs Klepser felt a warmth for Mr Crow, through his letters. Before long Mr Klepser took the important step of entrusting him with a list of the pieces of Worcester which he especially desired to purchase; Mr Crow's comments leave us in little doubt about the difficulty of this task.

Mr Crow diligently scoured the country and from time to time secured pieces which, after an exchange of letters, were dispatched to Seattle. The postman soon became familiar with these parcels, which at one period in the late 1940s were arriving with some frequency. When a parcel arrived, Mrs Klepser would phone her husband at his office in the city centre, several miles away. Mr Klepser would then catch a bus in his lunch hour, and hasten home in order to unwrap and inspect his latest acquisition. These were exciting moments and often the culmination of weeks of hope, anticipation and even anxiety.

Mr and Mrs Klepser's early purchases, stimulated by the chance discovery of the little creamjugs in Frederick and Nelson's department store, were mainly confined to blue and white Worcester. Soon after he first began to concentrate on Worcester porcelain, however, Mr Klepser's imagination was fired by an article in *Apollo* by Rissik Marshall on the so-called 'named services'. Some of the names referred to the persons for whom the service was made, others to more recent owners. In his article Marshall listed some twenty-nine of these services and, in doing so, presented Mr Klepser with the kind of challenge he could not resist. His search for examples of these services, many of them extremely scarce, was a central theme in his collecting, and his achievement in securing twenty-five of them is a tribute to his determination and persistence. Indeed this particular enthusiasm continued long after he had more or less ceased collecting, and his last two purchases were both examples from Marshall's list compiled some thirty years earlier. The pursuit of pieces from named services led Mr Klepser to a related area of specialisation: the coloured grounds. After his customary period of immersion in all the available literature on this form of decoration, he began to select the specimens which were eventually to form so impressive a representation. Soon afterwards, as was inevitable for a man with his scholarly and thorough approach to collecting, he widened his interests still further to include the earliest products of the factory, the wares of the 1750s, termed at that time 'Bristol Worcester'.

Through these overlapping phases, each preceded by a period of intensive study, Mr Klepser expanded his interest in the Worcester factory to embody almost every facet of its output during the first twenty-five years of production. Within a few years what had begun as an impulsive purchase of seven creamjugs had evolved into a consuming passion, and the foundation had been laid for one of the classic collections of Early English porcelain. The Klepser collection can stand comparison with almost any of the great Worcester collections of the past. It embraces pieces of the finest quality, together with a number of hitherto unrecorded shapes and patterns. But the great strength of the collection lies in its remarkably comprehensive nature. Given its breadth and importance, it is little known, either in the United States or in England, although a portion was exhibited at the Seattle Art Museum in 1955. To collectors of recent years, therefore, it represents an exciting and revealing 'terra nova'.

List of Colour Plates

15

Between pages 120–121

COLOUR PLATE 31
A Teabowl, Coffee Cup & Saucer *c.*1768 (No.123)

COLOUR PLATE 32
A Spoontray *c.*1772–75 (No.130)

COLOUR PLATE 33
A Teapot & Cover *c.*1765 (No.125)

COLOUR PLATE 34
A Teapot & Cover *c.*1768–70 (No.128)

COLOUR PLATE 35
A Butter Tub & Stand *c.*1770 (No.131)

COLOUR PLATE 36
A Plate *c.*1770 (No.136)

COLOUR PLATE 37
A Dish *c.*1770–72 (No.140)

COLOUR PLATE 38
A Plate *c.*1770–72 (No.142)

Between pages 136–137

COLOUR PLATE 39
A Plate *c.*1770 (No.147)

COLOUR PLATE 40
A Plate *c.*1770 (No.148)

COLOUR PLATE 41
A Saucerdish *c.*1772–75 (No.150)
A Mug *c.*1775 (No.149)

COLOUR PLATE 42
A Plate *c.*1770–72 (No.151)

COLOUR PLATE 43
A Teacup & Saucer *c.*1768–70 (No.152)

COLOUR PLATE 44
A Plate *c.*1772–74 (No.154)

COLOUR PLATE 45
A Teabowl & Saucer *c.*1767–68 (No.157)

COLOUR PLATE 46
A two-handled Cup & Saucer *c.*1770–72 (No.159)

COLOUR PLATE 47
A Plate *c.*1768–70 (No.160)

COLOUR PLATE 48
A Plate *c.*1768–70 (No.161)

COLOUR PLATE 49
A Saucer *c.*1772–75 (No.167)

COLOUR PLATE I
A fluted Vase *c.*1752 (No.1)

COLOUR PLATE 2
A fluted Vase *c.*1752 (No.2)

COLOUR PLATE 3
A helmet-shaped Jug *c.*1752 (No.3)

Chapter 1

The 1750–1755 Period

The forerunner of the Worcester factory was the short-lived manufactory of Benjamin Lund at Redcliffe Backs in Bristol, which was in operation between 1749 and 1751.

The celebrated traveller Dr Richard Pococke visited the Bristol factory in November 1750 and described in a letter to his mother what he saw there. Some of the china was 'painted blue' and some was undecorated. Significantly, he made no mention of coloured decoration and it remains uncertain whether any was undertaken at the Bristol factory.

Early in 1752, the Bristol factory was 'united' with the newly-established 'Worcester Tonquin Manufacture', founded in June 1751 and situated in the grounds of Warmstry House on the banks of the River Severn. This 'unification' involved the transportation of stock, moulds and all the utensils of porcelain manufacture, up the river from Bristol to Worcester. For a period of at least a year, Benjamin Lund himself was in the city, giving the Worcester partners the benefit of his expertise and practical knowledge and, indeed, he was described in bankruptcy proceedings, dated 23 February 1753, as a 'china maker, now of the city of Worcester'.[1]

The three years or so of experimentation at Bristol account for the extraordinary degree of sophistication evident even in the earliest Worcester wares. Whereas other factories gradually improved potting and decorative techniques, gaining an increasing mastery over their paste and glaze, at Worcester the required standards of excellence were achieved almost from the start.

The early decorative influences were primarily oriental; Chinese and, to a lesser extent, Japanese. The Chinese decoration on Worcester captured the spirit of chinoiserie in a manner which was attained at no other English porcelain factory. The Chinese scenes, painted with delicacy, subtlety and occasional naïvety, evoke a fairy-tale atmosphere of figures in loose-fitting robes, strutting birds, miniature islands, blossoming plants and meandering foliage. This elusive fantasy world was in a sense a pastiche, echoing the paintings of Boucher and Jean Pillement, the tapestries of Beauvais, the architecture and gardens of Henry Holland and the mirrors of Thomas Chippendale. It was an extension of the interaction between the rococo style and the vogue for all things oriental, which found expression in so many aspects of the decorative and applied arts.

Some of the early Worcester shapes were also derived from oriental forms but others, especially sauceboats, mugs and jugs, reflect the influence of contemporary English silver. This influence tended to be of a general rather than a specific nature and is most evident in handle forms, some having a powerful and almost uninterrupted curve, and others the complex and fanciful scrolling which so exemplifies the rococo style on English porcelain of the 1750s.

These graceful mid-eighteenth-century shapes which must have afforded so much

[1] Dr Bernard Watney: *English Blue and White Porcelain of the Eighteenth Century.* Page 36.

visual pleasure to those who beheld them, were perhaps less satisfying from a purely practical standpoint. The very elaboration of design which lends such allure to the ten-sided mug (No.4) or the twelve-sided teabowl (No.7) would have rendered them far from ideally suited as drinking vessels. Perhaps this is one reason why so many of the more intricate Worcester forms at this time had so brief a period of production.

Every specialist collection, by bringing together strongly related objects of a similar period, adds to our knowledge and appreciation of the subject. But whilst certain aspects are thrown into fresh perspective, other apparent paradoxes or unexplained anomalies can emerge.

For instance, the twelve-sided teabowl (No.7), the coffee cups (Nos 13 & 15) and the creamjug (No.17) are all, in varying degrees, rare pieces. Perhaps twenty or so teabowls exist; possibly double that number of creamjugs and several dozen of the coffee cups. All four of these shapes were produced in underglaze blue, but in each case, only a single example has been discovered. Whether this curious imbalance relates directly to the factory's output at the time, to an experimental approach to the decoration on certain shapes or is merely a reflection of the higher survival rate among coloured wares, is uncertain, but it is an indication of how much more we still have to learn about the first few years of the Worcester factory's production. None of the wares of this period bears a factory mark and indeed no factory mark occurs on *coloured* Worcester until the late 1760s.

These early wares are strongly represented in the Collection. When Mr Klepser first took an interest in this period of Worcester, in about 1947, it was not as widely collected as the later and more conventional Worcester. It was generally termed 'Lowdins' or 'Bristol-Worcester' and the ceramic reference books available at that time tended to concentrate on the later periods. This relatively unknown and mysterious early period was explored only by the more studious-minded collectors such as Dyson Perrins, Rissik Marshall and Kenneth Klepser himself. His fascination with this aspect of Worcester grew to such an extent that, by the late 1950s, he had turned his attention almost exclusively onto them, and they always remained among his favourite pieces.

This section of the Collection contains some outstanding items, four of which are the only examples of their type known. The creamboat (No.20) is the only 'Bristoll'-marked coloured creamboat so far recorded and is one of a handful of pieces in existence bearing this embossed mark. It is fairly certain that this creamboat was *made* in Bristol, but the decoration was possibly done after the move to Worcester. It seems unlikely that the Collection contains any other pieces of Lund's Bristol, though a possible candidate is the small white vase (No.12) which is also, as far as can be discovered, a unique piece. The curious similarity of its moulded Chinese decoration to painted decoration on other pieces is a distinctive and appealing feature of this rare vase.

Conceivably the outstanding item in the whole collection is the superb decagonal mug (No.4), a shape hitherto unrecorded in eighteenth-century English porcelain. Its startlingly strong outlines are softened by the more restful impact of the freely painted chinoiserie scene that embellishes it, and the overall effect is ideally presented on the relatively small proportions of this astonishing piece.

The Collection is also rich in the splendid vase forms of the period, equalled perhaps only by those made at the Bow factory during the same years. There are three of the early creamjugs and a group of the beautiful coffee cups with their exuberant scroll handles and cunningly tactile shapes.

Sauceboats, which formed so important an element of the first productions at Worcester, are also well represented. The wonderful pair of oval butter tubs (No.6) have swirling asymmetrical rococo scrolls in their moulded decoration allied to chinoiserie landscapes painted with birds, flowers and foliage in profusion, presented in a rich famille verte splendour. These butter tubs are characteristic of much early English porcelain, in that shapes derived from contemporary silver are adorned with landscapes and motifs of purely oriental inspiration.

The large helmet-shaped jug (No.3) is an important and imposing piece and one of only three of its kind recorded. Even rarer is a small 'scratch cross' class plate (No.32) which is another previously unrecorded form.

The mustard pot (No.9) aptly illustrates the humour sometimes evident in the decoration. A serpent, suddenly confronted by a Chinese figure, coils itself up into a hoop-like posture, resembling a French horn, whilst its potential assailant menaces it, waving a spear half-heartedly from behind the safety of a rock. This charmingly painted scene, slightly reminiscent of a comedy cartoon, has a spontaneity and a humour no less enjoyable for being completely unintentional.

However, if I were to suspend critical objectivity for a moment, from among this superb array of early wares I would unhesitatingly select the beautiful vase illustrated in Colour Plate I. Its slender baluster form, so subtly designed, is in perfect harmony with the long meandering plants and grasses, drawn with such feeling for the rhythm of the shape and in such beguilingly soft colours.

I

COLOUR PLATE I

1 A fluted Vase *c.*1752

of inverted baluster shape painted in famille verte taste with flowering plants and grasses, the reverse side with butterflies and insects.

Height: 7¾ inches

Mark: None

Provenance
The Frank Hurlbutt Collection
The H. Rissik Marshall Collection
Sotheby's 27 January 1953

For the companion vase, see H. Rissik Marshall: *Coloured Worcester Porcelain of the First Period.* Plate 3, No.45.

The painting exemplifies the superb effects which were attained at this early period with a relatively limited palette. As with No.2 in this Collection, the shape, derived from a K'ang Hsi original, also occurs in conjunction with Chinese figure decoration. Most of the early Worcester vase forms have no counterpart in underglaze blue, however, a blue and white version of this graceful form is in the reserve collection of the Plymouth Art Gallery.

Two coloured vases of this shape, painted with Chinese figures, are in the Dyson Perrins Museum at Worcester.

2

COLOUR PLATE 2

2 A fluted Vase *c.*1752

of baluster shape with a flared scalloped neck and spreading base, painted in famille rose taste with flowers growing from pierced rockwork, insects and a bird in flight.

Height: 7½ inches

Mark: None

Cf. letter No.38

Literature
Franklin A. Barrett: *Worcester Porcelain and Lund's Bristol*. Plate 5.
H. Rissik Marshall: *op.cit.* Plate 55, No.1111.

A pair of vases with similar decoration is in the Loan Collection in the Bristol City Art Gallery and discussed in an article by Simon Spero, 'Lund's Bristol and Early Worcester Porcelain', *Collector's Guide*, June 1977, Plate 4. Three vases of this shape are in the Fitzwilliam Museum in Cambridge.

This dark jade tone of green is a characteristic colour in this early period.

3

3 A helmet-shaped Jug *c.*1752

supported on a moulded pedestal base and painted with small floral sprays and insects in famille verte taste.

Height: 7½ inches

Mark: None

The moulded decoration on this jug differs from that on the other two examples so far recorded. Cf. Albert Amor Ltd: *Dr. John Wall, 1708–1776*, Exhibition Catalogue 1976, No. 1. Simon Spero: 'Lund's Bristol and Early Worcester Porcelain', *Collector's Guide*, June 1977, Plate 3.

This shape occurs in Böttger porcelain at Meissen in about 1713, modelled by Benjamin Thomae after a silver original by Johann Jacob Irminger, the Saxon Court silversmith. A comparable form is also known in Chinese K'ang Hsi porcelain and in Rouen faience. The painted decoration has been applied with an uncharacteristic restraint, perhaps because the form, unusual for Worcester wares, is so strong.

The swag and ribbon motif moulded around the lower terminal of the handle is a recurring embellishment at this period, echoed in the moulded and painted ornamentation on the pedestal sauceboat, No. 23 in the Collection.

4 A decagonal Mug *c.*1752

painted with two Chinese figures in a garden landscape, standing below a flowering prunus-blossom tree. The reverse side is painted with floral sprays, foliage and a bird in flight.

Height: 3¼ inches

Mark: None

This is the only ten-sided Worcester mug so far recorded.

The high curved thumb-rest on the handle, although prominent on Worcester sauceboats of this period, is a most unusual feature to encounter on a mug. The yellowish paste and slightly matt glaze on this piece link it to a group of early wares which includes the twelve-sided teabowl (No. 7), the dry mustard pot (No. 8) and the two creamjugs (Nos 17 & 18) in the Collection. This experimental glaze, only in use for a year or so, had a tendency to stain, a fault otherwise uncharacteristic of early Worcester porcelain.

The light sanding visible here, on the reverse side of the mug, is a recurrent characteristic on this early group of wares.

The shape is almost certainly based upon a silver original.

4

5 A lobed Teapot & Cover c.1753–54

of irregular form, painted in the Kakiemon taste with a flowering peony, bamboo, a pine tree, prunus blossom, a banded hedge and a bird flying overhead. The 'Banded Hedge' pattern.

Height: 5½ inches

Mark: None

Provenance
The Frank Arnold Collection
Sotheby's 28 January 1964

The 'Banded Hedge' pattern is known on Japanese porcelain as 'The Three Friends'. The pine is symbolic of longevity, the bamboo of upright character and the prunus blossom of sweetness. The design was widely utilised in Europe and occurs on French and German porcelain and, in England, on Chelsea, Bow, Longton Hall and Worcester.

This shape of teapot, derived from a silver form, was issued in three sizes and was confined to a relatively brief period from c.1753–56.

The earliest Worcester teapots were either of

5

6

hexagonal form or of a lobed or ribbed shape. The plain globular type, adapted from the Chinese, first appears in about 1754–55.

COLOUR PLATE 6

6 A pair of Butter Tubs *c.*1752

of moulded oval form painted in famille verte taste with a river scene, buildings, birds and sprays of flowers. The interior border is green with black latticework and panels of flowers.

Length: 7 inches

Width: 5¼ inches

Marks: None

Provenance
T. Leonard Crow (Cf. letters Nos 24 & 35)

Literature
Franklin A. Barrett: *op.cit.* Plate 4B

This lobed moulded form of Worcester butter tub seems confined to the period between 1752 and 1755. The paste and glaze of this pair strongly resemble that of the fluted vase (No.2). The basic shape also occurs in conjunction with decoration in the Kakiemon taste.

A pair of similar butter tubs is in the Victoria and Albert Museum.

7

COLOUR PLATE 7

7 A Teabowl *c.*1752

of twelve-fluted form, painted in famille verte taste with a heron-like bird, meandering flowers and foliage and an interior border of green with black latticework and panels of flowers.

Diameter: 3 inches

Mark: None

Literature
Henry Sandon: *Worcester Porcelain.* Plate 8.
This shows a similar teabowl and saucer together with two unglazed wasters, found on the factory site during the excavations in 1968.
Simon Spero: *op.cit.* Colour Plate II.

COLOUR PLATE 4
A decagonal Mug *c*.1752 (No.4)

COLOUR PLATE 5
A lobed Teapot & Cover *c*.1753–54 (No.5)

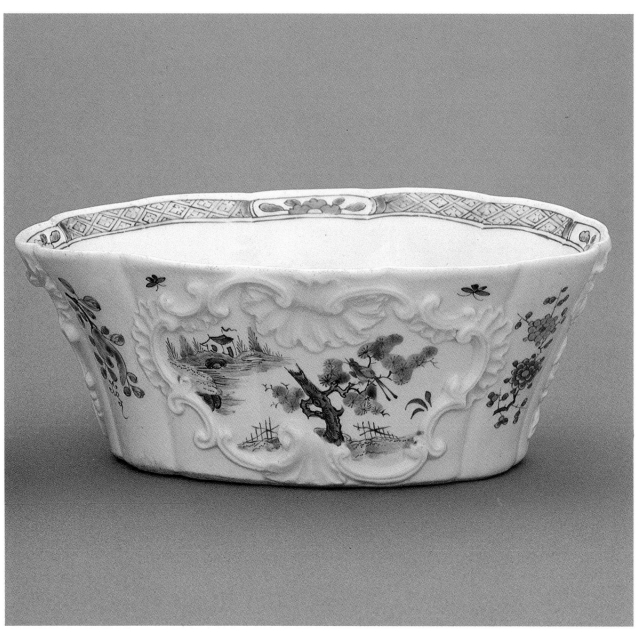

COLOUR PLATE 6
One of a pair of Butter Tubs *c.*1752 (No.6)

COLOUR PLATE 7   A bottle-shaped Vase *c.*1753 (No.10)   A bottle-shaped Vase *c.*1753 (No.11)
A Teabowl *c.*1752 (No.7)   A dry Mustard Pot *c.*1752–53 (No.8)
A Coffee Cup *c.*1753 (No.13)   A Coffee Cup *c.*1753 (No.14)

COLOUR PLATE 8   A Creamjug *c.*1752–53 (No.18)   A Creamjug *c.*1752–53 (No.17)
    A Creamboat *c.*1752–53 (No.21)   A Creamjug *c.*1753 (No.19)
    A fluted Creamboat *c.*1750 (No.20)   A wet Mustard Pot & Cover *c.*1753 (No.9)

Twelve-fluted teabowls and saucers would seem to be the earliest form of teabowl and saucer made at Worcester, and like the creamjugs (Nos 17 & 18), which they resemble in their paste and glaze, were made for a very brief period from about 1752-53. Both the teabowls and saucers and the creamjugs have a yellowish paste and matt, often sanded glaze, quite unlike the early quatrefoil coffee cups (No.14), small hexagonal vases (Nos 10 & 11) and lobed creamjugs (No.19) which probably date from a year or so later.

This form of teabowl was also produced in underglaze blue but presumably for a very short period, as only one example is known. The coloured version occurs in four different Chinese designs.

COLOUR PLATE 7

8 A dry Mustard Pot *c.*1752-53

painted in famille verte taste with a continuous design of a heron-like bird strutting upon the grass among rocks, trees and flowering plants.

Height: 3 inches

Mark: None

Literature
For two slightly later dry mustard pots, complete with their covers, see:
H. Rissik Marshall: *op.cit.* Plate 3, Nos 55 & 57.
Franklin A. Barrett: *op. cit.* Plate 7A.

This mustard pot would originally have had a high-domed cover. The shape is also known in underglaze blue during the 1755-68 period but the somewhat rarer coloured examples are confined to the 1750s.

Blue and white examples of this rare form were made at Lowestoft, Caughley and also in the controversial 'Reid' or 'Pomona' class of porcelain.

COLOUR PLATE 8

9 A wet Mustard Pot & Cover *c.*1753

of cylindrical form, painted with a landscape scene depicting two Chinese figures, one of whom is endeavouring to attack a coiled serpent with his spear from behind the safety of a rock.

Height: $3\frac{3}{4}$ inches

Mark: None

Provenance
T. Leonard Crow (Cf. letter No.37)

8

9

10

Literature
H. Rissik Marshall: *op.cit*. Plate 24, No.522, illustrates a slightly later mustard pot, lacking its cover.

The angular handle form was also used on Worcester creamboats of this period. Mustard pots of the early and mid-1750s are very scarce. A blue and white example is No.197 in this Catalogue.

Another example of this amusing and rare decoration, also on a mustard pot, is in the Loan Collection of Lund's Bristol and early Worcester porcelain in the Bristol City Art Gallery.

COLOUR PLATE 7

10 A bottle-shaped Vase *c.*1753

of hexagonal form painted on one side with a Chinese figure in a fenced garden and, on the reverse, with flowering plants.

Height: 4¾ inches

Mark: None

Literature
H. Rissik Marshall: *op.cit*. Plate 25, No.566.
Simon Spero: *op.cit*. Colour Plate II, illustrates three vases of this shape in differing patterns.

This, the most common Worcester vase form of the early and middle 1750s, dates from the period between 1753 and 1756. It occurs in Chinese and Japanese patterns, with 'pencilled' decoration and with overglaze transfer printing. No blue and white examples are known.

11

12

COLOUR PLATE 7

11 A bottle-shaped Vase *c.*1753

of hexagonal form, with double lug handles at the neck, painted on one side with a Chinese figure in a fenced garden and on the reverse with flowering plants.

Height: $3\frac{3}{4}$ inches

Mark: None

Provenance
The Frank Arnold Collection
Sotheby's 28 January 1964

Literature
H. Rissik Marshall: *op.cit.* Plate 25, No.558.
Simon Spero: *op.cit.* Colour Plate 11.

A rarer and smaller variant of the orthodox vase form (No.10).

The shape is a direct copy from Chinese porcelain. Like so many Worcester shapes of this period, it was in production for a very brief time, in this case, about two years. It can occur with either a flat smear-glazed base or a shallow foot rim.

12 An undecorated Vase *c.*1752

of quatrefoil lobed form with two small handles in the form of dolphins. The central panels on each side, moulded in low relief, show a Chinese lady holding a fan and standing in front of a fence.

Height: $3\frac{1}{4}$ inches

Mark: None

Provenance
Dr Bernard Watney Collection

A painted version of this moulded pattern is known on Worcester of this period. However, no other vase of this type has so far been recorded. The absence of painted decoration is an unusual feature, especially for a piece of Worcester of the 1750s. In this respect, the vase has stylistic affinities with the Lund's Bristol factory and such an attribution cannot be discounted.

13

14

COLOUR PLATE 7

13 A Coffee Cup *c.*1753

of quatrefoil lobed form, with a moulded scroll handle, painted in alternate panels with flowering foliage, a Chinese lady holding a parasol and a bird perched upon a flowering plant.

Height: 2½ inches

Mark: None

Literature
Simon Spero: *op.cit.* Colour Plate II.
Henry Sandon: *op.cit.* Plate 15.

This illustration shows a similar cup, together with an unglazed factory waster and the only known blue and white version of this shape.

Several dozens of these cups are known in museums and collections but, so far, not a single saucer has been discovered to match with them; nor are any saucers known to go with the coffee cups Nos 14 & 16 in this Catalogue. In the light of this, it must be considered extremely doubtful whether saucers were ever made to fit with this particular form of coffee cup.

Three quatrefoil lobed cups are recorded supported on three curved feet. All of these are in the Loan Collection in the Bristol City Art Gallery.

COLOUR PLATE 7

14 A Coffee Cup *c.*1753

of lobed form, with a moulded scroll handle, painted with a long-tailed bird perched among meandering oriental flowering plants and foliage.

Height: 2½ inches

Mark: None

Literature
Albert Amor Ltd: *Worcester Porcelain; The First Decade 1751–1761*, Exhibition Catalogue 1981, No.11.
Simon Spero: *op.cit.* Colour Plate II.

This pattern also occurs in the slightly more common quatrefoil lobed coffee cup form (No.13). Judging from their paste, glaze, form, style of decoration and from the relatively small number which have survived, these cups were made only for a brief period, probably *c.*1753–54.

A comparable lobed form of cup also occurs in the 'A' class of porcelains. Cf. No.17.

This form of coffee cup is not known in underglaze blue.

15

15 A pair of Coffee Cups *c.*1753–54

of octagonal form with moulded scroll handles, painted in famille verte taste with alternate panels of flowering plants and insects.

Height: $2\frac{1}{8}$ inches

Marks: None

Literature
Albert Amor Ltd: *Worcester Porcelain; The First Decade*, Exhibition Catalogue 1981, No.33.

Octagonal coffee cups, which are known with three different handle forms and in two sizes, occur with several Chinese-style patterns and, more rarely, with overglaze transfer-printed decoration. However, only a single blue and white example of this form is recorded.

Octagonal saucers occur in various Chinese-style patterns but the pattern illustrated here, although commonly found on cups, has not so far been discovered on an octagonal saucer.

With regard to Worcester tea and coffee ware, an octagonal or hexagonal shape is always a sure indication of manufacture before about 1762.

16

16 A Coffee Cup *c.*1753

of ogee shape, with a plain loop handle, painted in famille verte taste with flowering plants, Chinese symbols and insects.

Height: $2\frac{1}{4}$ inches

Mark: None

Literature
Albert Amor Ltd: *Dr. John Wall, 1708–1776*, Exhibition Catalogue 1976, No.12.

The strong colours, flared rim and narrow, rather poorly formed footrim, together with the slightly sanded glaze, indicate an earlier date than is usually suggested for this rare form of coffee cup. The shape is derived from silver forms of the period.

17

18

COLOUR PLATE 8

17 A Creamjug *c.*1752−53

with scroll handle, painted with a Chinese figure under a tree, in a garden landscape.

Height: 2¾ inches

Mark: None

Literature
Henry Sandon: *op.cit.* Plate 16.
Simon Spero: *op.cit.* Colour Plate II.

This is probably the earliest form of creamjug made at Worcester and the precursor of the standard 'sparrow beak' shape (Nos 74 & 75). It slightly predates the lobed form with the elaborately scrolled handle (No.19) and was produced for a period of no more than two years. It occurs in a number of polychrome patterns and with two different handle forms. As with several early shapes illustrated in this catalogue, only a single underglaze blue example has so far been discovered.

A slightly downward-tilting lip is a characteristic feature of this class of creamjug.

It is interesting to note that in certain respects the shape has affinities with a creamjug in the Victoria and Albert Museum from the problematical 'A' class of porcelains. This group of wares seems to date from about 1750−55 but it has not yet been established whether it is of English or Italian origin. Cf. a paper by R.J. Charleston and J.V.G. Mallet: 'A Problematical Group of Eighteenth Century Porcelains', *English Ceramic Circle Transactions*, Volume 8, Part I, 1970, Plates 75b and 77a.

COLOUR PLATE 8

18 A Creamjug *c.*1752−53

with a masked lip and scroll handle, painted in a vivid palette in famille rose style, with flowers, insects and two birds perched on rockwork.

Height: 2½ inches

Mark: None

Literature
Albert Amor Ltd: *Worcester Porcelain, The First Decade*, Exhibition Catalogue 1981, No.21, illustrates a bell-shaped tankard, formerly in the Hughes Collection, painted in the same distinctive pattern.

Only two examples of this 'masked' creamjug have so far been recorded, the other being painted with a stork, in a pattern similar to that on the dry mustard pot (No.8).

19

20

COLOUR PLATE 8

19 A Creamjug *c.*1753

of lobed form, with a scroll handle and irregular rim, painted with a snake in a basket beneath tall pine trees and, on the reverse, with a Chinese figure holding a parasol.

Height: 3 inches

Mark: None

Provenance
T. Leonard Crow

Literature
J. Emerson: *The Collectors: Early European Ceramics and Silver*, Exhibition Catalogue, No.84.
H. Rissik Marshall: *op.cit.* Plate 25, Nos 557 & 559.

This form of creamjug was issued in two basic sizes: 3 inches and 3½ inches. The smaller size was confined to a brief period of *c.*1753 to *c.*1756 but the larger one spans a slightly longer period from *c.*1754 to *c.*1758. The shape occurs also in blue and white, the smaller size being the rarer of the two.

The painted design is associated with hand-thrown pieces of the 'scratch cross' family and can be seen on the wine funnel, No.31 in this Catalogue.

COLOUR PLATE 8

20 A fluted Creamboat *c.*1750

on four pad feet, painted in famille verte taste with flowers and sprigs and with an inner border of green and black latticework and panels of flowers.

Length: 4¼ inches

Mark: 'BRISTOLL', embossed and painted over in green

Provenance
Mrs Dudley Cory-Wright Collection
Christie's 3 December 1962

Literature
Henry Sandon: *op.cit.* Plate 2, illustrates a similar shape in underglaze blue, also bearing the embossed 'Bristoll' mark on the base.

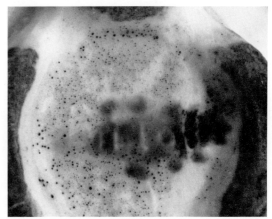

20 (detail)

21

22

The Klepser creamboat would appear to be the only 'Bristoll'-marked coloured example of this shape so far recorded.

The painted decoration has a tentative quality not evident on other early pieces in the Collection. It is reasonable to suppose from this lack of assuredness that this may be an example of the earliest coloured decoration carried out at Worcester.

This piece is discussed further in Appendix A.

COLOUR PLATE 8

21 A Creamboat c.1752–53

of hexagonal form with a scroll handle, moulded in relief with a continuous oriental mountain landscape of trees, temples, flowers and birds, the interior being bordered with Chinese symbols. The moulded decoration is picked out in bright colours.

Length: 4¼ inches

Mark: None

Literature
H. Rissik Marshall: *op.cit.* Part I, Chapter 2, Plates 1c & 1d, illustrates the celebrated creamboat with similar moulding, now in the Dyson Perrins Museum at Worcester, bearing the embossed mark 'Wigornia' on the underside of its base. The word is derived from the old Roman name for the city of Worcester.

Henry Sandon: *op.cit.* Plate 5, illustrates a blue and white creamboat with similar moulded decoration, together with an unglazed waster discovered on the factory site during the excavations in 1968.

S.M. Clarke of Chicago has categorised these moulded creamboats in a paper in *The American Ceramic Circle Bulletin, Number 3*; '"Wigornia" Type Cream Boats'. He has designated this mould as Type E, of which five examples have so far been recorded, three polychrome and two blue and white.

The bright vivid colours in which the moulding has been picked out are reminiscent of saltglaze. The overall effect of this continuous oriental landscape scene evokes the atmosphere of the second *tenture chinoise*, the Beauvais tapestries woven from models prepared by François Boucher in 1742. A blue and white creamboat with similar moulded decoration is illustrated in this Catalogue (No.198).

COLOUR PLATE 9

22 A Creamboat c.1754–55

of moulded form with scroll handle and irregular flared rim, painted in reserved panels with a Chinese figure holding a butterfly net beside a clump of bamboo and, on the reverse, with a Chinese figure standing beside a fence and a tall tree.

Length: 5½ inches

Mark: None

Provenance
T. Leonard Crow (Cf. letter No.31)

Literature
H. Rissik Marshall: *op.cit.* Plate 2, No.34.

This form of creamboat also occurs in underglaze blue and with overglaze transfer prints. The paste is invariably more creamy in appearance than that

COLOUR PLATE 9
A Creamboat *c.*1754–55 (No.22)

COLOUR PLATE 10
A Sauceboat *c.*1751–52 (No.23)

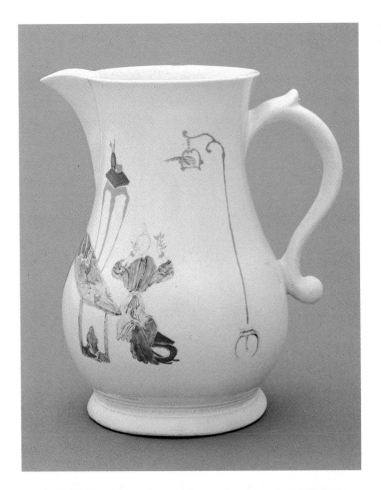

23

of other Worcester creamboat shapes of the period.

There are variations both to the moulded decoration and the handle forms associated with this form of creamboat. The shape was introduced in about 1754 and spans a period of about four years.

The handle form, which was also used on coffee cups and creamjugs, was introduced on creamboats in about 1754–55, postdating the earlier angular handle (Nos 9 & 20) by some four years.

COLOUR PLATE 10

23 A Sauceboat *c.*1751–52

supported on an oval pedestal foot and moulded in relief with cornucopia swags and ribbons picked out in bright colours. The interior border is painted in famille verte taste and the thumbrest on the scroll handle is coloured green.

Length: 8¾ inches

Mark: None

Literature
Albert Amor Ltd: *Dr. John Wall, 1708–1776*,
Exhibition Catalogue, No.7.
H. Rissik Marshall: *op.cit*. Plate 3, No.52.

This is a modified form of the celebrated 'Bristoll'-marked sauceboats, similar in their moulded decoration, but having a more elaborate, high, two-piece scroll handle, moulded with a dolphin. The unpainted versions of the latter were described by Dr Richard Pococke in a letter to his mother after he had visited the Bristol factory in the autumn of 1750, as 'beautiful white sauceboats adorned with reliefs of festoons which sell for sixteen shillings a pair'.

The sauceboat illustrated is probably Worcester rather than a Lund's Bristol piece, though an examination of its paste and glaze reveals it to be a very early piece. The moulded dolphin just under one side of the handle echoes the motif incorporated into the handle form of the Bristol-marked examples.

Similar sauceboats are in the Dyson Perrins Museum at Worcester and the Loan Collection of Lund's Bristol and Early Worcester in the Bristol City Art Gallery.

The four sauceboat shapes, Nos 23 to 26 are all forms confined entirely to the 1750s.

24

24 A Sauceboat *c.*1752

supported on an oval pedestal foot, painted with Chinese landscapes within reserved panels and with an interior border of green and black latticework and panels of flowers.

Length: 9 inches

Mark: None

Provenance
T. Leonard Crow

Literature
H. Rissik Marshall: *op.cit.* Plate 2, Nos 31, 33 & 39.

This is easily the most common of the Worcester sauceboat forms produced during the early and middle 1750s. It was issued in three basic sizes: 9 inches, 8 inches and 6½ inches, although the exact measurements vary slightly. The shape spans the period from *c.*1750–58 and was decorated in a wide variety of styles including European landscapes, birds, overglaze transfer prints and underglaze blue painting.

The palette and style of the decoration on the interior of this sauceboat are identical to those on the interior of the sauceboat with swags (No.23).

A similar sauceboat is in the Loan Collection in the Bristol City Art Gallery.

25

25 A Sauceboat *c.*1752–53

supported on an oval pedestal foot, painted in famille verte taste with crane-like birds and flowering shrubs within reserved panels, the interior border being of green and black latticework and panels of flowers.

Length: 6½ inches

Mark: None

Literature
H. Rissik Marshall: *op.cit.* Plate 1, No.16.

This form of sauceboat in its middle and smaller sizes is known in Lund's Bristol porcelain, with underglaze blue decoration. An example of the smaller size is in the Loan Collection in the Bristol City Art Gallery.

Sauceboats of this shape are frequently described as 'silver shape'. Whilst no exact counterparts seem to have been made in silver, some sauceboats of the early 1750s are of roughly comparable form, though lacking the moulded ornamentation of the porcelain examples.

As is usually the case with Worcester sauceboats of this period, the moulded decoration differs on each side.

26

26 A Sauceboat *c.*1753–54

with a flat base and moulded form, painted in a bright famille rose palette with floral sprays and insects and with an interior border of freely painted meandering flowers and leaves.

Length: 6 inches

Mark: P in a reddish brown

Provenance
T. Leonard Crow

Literature
Franklin A. Barrett: *op.cit.* Plate 4A.
H. Rissik Marshall: *op.cit.* Plate 1, No.1.

This shape is confined to a brief period of *c.*1753–56 and should not be confused with the earlier sauceboats decorated in underglaze blue, some of which bear the embossed 'Bristoll' mark (see Appendix A). The Lund's Bristol version tends to be less sharply moulded and almost invariably has a larger, better-modelled thumb-rest on the handle.

The Worcester version of this form also occurs with 'pencilled' decoration but is most commonly found in underglaze blue.

27

27 A Sauceboat *c.*1755

of elaborately moulded form with scroll handle
and painted within shaped oval panels, with a
Chinese figure and his dog chasing a stag, and on
the reverse with figures crossing a bridge. The
'Stag Hunt' pattern.

Length: 7½ inches

Mark: Painter's mark in red

Literature
Bernard Watney: *English Blue and White Porcelain
of the Eighteenth Century*, Plate 33B, illustrates a
similar shape in underglaze blue.

This pattern, derived originally from Chinese
porcelain, was used at several English factories
including Derby, Lowestoft, Chamberlain's Worcester, and the Liverpool factories of Richard
Chaffers, Philip Christian and Samuel Gilbody.

For a comparison between the Worcester and the
Chinese versions, see Klaber & Klaber: *Oriental
Influences on European Porcelain*, Exhibition Cat-
alogue 1978, Plate 26.

An identical sauceboat is in the Loan Collection in
the Bristol City Art Gallery.

Other examples of this pattern are Nos 32 & 55 in
this Catalogue.

28 An octagonal Bowl *c.*1753

painted in oriental taste with flowering plants,
bamboo and fencing.

Diameter: 6 inches

Mark: None

Literature
Albert Amor Ltd: *Worcester Porcelain: The First
Decade*, Exhibition Catalogue, No.41, illustrates
an octagonal teabowl and saucer in the same
pattern.

The design shows a happy blend of Japanese and
Chinese influences in its palette and style of
decoration.

It is likely that many of the artists at Worcester in
the early years had previously painted on tin-
glazed earthenware. This would account for the
delft-like style of some of the chinoiserie decoration.

This form occurs in silver for use as a sugar bowl in
about 1710.

29

28

29 A Teabowl & Saucer *c*.1754–55

painted in the oriental taste with two birds, one perched upon a flowering tree above a fence, the other strutting beside a banded hedge.

Diameter of saucer: $5\frac{5}{8}$ inches

Mark: None

Literature
Albert Amor Ltd: *Worcester Porcelain; The First Decade*, Exhibition Catalogue, No.54, illustrates a teapot stand painted in this pattern.

This pattern is a combination of Japanese and Chinese influences in its palette and subject, although the direct inspiration for the design may be that of Meissen.

30

31

COLOUR PLATE 11

30 A Cider Jug *c.*1754

of pear shape with a downward-turning curved lip, painted with Chinese figures and furniture in muted colours and embellished with touches of gilding.

Height: 6⅝ inches

Mark: Incised cross and incised line

Provenance
T. Leonard Crow (Cf. letter No.2)

Literature
Franklin A. Barrett: *op.cit.* Colour Plate C.

The 'scratch cross' family of Worcester wares is so named because of the presence of incised crosses or lines, cut into the bases of many of the hand-thrown pieces, most often opposite the handles of mugs, jugs, coffeepots, cups and teapots. This class of porcelain spans the period between *c.*1754 and 1756 and is characterised by a greyish-coloured often dry-looking glaze, a tendency to be thickly potted, strong, simple outlines and a sparing use of gilding.

The shape of the cider jug, derived from a much earlier silver original, also occurs in underglaze blue and, more rarely, with overglaze transfer prints.

A tankard, formerly in the Grant Dixon Collection, bearing an incised cross on its base, is inscribed 'E. 1754'. Cf. Appendix B.

COLOUR PLATE 12

31 A Wine Funnel *c.*1754

of accentuated trumpet shape, modelled after a silver original and painted with a Chinese figure holding a fan, flanked by a gnarled pine tree and with a narrow interior border of green and black latticework, with flowers in panels.

Height: 5 inches

Mark: None

Provenance
T. Leonard Crow (Cf. letters Nos 18 & 19)

Literature
Franklin A. Barrett: *op.cit.* Plate 8A.
H. Rissik Marshall: *op.cit.* Plate 2, No.38.

Worcester wine funnels are known in two polychrome patterns and they occur in three different sizes: 4 inches, 4½ inches and 5 inches. The author

32

knows of twelve coloured examples, eight in the Chinese-figure pattern and four in a famille rose 'root' design. In addition to these, three blue and white funnels are known, two painted and one transfer-printed. All of these fifteen specimens date from the middle 1750s with the solitary exception of a larger one, printed in underglaze blue, which is some fifteen years later in date.

The subdued palette and the greyish cast to the glaze indicate that this funnel belongs to the 'scratch cross' class although it is not marked.

32 A Plate *c.*1754

of small size, painted with Chinese figures on a bridge within a landscape and, in the distance, a man and two stags. The 'Stag Hunt' pattern.

Diameter: 7 inches

Mark: Incised cross

This form of plate is hitherto unrecorded in Worcester porcelain.

Worcester plates of the pre-1760 period are very rare, especially in colour. They are generally of a larger diameter and it is conceivable that this example was intended as a stand.

Although this pattern was clearly inspired by Chinese porcelain, this version is likely to have been derived from Meissen.

Other examples of this pattern are Nos 27 & 55 in this Catalogue.

39

33

33 A small Mug *c.*1754–55

or coffee can, with a grooved handle and slightly flared base painted in underglaze blue and overglaze red enamel with a Chinese figure crossing a bridge, a willow tree and bamboos.

Height: 2 inches

Mark: None

Provenance
T. Leonard Crow

Literature
L. Branyan, N. French & J. Sandon: *Worcester Blue and White Porcelain, 1751–1790,* IB 3.
H. Rissik Marshall: *op.cit.* Plate 24, No.540.

The overglaze red decoration is contemporary with the porcelain although several examples are known in purely underglaze blue.

The pattern occurs on Cookworthy's Plymouth porcelain.

R.W. Binns in his *First Century of English Porcelain,* 1906, Page 90, states that in 1770, there was a serious strike among the artists at the Worcester factory in protest against the introduction of transfer-printing, which was increasingly threatening their future. As a result many of these artists left the factory. At about this time, the Plymouth factory placed an advertisement in Berrow's *Worcester Journal,* 22 February 1770 for 'a number of sober, ingenious artists capable of painting in enamel or blue'. There is no absolute evidence that any of the Worcester artists took up employment at Plymouth, but Dr Bernard Watney has pointed out that this is highly likely, especially as many of the Worcester underglaze blue patterns were subsequently utilised at Plymouth.

A pair of similar mugs are in the Dyson Perrins Museum at Worcester.

34 A Saucerdish *c.*1755

of pleat-moulded form with four reserved panels, painted in famille rose taste with birds, foliage and scattered flower sprays.

Diameter: 8½ inches

Mark: None

Literature
H. Rissik Marshall: *op.cit.* Plate 6, No.104.

In contrast to other teaware shapes with similar moulded decoration this saucerdish is very thickly potted. This moulding occures more commonly on blue and white Worcester of the middle 1750s. Although the decoration is in the Chinese taste, the immediate inspiration was possibly that of Meissen.

35 A Coffee Can *c.*1755

of pleat-moulded form with an elaborate scroll handle, painted within reserved panels in Chinese taste with birds perched on branches and a green and black latticework border with panels of flowers.

Height: 2½ inches

Mark: None

Provenance
T. Leonard Crow (Cf. letter No.52)

This form of flattened scroll handle occurs only on moulded coffee cans, teacups and coffee cups. It is most often found in conjunction with underglaze blue decoration.

An exterior painted border design is uncommon at this period.

34

35

36

36 A Teabowl & Saucer *c.*1755

pleat-moulded and painted within reserved
panels in oriental taste with a bird, floral sprays
and sprigs and a green and black latticework
border with panels of flowers.

Diameter of saucer: 5½ inches

Mark: None

The saucers of these moulded teaware are invariably shallow, a feature common to most saucers of the 1750s and 1760s. As tea was sometimes
drunk from the saucer, there may be a correlation
with its cost at that time. The amount of tea drunk
in England greatly increased in the late 1760s,
despite continuing high taxation. Thereafter,
consumption fluctuated according to alterations in
the tax upon tea. In 1784, following the Com-
mutation Act, the price of tea fell sharply and within ten years consumption had quadrupled.

The subject of tea as revenue is discussed by Frank
Tilley in *Teapots and Tea*, Chapter 9.

A saucer of this pattern is in the Loan Collection in
the Bristol City Art Gallery.

Chapter 11

The 1755–1765 Period

In the ten years from 1755 onwards there was rapid expansion at the Worcester factory. Overglaze transfer-printing was developed into a technique that produced successful and sophisticated results economically, and the range and quality of the underglaze blue decoration increased greatly. Both of these important facets of the factory's production are discussed in later chapters of this Catalogue.

This period also witnessed a gradual change in emphasis, both in shapes and in styles of decoration. It was a time of transition from the subtle but exuberant forms of the early wares towards the progressively more simplified and standardised shapes of the middle 1760s.

The influence of rococo design, nourished by the prosperity of the emerging middle class, was generally less pronounced at Worcester than at Chelsea and it became manifestly more restrained during the 1760s. The elaborate moulded ornamentation on sauceboats, creamboats and some teapots, persisted through much of this period, but other forms, such as mugs, creamjugs and coffee cups became simpler in outline and less varied in their shapes. As the decade of the 1760s unfolded, the balance in artistic emphasis gradually shifted from 'shape' towards 'pattern'. In the early and middle 1750s, painted decoration had been a further adornment to the superb oriental and rococo forms of the period. Ten years later, many shapes had become far more standardised and the quality of the painted decoration largely determined the artistic impact of each piece.

These changes were of course dictated as much by the commercial realities of porcelain manufacture as by evolutions in fashion and taste. If the Worcester forms lacked some of their earlier flair and subtlety of outline, they fully compensated for this aesthetic loss in the practicality of their splendidly designed shapes. This factor, together with the hard, durable glaze, justly claimed to be able to withstand boiling water, was a major contribution to the success and prosperity of the Worcester factory throughout the third quarter of the eighteenth century.

Early on, the Worcester factory established a pre-eminence in the important field of tea and coffee services, which was maintained from the mid-1750s until the growing competition from Caughley and Derby, twenty years later. The success of Worcester in this endeavour was principally due to their glaze and it was this, which gave the factory an enormous advantage over their rivals. Whereas it is commonplace today to encounter Bow, Lowestoft, Liverpool and especially Derby teapots which have sustained cracks around the body, in a manner suggesting the impact of boiling water, Worcester teapots are seldom damaged in this way. This is supported by a contemporary reference in the *Gentleman's Magazine* in 1763, describing Worcester porcelain as among those wares sold more cheaply than imported porcelain '. . . but except Worcester they all wear brown and are subject to crack, especially the glazing, by boiling water. The Worcester has a good body, scarce inferior to that of Eastern china, it is equally tough and its glazing never cracks or scales off.'[1]

By the middle 1760s, a Worcester tea and coffee service comprised forty-three pieces. Some of these shapes, such as teapots and creamjugs, had been in use at the factory for over ten years, but others, among them teacaddies and milkjugs, had been introduced more recently. The Christie's sale of Worcester porcelain in December 1769 included eighty-one 'complete tea and coffee equipages' which were probably made up as follows:

	Item	Approximate date of introduction at Worcester
1	Coffeepot and cover	about 1752
1	Teapot and cover	about 1752
1	Teapot stand	about 1755
1	Bason (slop bowl)	about 1755
1	Bason plate (saucerdish)	about 1755
1	Sugar dish (sucrier or sugar bowl)	about 1755
1	Sugar dish cover (listed separately in the catalogue)	
1	Sugar dish plate (saucerdish)	
1	Milkpot (milkjug and cover)	about 1762-65
1	Spoon boat (spoontray)	about 1756
2	Teajars (teacaddies)	about 1765-68
1	Cream ewer (creamjug)	about 1752
12	Teacups	about 1756
12	Saucers	about 1752
6	Coffee cups	about 1752

The 'complete tea and coffee equipage' may also have included six chocolate cups, a form first introduced at Worcester in the early 1760s.

Whereas some of these Worcester shapes were still inspired by Chinese forms, by the late 1750s, the influence of Meissen had become prominent in such pieces as vases, teapots and especially in the leaf-moulded wares which were also imitated at Chelsea, Longton Hall, Bow and Derby. Much the same was true of the painted decoration. Oriental patterns remained very popular, although they tended to lack some of the spontaneity which characterised the earlier chinoiserie designs. However, by the late 1750s, the main decorative influence was that of the Meissen factory. The impact of the Meissen flower painting, which had so rapidly swept away the Chinese and Japanese patterns at Chelsea in 1754, was more gradual at Worcester, and took longer to fully manifest itself. Indeed, it was only by about 1758 that the characteristic style of floral decoration, so often associated with the artist James Rogers, had become fully established. As with the earlier period, no factory mark was used on polychrome wares and identification is based upon a familiarity and understanding of the paste and glaze and a recognition of the distinctive Worcester shapes.

The Klepser Collection is representative of most of the styles of decoration used during the 1755–65 period as well as the majority of the characteristic Worcester shapes. The vase and cover (No.53) is a fine specimen of the work of James Rogers, showing the painter's distinctive style of bird painting to its best advantage. Four contrasting teapots

[1] Bernard Watney: *English Blue and White Porcelain of the Eighteenth Century*, Page 45.

(Nos 37–40) illustrate the variety of forms in production during this period as well as the gradual movement towards simplicity of design and economy of form.

The two-handled sauceboat (No.42) is an early example of the Meissen influence at Worcester, in its moulded-border reserved panels, containing miniature scenes of European figures in landscapes. The leaf-shaped dish (No.41) is an outstanding piece, combining floral decoration in the Meissen style with 'pencilled' figures, also showing a Meissen influence. The pounce pot (No.59) is a shape previously unrecorded at Worcester and arouses speculation as to the possible existence of an inkpot to match.

The chinoiserie subjects are well represented in a series of dishes, mugs and a coffee cup (Nos 44–48) and they make an illuminating contrast to their counterparts of the early 1750s. By comparison with their predecessors, they are standard patterns, carefully composed, well executed in an attractive palette, but lacking the freshness and the delft-like vitality of the earlier pieces.

But perhaps the outstanding piece in this section of the Collection is the delightful, small teapot (No.37), the only other example of which is in the Victoria and Albert Museum. The swirling asymmetry of its heavy moulding partially obscures its hexagonal form and endows it with a gloriously restrained rococo splendour.

37

38

COLOUR PLATE 13

37 A Teapot & Cover *c.*1756-58

of small size, heavily moulded with swirling rococo-scroll cartouches, flanked by upward- and downward-moulded floral sprays. The moulding is repeated on the reverse side and also, on a smaller scale, on the cover. The painted decoration is of large moths and sprays of flowers, vividly depicted in bright colours.

Height: 4½ inches

Mark: None

Provenance
The Reverend C.J. Sharp Collection
Sotheby's 1 March 1955

Literature
H. Rissik Marshall: *op.cit.* Plate 54, No. 1102.

The freely painted decoration on this teapot is executed with no consideration for the prominent moulding, a feature most uncharacteristic of early Worcester. The possibility exists that the painted decoration was done outside the factory.

The only other example known, lacking its cover, is in the Victoria and Albert Museum.

COLOUR PLATE 13

38 A Teapot & Cover *c.*1758-60

of inverted pear shape with a faceted spout and flattened cover painted with a landscape scene, floral sprays in lilac and with the Arms of Hayward with Parsons of Quedgley House in pretence. The landscape and the Arms are repeated identically on the reverse side.

Height: 5 inches

Mark: None

Literature
Franklin A. Barrett: *op.cit.* 47A and 47B, illustrates a bell-shaped mug and a cup and saucer with the same armorial design.

Thomas Hayward of Quedgley House, Gloucester, was born in 1706 and died on 14 March 1781, having married Mercy, daughter and heir of Charles Parsons of Bredon.

The earliest examples of armorial decoration at Worcester date from about 1755 and the Arms are frequently incorporated into a landscape background as on this teapot. By the mid-1760s this feature is no longer encountered and armorial bearings are usually displayed on a white ground.

39

40

This shape of teapot, with its faceted spout, flattened cover and bud knop, ranges in period from *c*.1756–65.

39 A Teapot & Cover *c*.1760–62

of barrel shape, with a flat cover and floral knop, moulded in relief with a Chinese landscape, incorporating a house on an island with a seated figure fishing, a tree and flowering plants. The vivid palette with touches of gilding almost obscures the basic underglaze blue design.

Height: 5½ inches

Mark: Painter's symbol in underglaze blue

Literature
H. Rissik Marshall: *op.cit*. Plate 6, No.95.

This form of teapot occurs in several different moulded designs during the 1760s and the decoration can be polychrome, underglaze blue or simply left 'in the white'. Cf. No.196 for a blue and white example of this shape.

40 A Teapot & Cover *c*.1765

of globular shape with a conical knop, painted in Chinese taste with sprays of flowers and insects, embellished with touches of gilding.

Height: 4¾ inches

Mark: None

The standard form of globular Worcester teapot which first appeared in the mid-1750s and remained a popular shape until its gradual disappearance at Worcester in the 1770s. The palette is a little unusual and the size slightly smaller than average for a teapot of this period.

Until about 1768, the underside of the flange on teapot covers was fully glazed. Thereafter, covers were invariably unglazed, though occasionally smears of glaze are present.

41

41 A Dish *c.*1756–58

of moulded leaf shape with a serrated rim and short stalk handle, painted within a scroll-moulded central reserved panel with two figures 'pencilled' in black: a gentleman wearing a cloak and a feathered hat and a lady in a voluminous dress, holding a bird. The central panel is surrounded by sprays of European flowers.

Height: 7½ inches

Mark: None

Literature
Albert Amor Ltd: *Worcester Porcelain; The First Decade*, Exhibition Catalogue, No.57, illustrates a similar dish painted in lilac monochrome.

The 'pencilled' decoration in the moulded central panel is most untypical of Worcester and was probably derived from Meissen. This form of dish occurs in several polychrome designs, in monochrome lilac decoration and in underglaze blue.

An octagonal Worcester teapot in the Victoria and Albert Museum has similar figure decoration, including a lady holding a bird.

42

42 A two-handled Sauceboat
*c.*1755–58

with shell-moulded lips and scroll handles, the terminals moulded in the form of monkey heads. The elaborately moulded sides each contain two circular reserved panels, finely painted with European figures within a landscape. The interior is painted with butterflies and a large bouquet of flowers.

Length: 8 inches

Mark: None

Cf. letter No.15.

Literature
Franklin A. Barrett: *op.cit.* Plate 36A.
Albert Amor Ltd: *The Golden Age*, Exhibition Catalogue 1980, No.17.

Two-handled Worcester sauceboats were issued in three basic sizes of which this size, the largest, sometimes has the additional ornamentation of thumb-rests in the form of monkey heads. This shape of sauceboat occurs in a variety of styles including famille verte, European flowers, European figures, overglaze transfers and underglaze blue painting. The listed wholesale price for this shape of sauceboat in underglaze blue was from 24*s* to 28*s* per dozen according to size.

The shape of this sauceboat is loosely derived from a silver form, but the painted decoration shows the influence of Meissen.

A blue and white example is No.199 in this Catalogue.

49

43

44

43 A pair of Sauceboats *c.*1758

moulded in the form of overlapping cos-lettuce leaves, the handle being formed by a long stalk. The outer sides are decorated with flowers and insects and the interior with a spray of flowers.

Length: 7⅜ inches

Marks: None

Literature
H. Rissik Marshall: *op.cit.* Plate 5, Nos 80 & 82.
Simon Spero: *The Price Guide To Eighteenth Century English Porcelain*, Page 78.

These sauceboats, issued in two sizes and in several differing models, were derived from Meissen originals. They were made in great numbers from the late 1750s until the early 1760s and a few blue and white examples are also known, though these are rare. Some authorities have doubted that they are of Worcester origin, but recent excavations have established this attribution conclusively.

Cos-lettuce leaf sauceboats were also made at Derby, Longton Hall, Bow and at Champion's Bristol factory.

The palette and style of decoration strongly resemble that on the interior of the two-handled sauceboat (No.42).

44 A Dish *c.*1758

moulded in the form of two overlapping cabbage leaves, the crossed stalks forming a handle at one end. The decoration is in the Chinese taste with a lady seated upon a rock beneath a willow tree, flanked by a man holding a fan and, on the other side, a lady and a small boy, all enclosed in a green diaper border.

Diameter: 10¼ inches

Mark: None

Provenance
T. Leonard Crow (Cf. letter No.34)

Literature
Franklin A. Barrett: *op.cit.* Plate 33B, illustrates a coffee cup and saucer painted with a slightly simplified version of this pattern.
H. Rissik Marshall: *op.cit.* Plate 1, No.21, illustrates a sucrier and cover in this pattern, together with a Chinese stand.

The lady and the small boy on the left of the decoration are incorporated into a coloured outline transfer print which occurs on teaware, small

hexagonal vases and mustard pots of the mid-1750s.

This shape of dish occurs more commonly with coloured floral sprays and in underglaze blue and ranges in date from *c.*1756–70.

45 A Coffee Cup *c.*1756–58

of bell shape, with a wishbone handle, painted with Chinese figures in loose-fitting robes, carrying banners.

Height: 2½ inches

Mark: None

Provenance
T. Leonard Crow

Coffee cups of bell shape, with wishbone handles, occur in a variety of patterns in both polychrome and underglaze blue during the period from *c.*1756–65. An adaptation of this form was utilised at Derby during the first half of this brief period. By comparison with the early Derby examples, the Worcester version of this shape has a thinner, more precisely potted handle; the thumb-rest points upwards, rather than outwards, as on the Derby handle. The handle form itself was a simplified adaptation of a Meissen handle of the 1730s.

45

46

47

46 A Mug c.1756–58

of cylindrical form with a slightly flared base and curved strap handle, painted in vivid colours with a Chinese figure in a long purple robe and, on the reverse, with a spray of oriental flowers and foliage. The 'Beckoning Chinaman' pattern.

Height: 3½ inches

Mark: An arrow in red

Literature
H. Rissik Marshall: *op.cit.* Plate 5, No.76.
Simon Spero: *op.cit.* Page 80.

This well-known Worcester pattern occurs primarily on mugs, jugs and teapots, frequently painted in a very vivid palette. The design was also used at Philip Christian's Liverpool factory where it appears on fluted teapots. On Worcester, the pattern spans the c.1756–65 period. A rare variant shows a second, smaller Chinese figure, his arms held aloft.

The 'strap' handle form, flattened on the outer side and curving back below the lower terminal, is confined to cylindrical mugs of the 1753–58 period. It was a style of handle adapted from silver.

The slightly spreading base evident on this mug and on the smaller example (No.33) is a reliable indication of a date prior to about 1758. A more pronounced spreading base occurs during the 1750–55 period.

47 A Mug c.1762–65

of straight-sided cylindrical form, painted with Chinese figures, a dog and insects, within a puce scroll ground and reserved panels of flowers in black.

Height: 3 inches

Mark: None

Provenance
T. Leonard Crow (Cf. letter No.7)

Literature
F. Severne MacKenna: *Worcester Porcelain*, Plate 24, No.49, illustrates this mug.

By comparison with the 'Beckoning Chinaman' mug (No.46) which is eight years or so earlier in date, this mug has become more standardised in shape, more stylised in its decoration and more crowded in its overall composition. The pattern also occurs on teaware and vases.

48

49

COLOUR PLATE 16

48 A Sweetmeat Dish *c.*1758

moulded with a spray of rose leaves and buds, the stalk forming the handle and painted with three seated Chinese figures, one with a standing boy, with an insect hovering above. The moulded decoration is known as the 'Blind Earl' pattern.

Diameter: 6¼ inches

Mark: None

Provenance
T. Leonard Crow

Literature
Franklin A. Barrett: *op.cit.* Plate 33B, illustrates a cup and saucer in this painted design.

The moulded pattern on this dish takes its name from the blind Earl of Coventry who is traditionally believed to have taken pleasure in feeling the moulded decoration, even though he was unable to see the painted design. Although this moulding was first utilised at Worcester in the late 1750s, the hunting accident that caused the Earl of Coventry's blindness did not occur until 1780!

The painted pattern is also on the leaf-shaped dish, No.44 in this Collection.

COLOUR PLATE 16

49 A Sweetmeat Dish *c.*1758–60

moulded with a spray of rose leaves and buds, the stalk forming the handle, and painted with bouquets and sprays of flowers, a butterfly and with a purple scroll and 'sunburst' border.

Diameter: 6 inches

Mark: None

Provenance
T. Leonard Crow (Cf. letter No.34)

Literature
H. Rissik Marshall: *op.cit.* Plate 6, No.86, shows a teabowl and saucer of this pattern.

Sweetmeat dishes, plates and spoontrays with the so-called 'Blind Earl' moulding occur with various different designs, including some painted in the atelier of James Giles. The moulding is also found in conjunction with underglaze blue decoration. The painted decoration exhibits a strong Meissen influence.

Cf. Nos 48 & 96 in this Collection.

50

50 A Coffeepot & Cover *c.*1758–60

with herringbone moulding, painted with bouquets and scattered flowers beneath a puce scroll and foliage border.

Height: 10 inches

Mark: None

Provenance
T. Leonard Crow (Cf. letter No.1)

Literature
F. Severne MacKenna: *op.cit.* Plate 29, No.58, illustrates this coffeepot.

The style of flower painting, in its characteristically vivid palette, is traditionally associated with the artist James Rogers. However, there is no firm evidence linking him with this decoration.

This classic Worcester coffeepot shape of the 1756–68 period was derived from a silver original. This influence is particularly evident in the moulded motifs just below, and near the base of, the curved spout. A silver coffeepot by Paul de Lamerie, made in London in 1735, displays strong similarities with the moulding on the Worcester coffeepot. They also resemble one another in overall shape, in their domed covers and in their knops.

51

51 A Mug *c.*1758–62

of bell shape, with a grooved handle, painted with a bouquet and sprays of flowers and a butterfly.

Height: 4¾ inches

Mark: None

Literature
Simon Spero: *op.cit.* Page 81.

The style of decoration, similar to Nos 50 & 52 in this Collection, was derived from the Meissen factory.

A more direct influence for this style of flower painting is that of Chelsea. In 1757, due to the illness of Nicholas Sprimont, the proprietor, the Chelsea factory partially closed down for a year or so and, as a result, a number of workmen were discharged. Some are known to have obtained employment at Bow and it is possible that others found their way to Worcester. The flower painting on this mug has many similarities with Chelsea decoration of the late 1750s including the palette, the painting of the leaves, many of the flowers themselves, and even the composition and arrangement of the bouquet. The similarity is partially obscured by the brighter Worcester colours and the fuller bouquet, but the possibility exists that this so-called 'James Rogers' style of decoration may in fact reflect the influence, or even the presence, of artists from Chelsea.

This shape of mug, introduced at Worcester in the mid-1750s, spans a period of some fifteen years, and was the model used at several other English factories.

52

52 A pair of Vases *c.*1758–62

of quatrefoil lobed baluster shape with two
triangular handles at the neck, painted with
bouquets and sprays of flowers.

Height: 6½ inches

Mark: None

Cf. letter No.36

Literature
Franklin A. Barrett: *op.cit.* Plate 22.
H. Rissik Marshall: *op.cit.* Plate 25, No.578.

This distinctive Worcester vase form spans a period
from *c.*1753 to 1762 and is found with early Chinese
figure painting, European flowers, 'ho-ho' birds
and with 'pencilled' decoration.

Three similar vases of this shape are in the Victoria
and Albert Museum, and another pair is in the
Dyson Perrins Museum at Worcester. A further
pair is in the Katz Collection in the Boston
Museum of Fine Arts.

COLOUR PLATE 13
A Teapot & Cover *c*.1756–58 (No.37)
A Teapot & Cover *c*.1758–60 (No.38)

COLOUR PLATE 14
A Dish *c*.1756–58 (No.41)

COLOUR PLATE 15
A two-handled Sauceboat *c.*1755–58 (No.42)

COLOUR PLATE 16
A Sweetmeat Dish *c.*1758–60 (No.49)
A Sweetmeat Dish *c.*1758 (No.48)

COLOUR PLATE 17
A Coffeepot & Cover *c.*1758–60 (No.50)

COLOUR PLATE 18
A Vase & Cover *c*.1756–58 (No.53)

53

COLOUR PLATE 18

53 A Vase & Cover *c.*1756–58

of baluster shape, painted with a long-eared owl perched on a branch with a large bird with outstretched wings on a lower branch, surrounded by a host of other birds, perched and in flight.

Height: 8½ inches

Mark: None

Literature
Franklin A. Barrett: *op.cit.* Plate 18.

A vase of similar form, showing almost identical decoration in underglaze blue, is in the British Museum.

54

This style of decoration is usually ascribed to James Rogers. The key piece in this attribution is a small bell-shaped mug in the British Museum, painted with a pheasant and other birds and inscribed on the base in black enamel: 'I Rogers Pinxit 1757'. An examination of the mug reveals it to be a comparatively poor example of this artist's work, but it is clearly a crucial link with the well-known 'mobbed owl' vases, such as the example in this Collection. Hugh Tait, in an article in *The Connoisseur* of April 1963, 'James Rogers', points out the many similarities between the dated mug and the vases, in painting, composition and palette.

54 A Pickle Dish *c.*1756–58

the exterior moulded with overlapping artichoke leaves and the interior painted with sprays of flowers.

Diameter: $2\frac{3}{4}$ inches

Mark: None

Provenance
T. Leonard Crow

Literature
Albert Amor Ltd: *Worcester Porcelain; The First Decade*, Exhibition Catalogue, No.76.
H. Rissik Marshall: *op.cit.* Plate 1, No.13.

This well-known Worcester form is relatively unusual in colour and was made over a brief period from about 1755–58. The blue and white examples, which are much more common, were produced over a far longer period from about 1756–70, some of the later examples being transfer-printed.

As with the majority of the many pickle-leaf forms made during the second half of the eighteenth century, the exact use of this moulded dish is unknown. However, in the days before refrigeration, when only a handful of the largest homes had ice houses in their grounds, it was necessary to preserve meat by using salt. In these circumstances it is probable that these little dishes were used to contain pickles and the like, in order to counteract the salty or the 'high' flavour of the meat.

55 A Bowl *c.*1758

of pleat-moulded design, with two large rococo scroll-bordered reserved panels painted with Chinese figures in hunting scenes. 'The Stag Hunt' pattern.

Diameter: 5 inches

Mark: None

Literature
Albert Amor Ltd: *Worcester Porcelain; The First Decade*, Exhibition Catalogue, No.26, illustrates a teabowl, coffee cup and saucer.
R.L. Hobson: *Catalogue of the Frank Lloyd Collection . . . British Museum*, Plate 30, No.133, illustrates a sucrier and cover.

55

56

This well-known pattern was made at Worcester over a long period from about 1754 to 1770. It occurs on elaborately moulded cider jugs and teapots of about 1754–55, unmoulded teaware of the same period, often bearing 'scratch cross' marks, and moulded teaware of the late 1750s. It was also used throughout the 1760s and the pattern occurs on Worcester porcelain painted outside the factory, sometimes with additional bianco sopra bianco decoration. Later, towards the end of the century, the 'Stag Hunt' pattern was utilised at Chamberlain's factory.

The creamy appearance of the paste suggests a slightly later date than other moulded teaware in this Collection, Nos 34 & 36. Cf. Nos 27 & 32 in this Catalogue.

56 A Sucrier *c.*1760–62

painted in a soft palette of lilac and green with billing doves, a quiver of arrows, a 'tree of golden apples' and an altar on which lie two hearts, impaled by arrows. 'The Valentine' pattern.

Diameter: $4\frac{1}{8}$ inches

Mark: None

Provenance
T. Leonard Crow (Cf. letter No.23)

Literature
J.L. Dixon: *English Porcelain of the Eighteenth Century*, Plate 77b, illustrates a teapot in this design in the Cecil Higgins Collection in Bedford. H. Rissik Marshall: *op.cit.* Plate 11, No.203, illustrates a creamjug.

This famous and distinctive pattern was copied from Chinese porcelain. One variant of the pattern in underglaze blue is known on a Chaffers' Liverpool saucerdish, and one further underglaze blue variant, on Worcester.

For an example of the Worcester and the Chinese versions of this design, see Klaber and Klaber: *Oriental Influences on European Porcelain*, Exhibition Catalogue, No.23.

A teapot and a coffee cup and saucer painted in this pattern are in the Dyson Perrins Museum at Worcester.

59

57

57 A Scallop Shell c.1758–60

with moulded underside, painted with a bouquet and sprays of flowers in the interior and with the flared rim painted pink.

Length: 5¼ inches

Mark: None

Literature
Albert Amor Ltd: *Worcester Porcelain; The First Decade*, Exhibition Catalogue, No.65.
H. Rissik Marshall: *op.cit.* Plate 51, No.1049.

This shape in its polychrome version occurs principally during the late 1750s and also some ten years later with a gros bleu border. Three underglaze blue examples are known dating from the Lund's Bristol period, c.1750, but it appears that no blue and white Worcester versions of this shape were made until the transfer-printed examples of the late 1760s.

58 A Finger Bowl & Stand c.1760–62

boldly painted with bouquets of garden flowers, including pink cabbage roses and Turk's Cap lilies.

Diameter of stand: 6⅛ inches
Diameter of bowl: 4⅛ inches

Mark: None

Provenance
The Parkinson Collection
Sotheby's 29 March 1966

Literature
H. Rissik Marshall: *op.cit.* Plate 50, No.1035 and Plate 55, No.1118.

Finger bowls and stands were produced at Worcester from the mid-1750s until the early 1760s, in colour, underglaze blue and with transfer-printed and 'pencilled' decoration. Some blue scale examples were made in the mid-1760s but thereafter this shape seems to have been discontinued.

This is not a common shape in eighteenth-century English porcelain. Apart from the Worcester examples it was confined principally to Chelsea, during the red anchor period, and to Bow during the early 1750s.

This finger bowl and stand are in the largest of the three sizes made.

Cf. Nos 18 & 200 for further examples in this Collection.

58

59

59 A Pounce Pot or Sander
*c.*1760–62

with a perforated top, the curved sides painted with a large bouquet of flowers and smaller scattered sprays.

Diameter: 2 inches

Height: 1⅞ inches

Mark: None

Provenance
Dr Bernard Watney Collection

This shape is previously unrecorded in Worcester porcelain, although a larger, flared form of pounce pot is known, painted in underglaze blue and dating from some ten years later.

Pounce pots or sanders are rare in eighteenth-century English porcelain, especially in colour. This example, like its early Derby counterpart, would probably have been made together with an inkpot, as part of a desk set.

60

60 A Plate *c.*1765

in Chinese famille verte taste, painted in the centre with an elaborate basket of flowers and with a wide green cell border with rouge de fer flower heads and four reserved panels with chrysanthemums and lotus.

Diameter: 8¾ inches

Mark: None

Literature
H. Rissik Marshall: *op.cit*. Plate 55, No.1115.

The decoration is in a style more readily associated with Worcester painting of the middle 1750s and it is possible that this plate was made as a replacement for a Chinese famille verte piece.

61 A rectangular Dish *c.*1765

with canted corners, painted in famille verte style with birds in branches, chrysanthemums and scattered sprays of flowers.

Length: 10 inches

Mark: None

Literature
H. Rissik Marshall: *op.cit*. Plate 22, No.449.
Henry Sandon: *op.cit*. Plate 58.

Made as a replacement for a Meissen famille verte style service of about 1735. The decoration copies the Meissen original with great exactness, both in drawing and in composition, but the palette, although noticeably un-Worcester-like, is not quite as faithful to the original.

A replacement plate of this type is in the Dyson Perrins Museum at Worcester.

61

62

62 A Spoontray *c.*1760–62

of hexagonal lobed form, painted with a Chinese landscape scene in black, rouge de fer and gilt.

Length: 6 inches

Mark: None

Provenance
T. Leonard Crow

A very untypical style of decoration for Worcester, though in this case probably not a replacement piece.

This is the orthodox shape of spoontray at Worcester, introduced in about 1756 and continuing into the 1780s. From the early 1770s onwards, the standard lobed spoontray tends to have more steeply angled sides and becomes slightly larger in size. A lozenge-shaped spoontray was introduced from about 1760 to 1765 but this seems to have been only in conjunction with moulded patterns, cf. No.84.

Cf. No.130 in this Collection.

63

63

63 A Teabowl & Saucer *c.*1758–60

of fluted form, painted in Japanese taste with a
dragon descending from the clouds upon a pair of
crabs sitting between two flowering plants.

Diameter of saucer: 4¼ inches

Mark: None

Provenance
T. Leonard Crow (Cf. letter No.30)

Literature
Franklin A. Barrett: *op.cit.* Plate 28, illustrates a
large cabbage leaf jug decorated with this
pattern.

This design was derived from a Kakiemon original,
but the immediate inspiration was probably from
the Meissen factory. The predominance of orange
and gilt in the decoration of a piece of Worcester is
usually an indication of a Japanese influence in the
painted design.

A fluted teapot in this pattern is in the Victoria and
Albert Museum and a teabowl and saucer, are in
the Dyson Perrins Museum at Worcester.

This shape of teabowl and saucer was introduced
in about 1755–56 and occurs in association with a
number of polychrome designs, generally of oriental
inspiration, and also with the underglaze blue
'Prunus root' pattern.

Chapter III

The 1765–1776 Period

The commercial prosperity of the Worcester factory during its initial thirty years, from 1751 until 1781, can be likened to an arch, ascending through the first decade and reaching its apex during the middle and late 1760s. From the mid-1770s, its fortunes gradually declined, reaching a nadir by the early 1780s. The eventual recovery and return to artistic and commercial prosperity was not fully in progress until the turn of the century, and the 1780s can be seen in retrospect as one of the least successful decades in the factory's long and distinguished history.

The years from 1765 to 1776 were among the most successful experienced by the factory and some of the finest and most celebrated styles of decoration were produced in this period. The increased use of underglaze blue transfer-printing from the late 1760s onwards, was of crucial importance, reducing costs and, in certain respects, raising the standards of decoration. Overglaze transfer printing remained popular, although by the 1770s the quality of the printing had fallen far below the standards of the previous decade. These were also the years of the celebrated Worcester coloured grounds, inspired by Meissen and Sèvres, and this significant aspect of the factory's output is discussed in Chapters IV and V.

In 1767, the independent decorator, James Giles, entered into an arrangement with the Worcester factory which undertook to supply white porcelain to be painted in his London atelier. For the next four years a high proportion of the most elaborate decoration on Worcester porcelain was carried out in London, and the extensive use of 'outside decoration' is considered in Chapter VI.

By the late 1760s, Worcester's shapes had become secondary to the decoration, although those two facets of the overall design were still intended to complement one another. The porcelain body was primarily a canvas for the painted decoration and in many cases the shape of the object, whilst still of unerringly practical design, was little more than a framework for the painted decoration. The tureen stand from the 'Duke of Gloucester' service (No.64), aptly illustrates this change of emphasis. The 'Japan' patterns, the coloured grounds and many of the patterns inspired by Sèvres are laid out in such a way that the white porcelain is more or less obscured, and such pieces are admired almost entirely for the quality and visual impact of the decoration, rather than for any subtlety of form or beauty of paste and glaze. Indeed the Worcester paste showed a noticeable deterioration during the 1770s and the more elaborate patterns conveniently served to disguise this decline in quality.

Although factory marks were in common use by the late 1760s, they occur with regularity only where all or part of the decoration is in underglaze blue. The majority of pieces decorated entirely in overglaze colours do not bear a factory mark.

This section of the Collection contains five examples of the so-called 'Named Services',

65

first described by Rissik Marshall in an article in *Apollo*, in March 1945. Marshall listed twenty-nine of these services and Mr Klepser set out to collect a specimen from as many of them as possible, ultimately securing twenty-five examples. Some of these services are associated with their 'name' by proven ownership and, in a few instances, the service is recorded as having been made for the owner. But in other cases, the name has been given to the service by a collector or dealer of a later generation and the precise nature of the connection is not always readily apparent.

Several decorative influences on Worcester can be discerned through the 1765–76 period. The influence of Meissen, which had first appeared in the late 1750s, was by this time fully absorbed at the factory and can be seen in the 'Spinning Maiden' teabowl and saucer (No.83) and the 'Pecking Parrot' teacup and saucer (No.84). Other pieces, such as a plate (No.78) show a style of bird painting derived from Sèvres, which is quite distinct from the other types of bird decoration at Worcester. These derivations from Meissen and Sèvres were seldom exact copies of Continental patterns. More often they were adaptations or else designs in the Meissen or Sèvres taste. Almost invariably the Worcester patterns of this type have a freshness and an assuredness of composition rarely encountered on derivative styles at other factories.

The oriental influence at Worcester can be seen on the 'Bishop Sumner' dish (No.66) which is copied from a Chinese famille verte original, and on the 'Bengal Tiger' teabowl and saucer (No.87). 'Japan' patterns were very popular during the late 1760s, some incorporating underglaze blue in their decoration. These colourful compositions have none of the restraint and sense of space that characterised the Kakiemon designs of the mid-1750s and their visual impact is striking rather than subtle.

Bird decoration was also very popular at this time and several distinctive styles were evolved. In addition to the pheasant-like birds in watery landscapes derived from Sèvres, there were birds variously described as 'dishevelled', 'agitated' and 'exotic', as well as the naturalistic birds which were generally inspired by Meissen. Differing treatment of bird decoration on three items of approximately the same period can be observed in the pair of shell salts (No.68), the creamjug (No.76) and the plate (No.78).

Not all of the decoration at this time was colourful or in any sense flamboyant. During the early 1770s a great deal of simple floral decoration was done at Worcester, in very much the same unpretentious manner as that undertaken at Derby and at Bristol during the same period. This is exemplified by the teapot (No.72), the openwork basket (No.73) and the mustard spoon (No.71).

For the most part shapes were fairly simple in outline and most teaware forms were of a standard type which seldom varied. However, the Collection does contain some rarities in this respect. The shell salts (No.68) are an attractive and uncommon form, rarer than their Bow or Plymouth counterparts, and the pot of flowers (No.70) is an unusual and stylistically untypical Worcester form.

The Klepser Collection includes a fine representation of creamjugs, ranging in date from the early 1750s through to the late 1770s. These twelve little jugs form an instructive sub-section, tracing the gradual development of one basic form over a period of twenty-five or so years. Apart from the lobed creamjug with the scroll handle (No.19), all of them conform to the well-known Worcester 'sparrow beak' shape. If this form of creamjug did not actually originate at Worcester, it was surely brought near to perfection there.

What we term as the 'First Period' of the Worcester factory drew to a close in 1776, with the death of Dr John Wall. With it ended an era of continuous artistic and technical achievement. Dr Wall had been the guiding artistic spirit at Worcester and his loss, together with the departure of the engraver, Robert Hancock, were severe blows. The quality of the porcelain itself was beginning to show signs of deterioration from its previously high standards and the competition from Thomas Turner's newly established Caughley factory was beginning to make itself felt.

But amidst these problems and difficulties, the more ambitious styles of decoration were still being successfully carried out. Many of the most sumptuous Worcester designs date from this period and nothing could more vividly embody the decorative virtuosity still attained at the factory than the famous service decorated in the Chelsea style with the utmost splendour for the Duke of Gloucester (Colour Plate 19). The visual impression might be analogous to that of an oil painting, but the effect is none the less breathtaking in its sheer opulence.

64

64 A Tureen Stand *c.*1775–78

of shaped oval form with shell-shaped handles, richly decorated with clusters and sprays of fruit including peaches, cherries, grapes and plums. Four cartouches edged in blue and gilt scrolls each contain a single insect and on the underside of the dish are painted further sprays of fruit and flowers. The 'Duke of Gloucester' service.

Width: 11⅜ inches

Mark: Crescent in gold

Literature
Franklin A. Barrett: *op.cit.* Plate 54, illustrates a plate.
H. Rissik Marshall: *op.cit.* Plate 12, No.225, illustrates a small oval tureen and stand.
Henry Sandon: *op.cit.* Colour Plate IV illustrates a large tureen and cover of the type which would have fitted on this stand.

This service is reputed to have been designed for William Henry, Duke of Gloucester (1743–1805), the third son of Frederick, Prince of Wales. The seventy pieces from this service were sold at the Duke of Cambridge Sale, at Christie's on 8 June 1904.

This decoration has in the past often been attributed to the London atelier of James Giles. It is painted in the style of gold anchor Chelsea and indeed a Chelsea service is known, believed to have been made for the Duke of Cambridge in the mid 1760s, with a very similar style of decoration.

Gerald Coke, in his book *In Search of James Giles*, points out that the decoration is uncharacteristically ornate for Giles and utilises a real turquoise as opposed to the bleu céleste which is the equivalent colour in the Giles palette. Furthermore, the gilding on this service is flat and quite unlike the fine ciselé style which Giles used on his most opulent patterns. His conclusion is that this service may have been decorated by former Chelsea painters who were taken on at the Worcester factory, after the closure of James Giles's London business in 1776.

Two large tureens from this service, together with a stand, are in the Dyson Perrins Museum at Worcester.

68

65

66

COLOUR PLATE 20

65 A Plate *c.*1770–72

of flat shape with a narrow border, painted in Japanese Imari style with two large sprays of peonies in underglaze blue and rouge de fer with shades of green, yellow and gilt. The 'Sebright' service.

Diameter: 8 inches

Mark: Simulated Chinese character mark of Ch'eng Hua

Provenance
The Geoffrey Hart Collection
Sotheby's 23 June 1959

Literature
Albert Amor Ltd: *Dr. John Wall, 1708–1876*, Exhibition Catalogue, No.36.
H. Rissik Marshall: *op.cit.* Plate 9, No.156.

This is one of a small number of rare Worcester plates made as replacements for an oriental service belonging to Sir John Sebright, Bt of Worcestershire. This would account for the very untypical shape, palette and use of underglaze blue. The remnants of this service, both Japanese and Worcester, were sold to the firm of Stoner and Evans, in the early part of this century.

A similar plate from this service is in the Dyson Perrins Museum at Worcester.

COLOUR PLATE 21

66 A Dish *c.*1770–72

painted in rich famille verte style with a kylin and a phoenix in a Chinese landscape, surrounded by eight radiating panels containing oriental flowers and foliage, fabulous birds and monsters. The 'Bishop Sumner' pattern.

Diameter: 9¾ inches

Mark: Crescent in gold

Provenance
T. Leonard Crow

Literature
Albert Amor Ltd: *Worcester Porcelain 1751–1784*, Exhibition Catalogue, No.83.
H. Rissik Marshall: *op.cit.* Plate 10, No.177.

This well-known pattern is traditionally associated with Bishop Sumner, though there is some confusion as to the identity of the bishop. John Bird Sumner, Archbishop of Canterbury, was born in

67

1780 and died in 1862 and Charles Richard Sumner, Bishop of Winchester, lived from 1790 until 1874. In either case, the association could only have been one of ownership. At any event, far too many examples of this pattern exist for there to have been only one service.

The pattern occurs on dessert services but never on teaware. It is sometimes confused with the 'Bengal Tiger' pattern (see No.87).

67 A Teacaddy & Cover *c.*1772

decorated with five festoons of turquoise drapery pendent with bows and fringed in gilt upon a white ground. The 'Lord Stormont' service.

Height: 5½ inches

Mark: None

Provenance
T. Leonard Crow (Cf. letter No.9)

Literature
H. Rissik Marshall: *op.cit*. Plate 21, No.394.

The 7th Viscount Stormont was born in 1727 and died in 1796.

This very unusual and distinctive pattern occurs in conjunction with a series of untypical Worcester shapes. The teacaddy is comparable in form to that of the 'Duchess of Kent' service (No.129) but the teapot, for instance, is of 'squared' shape with a flat cover and the sucrier and cover are of a curiously squat form. The latter are in the Victoria and Albert Museum.

The pattern also occurs in carmine.

COLOUR PLATE 22

68 A pair of Salts *c.*1765

moulded in the form of shells and supported upon a rockwork base encrusted with shells, corals and seaweed, painted in vivid colours. The interior of the shells are painted with 'agitated birds' and have pink borders.

Width: 4 inches

Marks: Impressed 'T' on both pieces

Provenance
The Alfred Trapnell Collection
Illustrated in the Catalogue of the Trapnell Collection No.500 as Champion's Bristol

Literature
Albert Amor Ltd: *Worcester Porcelain 1751–1784*, Exhibition Catalogue, No.60, illustrates a salt with fruit decoration.
H. Rissik Marshall: *op.cit*. Plate 21, No.389, illustrates a pair of salts with floral decoration.

Worcester salts of this shape and with this style of bird decoration are sometimes wrongly attributed to Richard Champion's Bristol factory, possibly because the shape was made at Bristol and these 'agitated birds' occur on Bristol, Bow and Derby porcelain, and also on creamware.

'Agitated' birds, sometimes described as 'dishevelled', are often attributed to the atelier of James Giles, but the style of painting and especially the palette are strongly indicative of factory decoration and these birds do not appear in conjunction with any Giles characteristics in the subsidiary decoration.

This distinctive style of bird painting occurs on Worcester double leaf-shaped dishes, chestnut baskets and stands and junket dishes, among other shapes, and also in association with powder blue, gros bleu and blue scale decoration.

Three similar salts are in the Victoria and Albert Museum.

68

69

COLOUR PLATE 23

69 A Creamboat *c.*1768

of 'Dolphin Ewer' form, shell moulded, with moulded dolphins under the lip and the handle modelled in the form of a lamprey.

Length: 3¾ inches

Mark: None

Literature
Albert Amor Ltd: *Dr. John Wall, 1708–1776*, Exhibition Catalogue, No.43.
H. Rissik Marshall: *op.cit.* Plate 10, No.179 and Plate 50, No.1015.

This form of creamboat, known in the eighteenth century as a 'Dolphin Ewer', was made at Worcester in two sizes. Some rare examples, lacking any relief moulding and painted in underglaze blue, date from the late 1750s, but the majority of these creamboats span the period from *c.*1765–72. Other factories which produced this shape include Derby, Lowestoft, Caughley and the Liverpool factories of Philip Christian and Seth Pennington.

According to Rissik Marshall, there were lampreys in the River Severn in the eighteenth century.

70

71

COLOUR PLATE 23

70 A Pot of Flowers *c.*1768–70

made in two sections. The bucket-shaped pot has a petal-moulded rim, moulded ring handles and is painted with a bouquet and sprays of flowers. The detachable cover consists of a pyramid of naturalistically modelled flowers, including roses, daisies and carnations, all painted in bright colours.

Height: 5½ inches

Mark: None

Literature
Albert Amor Ltd: *Dr. John Wall, 1708–1776*, Exhibition Catalogue, No.72.
H. Rissik Marshall: *op.cit.* Colour Plate 22.

These rare pieces seem not to vary in shape, but the painted decoration on the pot and the exact composition of the modelled flowers is not always the same. The inspiration for this basic form, which also occurs in Chelsea, Bow, Derby, Champion's Bristol, Longton Hall and even Chaffers' Liverpool, was that of the French factory at Vincennes, although a comparable form also occurs in Mennecy porcelain of the late 1740s.

The style of flower painting on the pot resembles that on the yellow ground basket, No.95 in this Collection.

An unglazed waster of part of the bucket-shaped pot was found on the factory site.

71 A Mustard Spoon *c.*1772–74

with moulded foliate scroll handle picked out in puce and the small circular bowl decorated with a flower spray and gilt rim.

Length: 4 inches

Mark: None

Literature
Henry Sandon: *op.cit.* Plate 89, illustrates a blue and white example.

Coloured mustard spoons (and mustard pots) are considerably rarer than blue and white specimens. This approximate shape was the model for Caughley and Lowestoft examples, though both are scarce.

COLOUR PLATE 19
A Tureen Stand *c*.1775–78 (No.64)

COLOUR PLATE 20
A Plate *c.*1770–72 (No.65)

COLOUR PLATE 21
A Dish *c.*1770–72 (No.66)

COLOUR PLATE 22
A pair of Salts c.1765 (No.68)

COLOUR PLATE 23
A Creamboat c.1768 (No.69)
A Pot of Flowers c.1768–70 (No.70)

72

72 A Teapot & Cover *c.*1770–74

of globular form, decorated with a bouquet and sprays of flowers, the cover having a gilt rim and floral knop.

Height: 5¾ inches

Mark: None

Literature
H. Rissik Marshall: *op.cit.* Plate 17, No.310.
Simon Spero: *op.cit.* Page 71, illustrates a fluted teapot with similar decoration.

A small bowl in the Museum of Fine Arts, Houston, Texas decorated in this simple manner is inscribed on the underside, in overglaze red, within a double circle: 'John Evans Feb. 11 1773'.

This unpretentious style of painting is typical of the decoration undertaken at the Worcester factory during the early 1770s when so many of the more elaborate patterns were done at the 'Enamelling Branch' in James Giles's atelier in London.

73

73 A pierced Basket *c.*1768–72

of oval shape with entwined twig handles with floral terminals, painted on the interior with a bouquet of flowers.

Length: 9¼ inches

Mark: None

Literature
H. Rissik Marshall: *op.cit.* Plate 20, Nos 376, 377 & 378, illustrates three baskets of this shape, but with differing decoration.

The catalogue of the Sale of Worcester porcelain at Christie's in December 1769 mentions 'Baskets with green handles' and 'Ditto, white handles' and as, for the most part, only oval-shaped baskets would have had handles, it is possible that the reference is to specimens such as the one illustrated here.

This form of basket, made in three sizes, occurs in a wide range of decoration, including fruit, bird and floral patterns, coloured grounds and underglaze blue.

Cf. No.211 in this Collection for a blue and white example.

74

74

74 A Creamjug *c.*1768

of 'sparrow beak' form painted with two bouquets of naturalistic flowers and scattered sprigs.

Height: 3 inches

Mark: None

Literature
H. Rissik Marshall: *op.cit.* Plate 22, No.417.

This is the standard Worcester 'sparrow beak' creamjug form, evolved from the early prototype, No.17 in this Collection, and spanning the period from the late 1750s to about 1780. The shape combines a practical simplicity of design with a balance of form and weight. This sense of balance, so characteristic in the design of Worcester cream-jugs of the 1760s, is less evident in three pro-gressively later examples in this Catalogue (Nos 75, 76 & 77).

The shape itself was probably an adaptation of a silver model of the 1720s.

75 A Creamjug *c.*1770

painted with flowers and foliage and a 'harvest bug' in tones of green, turquoise, blue, sepia, a deep red and black.

Height: 3½ inches

Mark: None

Literature
H. Rissik Marshall: *op.cit.* Plate 10, No.180, illustrates a creamjug in this same pattern, but about two years earlier in date.

Basically similar in form to No.74, but its slightly later date is suggested by its less pear-shaped outline and sharper 'sparrow beak' lip. The tur-quoise is a characteristic Worcester colour of this period and a likely indication of Factory decoration.

75

76

76 A Creamjug *c.*1772–74

of tall size, with a dentil gilt edge and gilding along its loop handle, painted with exotic birds in a floral landscape.

Height: $4\frac{5}{8}$ inches

Mark: None

Provenance
T. Leonard Crow (Cf. letter No.30)

This piece is possibly a milkjug, lacking its cover, rather than a creamjug.

Though taller, this jug is roughly similar in outline to No.75. It has a rounded handle, rather than a grooved one, which is generally an indication of a post-1765 date.

This style of bird painting, in a fresh bright palette, occurs both on a white ground, as here, and in conjunction with blue ground colours, in particular, the blue scale decoration.

Cf. No.102 for a similar style of bird painting.

77

77 A Creamjug *c.*1775–78

painted in shades of green, picked out in gilt, with fruit, flowers and scattered sprigs.

Height: $3\frac{5}{8}$ inches

Mark: None

Provenance
T. Leonard Crow (Cf. letter No.6)

Literature
Albert Amor Ltd: *Worcester Porcelain 1751–1784*, Exhibition Catalogue, No.69, illustrates a teacup, coffee cup and saucer in this pattern.

The general outline of this creamjug resembles Nos 75 & 76, but the slightly smaller handle and a noticeable deterioration in the quality of the paste suggests that this is the latest of this series of four jugs (Nos 74–77).

78

78 A Plate *c.*1770–72

with a fluted gilt dentil rim, painted with two
exotic pheasants in tones of puce, lilac, yellow and
dry blue, in a verdant landscape, with other small
birds perched and flying.

Diameter: 9 inches

Mark: None

Provenance
T. Leonard Crow (Cf. letter No.30)

Literature
R.L. Hobson: *Catalogue of the Frank Lloyd Collection
... British Museum*, Plate 21, No.113, illustrates a
similar plate with a moulded border.

George Savage: *Eighteenth Century English
Porcelain*, Plate 100(b), illustrates a square dish
with this style of bird painting.

This characteristic style of bird painting was
produced at the Worcester factory during the early
1770s and was derived from Sèvres and Tournai.
The use of a bright 'dry blue' colour in the palette
is usually indicative of a post-1770 date. The
Worcester birds are more fanciful than their
relatively naturalistic Sèvres counterparts.

A representative selection of plates and dishes
painted in this style can be seen in the Dyson
Perrins Museum at Worcester.

79

79 A Plate *c.*1772–75

with a fluted rim, painted in Japanese taste with radiating panels of a dragon, prunus branches and green scrolls between panels of diaper and mons. The 'Brocade' pattern.

Diameter: 8¼ inches

Mark: Crescent in gold

Provenance
T. Leonard Crow (Cf. letter No.1)

Literature
F. Severne MacKenna: *op.cit.* Plate 25, No.51, illustrates this plate.
Simon Spero: *op.cit.* Page 90.

The 'Brocade' pattern occurs on coffeepots, tea services and dessert services. The dessert ware seem always to be marked with a crescent in gold, whereas the teaware are unmarked. The pattern was continued into the middle 1770s.

An adaptation of a Japanese Imari pattern.

80

80 An openwork Basket *c.*1768–70

of circular form, with a scalloped rim, painted in Japanese taste with eight radiating panels, four in underglaze blue and gilt and four with flowers and diapers on a white ground with mons. The 'Old Mosaick' pattern.

Diameter: 6 inches

Mark: Simulated Chinese characters

Provenance
T. Leonard Crow

Literature
R.L. Hobson: *op.cit.* Plate 10, No.58, illustrates a plate in this pattern.

This pattern is found on a wide range of Worcester shapes including tea and coffee services and tureens, but it occurs more rarely on openwork baskets. It is a compressed and simplified version of an original Japanese Arita pattern.

The Catalogue of Worcester porcelain, sold at Christie's on 14 December 1769 and on the five following days, refers to numerous Japan patterns including an 'Old rich Mosaic japan pattern', a description which fits the 'Old Mosaick' pattern very adequately.

A pair of similar baskets is in the Dyson Perrins Museum at Worcester.

81

81 A Dish *c.*1768–70

of lozenge shape, with fluted sides painted with alternating 'fans' or formal chrysanthemums and mons in underglaze blue, rouge de fer and green. The 'Old Japan Fan' pattern.

Length: 10½ inches

Mark: Simulated oriental characters

Provenance
T. Leonard Crow

Literature
R.L. Hobson: *op.cit*. Plate 10, No.60, illustrates a plate.
H. Rissik Marshall: *op.cit*. Plate 7, No.127, illustrates a punch pot.

This pattern could be the 'Fine old japan fan pattern' listed in the catalogue of the Sale at Christie's on 14 December 1769. It occurs on teaware, dessert services, vases, punch pots and punch bowls.

82 A Punch Bowl *c.*1768

painted with Chinese figures, two seated at a table and others singly or in groups with foliage and trees, in one of which is seated a monkey with a human face. The interior is decorated with four further Chinese figures smoking long pipes.

Diameter: 9 inches

Mark: None

Provenance
T. Leonard Crow (Cf. letter No.23)

Literature
H. Rissik Marshall: *op.cit*. Plate 19, No.337.

The enamel colours on this bowl are unusually thickly applied, and the outlines printed.

Another example of this rare pattern can be seen on a punch bowl in the Dyson Perrins Museum at Worcester.

79

82

83

84

83 A Teabowl & Saucer *c.*1768

painted with a Chinese woman wearing a green coat and puce skirt seated spinning, in cartouches edged with feathery scrolls in rouge de fer and puce, and with a gilt spearhead border. The 'Spinning Maiden' pattern.

Diameter of saucer: 5 inches

Mark: None

Provenance
T. Leonard Crow

Literature
Albert Amor Ltd: *Dr John Wall. 1708–1776*, Exhibition Catalogue, No.48.
H. Rissik Marshall: *op.cit*. Plate 20, No.375.

Whilst the pattern is clearly of Chinese inspiration, the presence of the gilt spearhead border suggests that the decoration is copied from a Meissen original.

A Worcester pattern of a slightly later date is known by the same name, but although it depicts a similar subject, with a Chinese woman seated at a loom, the treatment is far less elaborate and it appears to have been derived directly from a Chinese original.

A teabowl, coffee cup and saucer of this pattern, together with a teacaddy, are in the Dyson Perrins Museum at Worcester.

84 A Teacup & Saucer *c.*1768

moulded in relief and painted in the centre of both the cup and the saucer with a parrot encircled by a wreath of flowers and leaves. There is a continuous border pattern of flowers and leaves. The 'Pecking Parrot' pattern.

Diameter of saucer: $5\frac{1}{4}$ inches

Mark: Crossed swords and numeral 9

Provenance
T. Leonard Crow (Cf. letter No.30)

Literature
H. Rissik Marshall: *op.cit*. Plate 22, No.431, illustrates a saucerdish with a differing border pattern.
Henry Sandon: *op.cit*. Plate 87, illustrates a biscuit waster showing the quality and clarity of the moulded decoration in its unglazed state.

The 'Pecking Parrot' pattern also occurs on ribbed teaware, and the moulded decoration is found in conjunction with an underglaze blue pattern of the 1760s, the 'Chrysanthemum' pattern, and with yellow and green ground colours.

The 1769 Christie's catalogue mentions 'Twelve ribb'd handle cups and saucers, six coffee cups, teapot and stand, basin and plate, sugar dish, cover

85

and plate, tea jar and spoon boat, enamell'd in parrots'. This description would fit the ribbed version of the 'Pecking Parrot' pattern.

The direct influence of this pattern is from Meissen, although it also occurs on Chinese porcelain.

85 A Coffee Cup & Saucer *c*.1770

of fluted form, with a dentil gilt edge, painted in bright colours with exotic birds in landscapes, butterflies and insects.

Diameter of saucer: 4½ inches

Mark: Fretted square

Provenance
T. Leonard Crow

Literature
H. Rissik Marshall: *op.cit.* Plate 32, No.702.

S.M. Clarke in his paper 'Marks on Overglaze-Decorated First Period Worcester Porcelain; A Statistical Study' has noted that the fretted square mark is nearly always found in conjunction with fluted shapes. In respect of underglaze blue marks, it is logical to suppose that they would relate to shape, rather than to pattern, as they were applied without foreknowledge of the overglaze decoration.

Cf. the creamjug (No.76) for a similar style of exotic bird decoration.

86

86 A Coffee Cup & Saucer
*c.*1768–70

of fluted form and with a gilt-edged rim, painted with a Chinese garden scene in famille verte style, with a triangular fence, rocks, flowering plants and a bird in flight.

Diameter of saucer: 4½ inches

Mark: Fretted square

Literature
Gerald Coke: *In Search of James Giles*, Plate 65(b).
H. Rissik Marshall: *op.cit.* Plate 19, No.358.

An unusually late use of famille verte decoration, a style normally associated with Worcester porcelain of the middle 1750s.

This pattern is ascribed by R.L. Hobson to the London atelier of James Giles. However, neither the style of decoration, nor the very bright palette is in any way reminiscent of the Giles atelier and this attribution must be considered doubtful.

87 A Teabowl & Saucer *c.*1770

of fluted form, decorated with panels of fabulous animals, divided by Antiques, within a black dotted green border and cell diaper. The 'Bengal Tiger' pattern.

Diameter of saucer: 4½ inches

Mark: Fretted square

Provenance
T. Leonard Crow

Literature
H. Rissik Marshall: *op.cit.* Plate 10, No.178, illustrates a two-handled cup and saucer.

A very popular design used at many of the eighteenth-century factories including Caughley, Chamberlain's Worcester and later, at Coalport and elsewhere. It also occurs on Chinese porcelain. A version of this pattern occurs on Cookworthy's Plymouth porcelain, in particular on teapots and mugs. The pattern was known at Chamberlain's factory as the 'draggon in compartments'.

The 'Bengal Tiger' pattern also occurs on plain and ribbed teaware.

87

88 A Coffee Cup & Saucer

*c.*1768–70

of fluted form, painted with a red 'Jabberwocky'
on the branch of a flowering tree, above flowering
plants and a banded hedge, the shaped turquoise
border with pendent flower sprays. The 'Jabberwocky' pattern.

Diameter of saucer: 5⅛ inches

Mark: Fretted square

Provenance
T. Leonard Crow

Literature
Gerald Coke: *op.cit.* Plate 50a, illustrates the
version which he attributes to the Giles atelier.
H. Rissik Marshall: *op.cit.* Plate 28, Nos 608 &
613, illustrates examples with Factory decoration.

Fluted coffee cups, teacups and saucers in this
pattern were made in two sizes and teabowls occur
to match with the smaller size. An extremely rare
variant has a border of shagreen. Dessert wares
have a border of royal blue instead of turquoise.

The Giles version of this pattern tends to be less well
set out and more confused in its composition.

This design was described in Christie's 1769 catalogue as 'fine old rich dragon pattern, bleu céleste
borders'.

89 A Coffee Cup & Saucer

*c.*1770–72

of fluted form, decorated in Kakiemon taste with
two quails, one blue and the other red, beneath a
flowering prunus tree, within a shaped turquoise
border, edged with scrolls and pendent flowers.
The 'Quail' or 'Partridge' pattern.

Diameter of saucer: 5½ inches

Mark: None

Provenance
T. Leonard Crow

Literature
H. Rissik Marshall: *op.cit.* Plate 28, No.631,
illustrates a sucrier and cover in this pattern.

As many as nine different versions of the 'Quail'
pattern occur on Worcester although several of
these were not Factory patterns. The earliest
version, introduced in about 1758, was fairly close
to the Kakiemon original, although probably
derived directly from Meissen. Later versions of the
design became increasingly elaborate and colourful, though the central quail and flowering-prunus
motif remained more or less unchanged.

Other versions of this pattern occur on Chelsea,
Longton Hall, Chaffers' Liverpool, West Pans and
most commonly on Bow.

Cf. No.166 for one of the Giles versions of the
'Quail' pattern in this Collection.

84

88

89

90

90 A Teacup & Saucer *c.*1770

painted in rouge de fer, green and underglaze blue, enriched with gilding, with sprays of oriental flowers within a cross-hatched border diaper, interspersed with floral vignettes. The 'Kempthorne' pattern.

Diameter of saucer: $5\frac{1}{4}$ inches

Mark: Crescent in underglaze blue

Provenance
T. Leonard Crow

Literature
H. Rissik Marshall: *op.cit.* Plate 8, No.131, illustrates a basin and a masked jug and cover.
R.L. Hobson: *op.cit.* Plate 12, No.70, illustrates a coffee cup and saucer.

The origin of this famous Worcester pattern was related by W.W. Kempthorne in April 1870. John Thorneloe, one of the proprietors of the Worcester Company, visited Cornwall in search of soap rock. He discovered this in the parish of Mullion and lodged at the home of a local resident, Mr Renatus Kempthorne. Mr Kempthorne would take no payment for his hospitality but agreed to accept a china service decorated in a 'Japan' pattern. This became known as the 'Kempthorne' pattern and remained a popular design at Worcester for many years.

R.W. Binns describes John Thorneloe's journey to Cornwall as having taken place before 1760, but whether or not this is accurate, the earliest examples of the 'Kempthorne' pattern cannot be dated before 1765.

This pattern can be marked with either a fretted square or a crescent in underglaze blue.

A version of the 'Kempthorne' pattern occurs on Worcester decorated outside the factory. It is easily distinguished from its palette, the underglze blue being replaced by an overglaze blue.

Chapter IV

The Overglaze Coloured Grounds

The mastery of the coloured grounds was one of the major achievements of the Worcester factory. No other English factory emulated their range of colours, nor the success with which they were applied and used, until the Derby coloured grounds of the 1790s.

The Klepser Collection includes a superb representation of this important facet of the factory's output. Apart from the underglaze blue grounds discussed in the next chapter, Kenneth Klepser assembled examples of yellow ground, yellow scale, claret ground, apple-green ground, pink scale, purple scale, and sea-green, royal blue and turquoise grounds, together with many of the colourful border patterns which I have included here under the same heading. Although it was tempting to incorporate all of the coloured grounds into one comprehensive section of this Catalogue, it seemed more logical, from an academic standpoint, to consider the group from the Giles atelier separately.

The first ground colour to be introduced at Worcester was yellow. This colour had appeared at Chelsea by about 1753 and is listed three times in the 1755 catalogue. It was also in use at Derby by 1756. The date of its introduction at Worcester can be ascertained with some accuracy. A yellow ground cabbage-leaf masked jug, illustrated by Rissik Marshall (Plate 29, No.652), bears the arms of the Fourteenth Countess of Errol. She died in 1758, suggesting that the colour was already in use by this date. This conclusion is borne out by an examination of the paste and chinoiserie decoration of a series of mugs painted in a pale-yellow ground, one of which is illustrated in this Catalogue (No.94).

At what precise date the other ground colours were introduced at Worcester is more speculative. The advertisement for the Sale of Worcester held in London in May 1769, lists porcelain decorated 'in the beautiful colours of Mazarine Blue and Gold, Sky Blue, Pea Green, French Green, Sea Green, Purple, Scarlet and Gold', and the catalogue for the sale in December of the same year refers to 'Four enamelled yellow ground sauceboats'. From this it is clear that the majority of coloured grounds were in use by 1769, but, in my view, it is unlikely that many of the *overglaze* grounds had been in production for more than two years or so prior to this date.

A pink scale creamjug inscribed 'Henry Cook 1761' in the Dyson Perrins Museum, is often cited as evidence that the ground colour was in use by this early date. Implicit in this assumption is the likelihood that other ground colours would have been introduced by the early 1760s. This seems very doubtful. An examination of the pink scale jug reveals the porcelain to be at least ten years later in date than the inscription implies.

The origin of the Worcester coloured grounds presents an intriguing puzzle. Most of the colours were in use at Meissen by 1730 and, at Sèvres, they were introduced gradually during the 1750s. These two factories are the most likely sources, but it is possible that some grounds were derived directly from Chelsea, where several of the colours had been mastered by 1760. Indeed the beginnings of the prominence of the full range of coloured grounds at Worcester coincided with the decline of the Chelsea factory.

The relatively scarce early examples of the yellow ground on Worcester are, from their style of decoration, clearly derived from Meissen. Thereafter, it is probable that Sèvres provided the main source of inspiration, except in the case of the scale grounds, which would have been taken from Meissen. The yellow grounds are represented by five contrasting specimens. The bough pot (No.91) is an unusual example for this period, of a rococo form, and the yellow ground enhances its exuberant shape, adding to its sense of élan. The sucrier and cover (No.92) suggest the influence of Sèvres, whilst the milkjug and cover (No.93), painted in a yellow scale ground, are inspired by a Meissen prototype.

The famous rose Pompadour of Sèvres has no exact counterpart at Worcester and the claret ground on the sweetmeat dish (No.96) and the milkjug (No.97) is probably derived from Chelsea, where the colour was firmly established. It has been suggested that this is the colour described as 'Scarlet' in the sale advertisement for May 1769, but there is reason to believe that a more likely candidate exists.[1] Furthermore, the claret ground would appear to have been one of the last colours to have been introduced at Worcester.

The turquoise ground cup and saucer (No.99) is the equivalent colour to the 'Sky Blue' of the 1769 advertisement and was inspired by the bleu céleste of Sèvres, though the colour was also used at Meissen. This bright tone of turquoise was 'invented' at Sèvres in 1752 and owes its origins to the use of a similar colour on Chinese porcelain of the K'ang Hsi dynasty. The apple-green ground, represented in the Collection by a teapot (No.100) and a plate (No.101), is almost certain to have been the colour listed as 'pea green', a somewhat more faithful description of this particular tone. This too, probably reflects the influence of the Sèvres factory, where it was introduced in 1756.

The rare pair of plates (No.102) utilises the Sèvres bleu de roi, a ground colour which was common at the French factory but seldom occurs on Worcester. Perhaps the designers at Worcester, with their unerring taste, perceived that this royal blue was altogether too strong a colour to incorporate into a pattern in so prominent a manner. At any event, the royal blue was mainly confined to narrow borders, edged in gilt and framing many of the numerous patterns inspired by Sèvres.

The remainder of this section is devoted to a series of pieces with colourful border patterns, not strictly termed coloured grounds, but which in their decoration and visual purpose are sufficiently similar to them to form a coherent group. The principal thread linking these last nine specimens is that of Sèvres. This influence was so absorbed into the Worcester style that it is seldom possible to identify any particular pattern as an exact copy of Sèvres painting. It was a framework, adapted and developed in such a way that it became distinctive to Worcester, despite its French origins. Some of the most delightful Worcester patterns of the 1770s were evolved in this way, all having a freshness and a softness of palette that contrast with the underglaze blue grounds of the same period.

It should be stressed, however, that just as many of the earliest chinoiserie patterns show the immediate influence of the delftware painters, and the Meissen style of the late 1750s was often absorbed by way of Chelsea, the borrowing and adaptations of designs and motifs from Meissen, Sèvres and Tournai in the 1770s often reveal overlapping influences, sometimes discernible on a single piece.

[1] Cf. No.165 in this Catalogue.

COLOUR PLATE 24
A Bough Pot *c.*1768 (No.91)

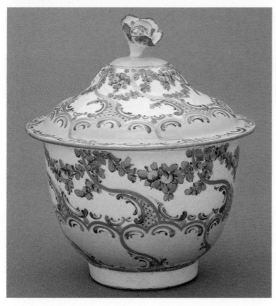

COLOUR PLATE 25
A Sucrier & Cover *c.*1770–72 (No.92)

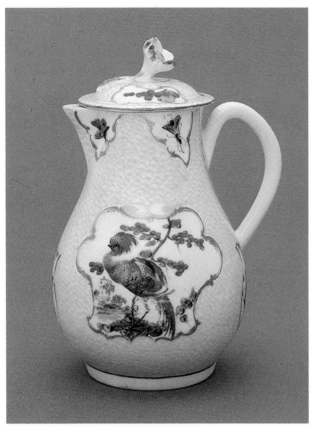

COLOUR PLATE 26
A Milkjug & Cover *c.*1765–68 (No.93)

COLOUR PLATE 27
A Mug *c.*1758 (No.94)

COLOUR PLATE 28
A Sweetmeat Dish *c.*1776 (No.96)
A Milkjug *c.*1776 (No.97)

COLOUR PLATE 29
A Teapot & Cover *c.*1765–68 (No.100)

COLOUR PLATE 30
An oval Dish *c.*1770 (No.103)

91

92

COLOUR PLATE 24

91 A Bough Pot *c.*1768

of bombé form, with a moulded scroll-edged rim, painted with bouquets of flowers within cartouches, upon a yellow ground.

Height: 6½ inches
Width: 8½ inches

Mark: None

Provenance
T. Leonard Crow

Literature
The shape is illustrated by:
Franklin A. Barrett: *op.cit.* Plate 19.
H. Rissik Marshall: *op.cit.* Plate 32, No.696.
Henry Sandon: *op.cit.* Plate 78.

Bough pots, sometimes referred to as crocus pots, were made at Worcester from *c.*1758–70. They occur most often with naturalistic birds in the Chelsea style, with exotic birds upon a scale blue ground or transfer-printed in underglaze blue.

The use of this very bright shade of blue is more readily associated with Factory decoration than with the Giles atelier.

It is unusual at this period to encounter a Worcester shape so strongly influenced by the rococo style.

COLOUR PLATE 25

92 A Sucrier & Cover *c.*1770–72

decorated with wide yellow ground borders and scroll gilding, with green floral wreaths and fruit.

Diameter: 4 inches

Mark: None

Literature
Franklin A. Barrett: *op.cit.* Plate 58A, illustrates a teapot.
H. Rissik Marshall: *op.cit.* Plate 30, No.662, illustrates a caudle cup and saucer.

The shade of yellow used as a ground colour at Worcester varies from a pale lemon colour to the strong sulphur tone seen on this sucrier and cover.

This rare pattern is adapted from Sèvres, where the ground colour was known as 'jaune jonquille'.

As with teapots, the undersides of the flanges of sucrier covers were fully glazed until about 1768. Thereafter they were unglazed like their Caughley counterparts of the same shape.

A yellow ground bough pot similar to No.91 is in the Lady Ludlow Collection at Luton Hoo, together with an extensive display of yellow ground Worcester.

93

94

COLOUR PLATE 26

93 A Milkjug & Cover *c*.1765–68

painted with dishevelled birds within gilt-edged mirror-shaped panels interspersed with insects, upon a yellow scale ground.

Height: 5¼ inches

Mark: None

Provenance
The Lady Heilbron Collection
Sotheby's 7 December 1954

Literature
J. Emerson: *The Collectors: Early European Ceramics and Silver*, Exhibition Catalogue, No.98, colour plate, illustrates this milkjug.
F. Severne MacKenna: *op.cit*. Plate 56, No.114, illustrates a teacup and saucer.
Frank Tilley: *op.cit*. Colour Frontispiece, illustrates a teapot and stand.

Yellow scale decoration is considerably rarer than the yellow ground and seems only to occur in conjunction with dishevelled birds. It is found principally on teaware and caudle cups and saucers. Although scale grounds do occur on Sèvres, they are rare, and the inspiration for this milkjug is more likely to have been from Meissen.

This particular bird, with its brilliant blue crest, is frequently found in association with yellow scale decoration, although the artist also worked on blue scale grounds.

Covered milkjugs seem to have been introduced at Worcester in about 1762–65.

COLOUR PLATE 27

94 A Mug *c*.1758

of bell shape, each side painted in puce monochrome with an oriental landscape within a lobed quatrefoil-shaped panel, upon a pale-yellow ground with scattered chrysanthemum sprays and leaves.

Height: 4½ inches

Mark: None

Literature
H. Rissik Marshall: *op.cit*. Plate 29, No.639.
Henry Sandon: *op.cit*. Plate 51.

The decoration on this mug displays a curious combination of influences. The floral sprays and the border design show a Kakiemon derivation,

95

whilst the landscape painting is in the Chinese style. The overall composition, however, is clearly derived from Meissen.

This is an example of the earliest use of a coloured ground at Worcester. The paste, the glaze and the shape are indicative of an early date and the finely executed Chinese landscape is reminiscent of such underglaze blue designs as the 'Romantic Rocks' pattern which occurs on octagonal teabowls and saucers.

Three bell-shaped mugs and one straight-sided example in this pattern are in the Victoria and Albert Museum, and a further bell-shaped mug, together with two vases, are in the Dyson Perrins Museum at Worcester.

95 A pierced Basket *c.*1768–70

of circular form, with a scalloped rim, painted in the interior with a large bouquet of flowers and around the border with floral sprays, the exterior having a pale-yellow ground.

Diameter: 8¼ inches

Mark: None

Provenance
The Trapnell Collection

Literature
H. Rissik Marshall: *op.cit.* Plate 13, No.232, illustrates a slightly earlier example.

Openwork baskets were first produced at Worcester in about 1758.

Cf. the pot of flowers (No.70) for similar floral decoration.

96 and 97

COLOUR PLATE 28

96 A Sweetmeat Dish *c.*1776

moulded with a spray of rose leaves and buds, the stalk forming the handle, and painted in the centre with fruit, within a claret cornucopia-shaped border with ciselé gilding. The 'Hope-Edwardes' pattern.

Diameter: 6 inches

Mark: None

Provenance
T. Leonard Crow (Cf. letter No.29)

Literature
Albert Amor Ltd: *The Elegant Porcelain of James Giles*, Exhibition Catalogue, 1983, No.38.
H. Rissik Marshall: *op.cit.* Plate 34, No.735.

Three versions of this basic design are known, two dessert services both decorated in the atelier of James Giles, and a tea and coffee service which appears to be painted by a different hand. This sweetmeat dish has many features which suggest Factory decoration rather than an attribution to the Giles atelier. The composition of the central cluster of fruit is tighter and more compact than on

the Giles examples and the palette is brighter. On the other hand, the style of gilding is very much in the manner of Giles. Gerald Coke, in his book *In Search of James Giles*, concludes that this may have been one of the patterns taken over by the Factory after the closure of the Giles atelier in 1776 and possibly executed by one of his former artists.

Cf. Nos 48 & 49 for other dishes with this so-called 'Blind Earl' moulding.

COLOUR PLATE 28

97 A Milkjug *c.*1776

painted with a group of fruit and flowers below a richly gilded claret cornucopia-shaped border. The 'Hope-Edwardes' pattern.

Height: $4\frac{1}{2}$ inches

Mark: None

Literature
Gerald Coke: *op.cit.* Plate 52(a), illustrates a teabowl and saucer from this service.

The 'Hope-Edwardes' service was reputedly made for Sir Thomas Edwardes, 6th Baronet, who died

98

in 1790. His niece, who succeeded to the family estates, married John Thomas Hope of Netley Hall, Salop, in 1794 and her son assumed the name and arms of Hope-Edwardes, in 1854.

As with the sweetmeat dish, No.96 in the Collection, this milkjug appears to be the Factory version of this pattern, rather than the slightly earlier Giles version. A comparison with the palette, composition and style of painting on the tureen stand from the 'Duke of Gloucester' service (No.64) shows many similarities with both this milkjug and with the sweetmeat dish (No.96).

The gilt decoration on the handle is an embellishment which can be traced back to Meissen, but in this instance, the immediate influence is that of the Giles atelier.

98 A Bowl c.1776

with a turquoise cornucopia-shaped border, enriched with ciselé gilding and painted with fruit and flowers.

Diameter: 6½ inches

Mark: Crossed swords and numeral 9

Provenance
T. Leonard Crow (Cf. letter No.9)

Literature
Gerald Coke: op.cit. Colour Plate VI, illustrates a lozenge-shaped dish with the Giles version of this form of decoration.

In the past, this decoration, together with the two preceding examples of the 'Hope-Edwardes' pattern, were attributed to the atelier of James Giles. However, modern scholarship, and in particular the research of Gerald Coke, has suggested the probability that all three pieces were Giles patterns, later taken over by the factory.

The presence of a pseudo-Meissen crossed swords mark is sometimes, but as in this case, not invariably, an indication of Giles decoration.

Cf. No.151 for the Giles version of this ground colour.

99

99 A Coffee Cup & Saucer *c.*1772

with fluted sides and entwined handles, painted in solid turquoise, enriched with gilding.

Diameter of saucer: $5\frac{1}{4}$ inches

Mark: Fretted square

Literature
Gerald Coke: *op.cit.* Plate 51(a), illustrates a two-handled cup and saucer decorated in the Giles atelier.
H. Rissik Marshall: *op.cit.* Plate 21, No.395, illustrates the Factory version.

A Sale of Worcester porcelain was held by Mr Burnsall at Christie's in May 1769. Although no catalogue of the contents of this sale has survived, an advertisement lists some of the coloured grounds at that time available on Worcester porcelain. Among these was a sky blue, which is almost certainly the solid turquoise of Worcester. Both the Factory and Giles used this colour ground, and the type and style of gilding are the principal clues as to the place of decoration.

This ground colour was probably derived from Sèvres, where it was introduced in 1752. The entwined handle form, introduced at Worcester in the late 1760s, was derived from Vincennes.

COLOUR PLATE 29

100 A Teapot & Cover *c.*1765–68

of inverted pear shape with a loop handle and a faceted spout, painted with exotic birds in mirror-shaped panels, upon an apple-green ground.

Height: $5\frac{1}{4}$ inches

Mark: None

Provenance
The Edmund Darcy Taylor Collection
Sotheby's 9 April 1957

Literature
Albert Amor Ltd: *Worcester Porcelain 1751–1784,* Exhibition Catalogue, Colour Plate IV, illustrates a sucrier and cover.
Henry Sandon: *op.cit.* Plate 68, illustrates a masked jug.

Apple green is probably the colour described in the Christie's 1769 Sale advertisement as 'pea green'. This ground colour was used at Worcester on a variety of shapes including teaware, dessert services, mugs and vases.

An element of controversy surrounds the Worcester apple-green grounds, especially those found in conjunction with bird decoration. Like

100

101

the yellow ground, the green ground would not take gilding.

The shape of this teapot is more usually associated with the late 1750s and early 1760s, but the decoration, in this instance, is clearly nearer to 1770 in date.

A large selection of Worcester decorated with green grounds is in the Lady Ludlow Collection at Luton Hoo.

101 A Plate *c*.1768–72

with a scalloped edge, painted with festoons of flowers trailing obliquely into the centre and an apple-green border, edged with gilt scrolls. The 'Marchioness of Huntly' pattern.

Diameter: 6 inches

Mark: None

Literature
Albert Amor Ltd: *Worcester Porcelain 1751–1784*, Exhibition Catalogue, No.80.
H. Rissik Marshall: *op.cit.* Plate 33, No.720.

A dessert service in this pattern was sold on 16 June 1882 by the Marchioness of Huntly, second wife of the 10th Marquess. This pattern has since been named after the Marchioness of Huntly, though far too many examples still exist for them all to have come from a single service.

Although doubt exists as to the genuineness of some of the apple-green grounds, this pattern is clearly above suspicion in this respect. Apple green is the most common of the overglaze grounds found on Worcester, although it is a colour that was seldom used at the Giles atelier. The colour was probably inspired by Sèvres, where it was introduced in 1756.

95

102

102 A pair of Plates *c.*1772–74

painted with royal blue cornucopia-shaped borders, enriched with gilding, and in the centre, exotic birds and flowering plants.

Diameter: 8¾ inches

Marks: Script W on both pieces. Very faint

Provenance
T. Leonard Crow (Cf. letter No.25)
The Eckstein Collection

Literature
H. Rissik Marshall: *op.cit.* Plate 37, No.808.

This very bright overglaze blue is a rare but not entirely successful ground colour. Rissik Marshall suggested that this decoration originated in the Giles workshop, and there are certainly aspects of the overall design which seem very untypical of Factory decoration. However, the bird painting does seem characteristic and strongly resembles that on the milkjug, No.76 in this Collection.

COLOUR PLATE 30

103 An oval Dish *c.*1770

of twelve-sided form, painted in the centre with exotic birds in a verdant landscape, surrounded by insects. The elaborate border design is of alternating pink herringbone, turquoise trellis diaper, purple caillouté and gilt floral panels, edged with scrolls and lambrequins in gilding.

Length: 12 inches

Mark: None

Literature
Albert Amor Ltd: *Worcester Porcelain 1751–1784*, Exhibition Catalogue, Colour Plate vi, illustrates a plate from this service.
H. Rissik Marshall: *op.cit.* Plate 31, No.690, illustrates a lozenge-shaped dish.
F. Severne MacKenna: *op.cit.* Plate 64, No.130, illustrates an identical dish.

The influence of the Sèvres factory had by this period become more prominent than that of Meissen, and this fine dish is illustrative of the more

103

delicate style of decoration associated with the French factory.

A tureen, cover and stand in this pattern are in the Dyson Perrins Museum at Worcester.

The gilt decoration is in a restrained style by comparison with the characteristically rich gilding associated with Giles. Cf. Colour Plates 42 & 44 for a comparison with Giles gilding.

104 A pair of pierced Baskets *c.*1775

of oval form, with rope twist handles and applied leaves to the exterior, painted on the interior with a border of pink diaper panels, alternating with green florettes reserved within gilt scrollwork on a stippled ground, the centre with radiating lilac scrolls, entwined with festoons of green foliage with red berries, and in the centre, a cluster of plums. The 'Earl Manvers' service.

Length: 7½ inches

Marks: None

Provenance
The Frederick Carter Collection
Marshall Field & Co., Chicago

Literature
R.L. Hobson: *op.cit.* Plate 39, No. 194.

This service was reputedly made for Charles Meadows, who upon succeeding to the estate of his uncle, the 2nd Duke of Kingston, assumed the surname and arms of Pierrepont. He was raised to the peerage in 1796 and advanced to the dignity of Earl Manvers in 1806.

97

104

The composition of the pattern and the relatively soft palette are typical of the Sèvres influence.

This is a relatively late form of basket, not introduced at Worcester until about 1770.

105 A Plate *c.*1775

with a fluted rim, painted with a border of pink diaper panels, alternating with green florettes reserved within gilt scrollwork on stippled ground, the centre with radiating lilac scrolls, entwined with festoons of green foliage with red berries, and in the centre, a cluster of plums. The 'Earl Manvers' service.

Diameter: 8½ inches

Mark: None

Provenance
T. Leonard Crow (Cf. letter No.12)

Literature
Franklin A. Barrett: *op.cit.* Plate 56B, illustrates a dish from this service.
H. Rissik Marshall: *op.cit.* Plate 15, No.258.

An examination of the paste, glaze and decoration of this service reveals it to be comparatively late in period and some examples appear to date from the late 1770s.

Several examples of this pattern are in the Dyson Perrins Museum at Worcester.

Cf. the pair of baskets, No.104 in this Collection.

106 A Bowl *c.*1770

of fluted form, painted with four groups of pink and gilt trelliswork, linked by festoons of berried hops, the rim and foot decorated with a gilt-edged turquoise scale border. A 'Hop Trellis' pattern.

Diameter: 6½ inches

Mark: None

Provenance
T. Leonard Crow (Cf. letter No.53)

Literature
H. Rissik Marshall: *op.cit.* Plate 28, No.622, illustrates a two-handled cup and saucer in this pattern.
George Savage: *op.cit.* Plate 106(c), illustrates a teacaddy.

This is one of the 'Hop Trellis' patterns, inspired by Sèvres. These patterns also occur with borders in pink, mauve and royal blue, and at least ten variations upon this theme were devised at Worcester.

105

106

107

107 A Teacup & Saucer *c.*1770–72

of fluted form, painted with exotic birds and insects, with a border of alternating pink herringbone, turquoise trellis diaper, purple caillouté and gilt floral panels, edged with lambrequins in gilding.

Diameter of saucer: 5¼ inches

Mark: None

Literature
H. Rissik Marshall: *op.cit.* Plate 31, No.690, illustrates a lozenge-shaped dish with similar decoration.

This style of fluted teaware is invariably found in conjunction with ogee handle forms on cups, milkjugs and barrel-shaped teapots. The shape was introduced at Worcester in about 1770 and is associated with the Sèvres style of decoration and, to a lesser extent, with patterns derived from Meissen.

A saucerdish of this pattern is in the Victoria and Albert Museum.

Cf. the twelve-sided dish, No.103 in this Collection.

108

108 A Teabowl, Coffee Cup &
Saucer *c.*1770−72

of fluted form, decorated with curving swags of
green and red hops and berries with radiating
scrolls and borders of pink chevron patterns.

Diameter of saucer: $4\frac{5}{8}$ inches

Mark: None

Provenance
T. Leonard Crow (Cf. letter No.43)

Literature
Albert Amor Ltd: *Worcester Porcelain 1751−1784*,
Exhibition Catalogue, No.72.
H. Rissik Marshall: *op.cit.* Plate 18, No.327,
illustrates a saucerdish in this pattern.

A pattern very similar in style and palette to the
'Earl Manvers', Nos 104 & 105 in this Collection.
This design occurs in conjunction with teaware of a
slightly smaller size than normal for this period.

109 A Teabowl & Saucer *c.*1772−75

of fluted form, painted with a star-shaped
arrangement of hop festoons and puce flowers,
pendent from a scalloped turquoise border
decorated in black with a caillouté motif.

Diameter of saucer: $5\frac{1}{4}$ inches

Mark: None

Literature
F. Severne MacKenna: *op.cit.* Plate 35, No.70,
illustrates a teapot and stand in this pattern.

This form of fluted teaware was continued into
the Flight period in the 1780s.

109

110

111

110 A Teacup & Saucer *c*.1772–75

of fluted form, with a turquoise border overlaid with black loops and œil de perdrix interspersed with panels of diaper, edged with gilt scrollwork, three floral sprays in mauve, and in the centre, within a gilt circle, a bouquet of flowers.

Diameter of saucer: 5¼ inches

Mark: None

Provenance
T. Leonard Crow

Literature
H. Rissik Marshall; *op.cit.* Plate 21, No.393, and Plate 43, No.908.

The ogee handle on this teacup was a form introduced at Worcester in about 1770. This handle form was widely used on English porcelain teaware during the period 1770–1800.

111 A Teabowl & Saucer *c*.1772

of fluted form, decorated alternately with red hop trellis and garlands of berried hops, pendent from gilt scrolls on a royal blue rim and with a shaped inner border of turquoise caillouté.

Diameter of saucer: 5½ inches

Mark: Crescent in underglaze blue

Provenance
T. Leonard Crow (Cf. letter No.28)

Literature
F. Severne MacKenna: *op.cit.* Plate 35, No.71.
H. Rissik Marshall: *op.cit.* Plate 23, No.477.

This is an adaptation and elaboration of a Sèvres pattern of about 1763. By comparison with the Sèvres original, the number of trellis panels has been reduced and the size of each expanded. The wide inner border of turquoise caillouté has been inserted in place of a crenellated bleu de roi design.

The catalogue of the Sale of Worcester porcelain at Christie's from 21 March–25 March 1774 lists 'Pair caudle cups ribb'd to a rich seve pattern'. An example that fits this description, decorated in the Giles atelier, is illustrated by Gerald Coke in *In Search of James Giles*, Colour Plate XI. It is interesting to note how much closer the Giles version is to the Sèvres original than the Factory example illustrated here.

Chapter V

The Blue Grounds

The ten years from 1765 to 1776 witnessed the pre-eminence of the Worcester blue grounds. To generations of collectors this form of decoration is synonymous with Worcester porcelain and, indeed, the imagination and inventiveness with which these grounds were used were seldom attained by any other European factory.

For the purposes of this Catalogue, I have grouped the three underglaze blue grounds: blue scale, powder blue and gros bleu, together with the overglaze royal blue, which was used as a border design. The first of these grounds was the 'powder blue' which was introduced in about 1760, although the earliest examples were decorated purely in underglaze blue and it was not until about 1765 that it occurred in conjunction with overglaze colours. The blue scale ground was certainly in production by about 1767–68, and probably by a year or so earlier. The gros bleu ground is mentioned under the description of 'Mazarine Blue' in the 1769 advertisement and this colour had probably been introduced only a year or so before, although it had been mastered at Chelsea by the late 1750s.

The 'powder blue' ground was derived from Chinese porcelain of the K'ang Hsi dynasty. It takes its name from the original method of production whereby the cobalt blue was blown in powdered form through a bamboo tube, covered at the end with a silk screen. It is distinguished from the other blue grounds by a granular effect which is especially noticeable on the lighter blue examples, such as the teapot (No.125) in this Collection. At its best, the 'powder blue' affords a harmonious background for the flowers or birds which appear in the characteristically fan-shaped reserved panels. This ground colour occurs in conjunction with three principal styles of overglaze decoration: birds, which are usually of the 'agitated' variety (Nos 125 & 126), English flowers and oriental flowers (No.127). It spans a period of about ten years from 1760 to 1770 and the softer, lighter-toned grounds tend to be earlier than the darker examples.

The inspiration for the famous Worcester blue scale ground is obscure. Rissik Marshall refers to a large Chinese bowl in the Drane Collection (Item 152), dating from about 1723, which is 'covered externally with a small downward scale blue ground with white reserves'. This, he concludes, is the likely source for the Worcester scale grounds. In considering this hypothesis, it should be emphasised that a blue scale ground is exceedingly rare on Chinese porcelain and indeed on European porcelain with the single exception of Worcester. Alternatively, the derivation may have been the Mosaik border designs used at Meissen in overglaze colours from about 1760 onwards. However, if this form of decoration was not actually invented at Worcester, it was certainly developed and refined there, in all its variations, into a distinctive and often sumptuous style.

The ground itself varies from a well-defined pattern, where each 'salmon scale' can be identified, to a darkish blue where the scales are barely perceptible. It seems likely that the clearly-defined scaling is often an indication of an early piece, although there are too many exceptions to this generalisation for it to be a positive guide to the dating of blue scale decoration.

The Klepser Collection includes sixteen examples of the blue scale ground, three of which are discussed in the following chapter. The exotic bird decoration, so inextricably associated with Worcester porcelain, is shown to good effect on the mug (No.115), the leaf-shaped dish (No.118) and the plate (No.119), whilst the coffeepot (No.112) and the vase (No.114) exhibit contrasting styles of oriental designs. The spectacular dish (No.122) illustrates the splendour of European floral painting and the small mug (No.117) is a rare and successful alliance of Chinese figures and a blue ground. Another unusual combination, perhaps inspired by gold anchor period Chelsea, can be seen in the teabowl, coffee cup and saucer (No.123). Here, in the manner associated with the French painter Antoine Watteau, figures resplendent in Chinese costume play musical instruments amidst fanciful rococo trelliswork, in surroundings redolent of 'Chinese Chippendale'. This exuberant richly gilded design occurs upon a blue scale ground of remarkable clarity and it is perhaps significant that the best examples of this ground so often coincide with the more elaborate and ambitious Worcester patterns. The blue scale ground, introduced in about 1766–67, seems gradually to have been phased out in the late 1770s and the later examples show a distinct deterioration in every aspect of their decoration.

The gros bleu ground was derived from Sèvres where the equivalent colour was known as bleu lapis. At Chelsea it was described as mazarine blue and at Worcester it has been variously named by writers as 'dark blue', 'wet blue' and more accurately 'solid blue'. By comparison with the 'powder blue' and blue scale it is indeed a solid blue and, as may be observed from the illustrations, it forms a frame that sometimes threatens to overwhelm the painting within it. It occurs in conjunction with a similar range of decorative motifs as the blue scale, although the visual effect can sometimes be strikingly different. The heaviness of the 'solid blue' ground is usually alleviated by the subtle use of gilded decoration and, at its best, the combination can be arresting. The plate from the 'Burdett Coutt's service (No.134), for instance, combines a design, composed and laid out with the sophistication and flair of the finest gold anchor period Chelsea, with the technical control of the underglaze blue and the high quality gilding which were among the hallmarks of the Worcester factory. Much of the work of Jefferyes Hamett O'Neale occurs in conjunction with a gros bleu ground and this is represented by a plate painted with the fable of 'The Eagle and the Tortoise' (No.136). The gros bleu ground first appeared at Worcester in about 1768, shortly after the introduction of the blue scale. The two colours seem to have fallen out of fashion at roughly the same time, during the late 1770s.

The remainder of this section of the Collection is devoted to patterns which have a narrow royal blue border. This is an overglaze colour, resembling the bleu de roi of Sèvres, and its characteristic brightness made it unsuitable as a ground colour, as can be seen from the pair of plates (No.102) in Chapter IV. A number of the named services which so fascinated Mr Klepser were painted with this form of border design, including several with the distinctive landscape scenes framed by turquoise husk borders. These royal blue borders were the last of the Worcester 'blue grounds', first appearing in about 1770 and continuing until the end of the decade.

  Unlike the porcelain in the other seven sections of this Catalogue, the majority of these blue ground pieces bear a factory mark. The 'powder blue' ground is an exception and is generally not marked, except in the case of examples decorated solely in underglaze blue. The blue scale is nearly always marked, most commonly with a fretted square. Gros bleu grounds also tend to be marked, either with a crescent or a fretted square. In contrast, the royal blue borders are associated with the crescent and sometimes script W marks, but not with the fretted square.[1]

[1] For a detailed analysis of this subject, see S.M. Clarke: *Marks on Overglaze-Decorated First Period Worcester Porcelain; A Statistical Study.*

112

112 A Coffeepot & Cover *c.*1765–68

decorated with star-shaped blossoms and half chrysanthemums edged with gilt scrolls, within mirror- and vase-shaped reserved panels upon a blue scale ground.

Height: 8¼ inches

Mark: Fretted square

Provenance
The Esperance Collection

Literature
Gerald Coke: *op.cit.* Plate 46(b), illustrates the Giles version of this pattern on a teabowl and saucer.
R.L. Hobson: *op.cit.* Plate 12, No.72, illustrates the Factory version on a milkjug and cover.

This is probably the 'Fine old Japan star pattern' referred to in the catalogue of the Christie's Sale in December 1769.

Coffeepots of this form were introduced in the early 1760s and it remained the standard Worcester shape for the next fifteen years.

By comparison with this pattern, the related version, attributed by Gerald Coke to the Giles atelier, has the star-shaped blossoms placed upon a white ground, between four underglaze blue panels.

113

113 A Teapot, Cover & Stand
*c.*1765–68

decorated with wheat-sheaves and Japanese flowers, edged with gilt scrolls, within vase- and mirror-shaped panels upon a blue scale ground.

Height of teapot: 6½ inches
Width of stand: 5⅞ inches

Mark: Fretted square

Provenance
The Esperance Collection

Literature
R.L. Hobson: *op.cit.* Plate 15, No.89.
H. Rissik Marshall: *op.cit.* Plate 47, No.969.

A teapot formerly in the Drane Collection and painted in this same 'Japan' style, with a clearly defined blue scale ground, has the unusual feature of a gold cartouche under the spout, inscribed 'No.45'. Attached to the knop is a gold brooch of the numerals 45 and the word 'Liberty'. This alludes to John Wilkes and the famous issue 'Number 45' of his paper, *The North Briton*, published on 23 April 1763. Wilkes was popularly regarded as a champion of liberty and this issue of his paper was widely commemorated on ceramics. However, the issue seems to have caught the public attention, *not* at the time of its publication, but during the Middlesex Elections of 1768 and the commemorative ceramics date from that year. This teapot, therefore, can be dated to within a year or so and consequently has a certain 'documentary' significance.

This lobed hexagonal form is the standard shape for a Worcester teapot stand. It was introduced in about 1756 and invariably has an unglazed base. As with spoontrays the later examples have more sharply angled sides and tend to be of a larger diameter.

114

115

Literature
English Ceramic Circle: Exhibition Catalogue
1948, No.427, illustrates a vase of the same shape,
with a similar 'Japan' design.

This pattern occurs on a variety of shapes including
teaware, coffeepots and a wide range of vase forms.

A garniture of five similar vases is in the Untermyer Collection in the Metropolitan Museum,
New York.

Another example of this well-known Worcester
shape is No.187 in this Collection.

115 A Mug *c.*1768

of cylindrical form, with a grooved handle,
painted with exotic birds among foliage within
asymmetrical panels edged with gilt scrolls, upon
a blue scale ground.

Height: $4\frac{3}{4}$ inches

Mark: Fretted square

Provenance
T. Leonard Crow

Literature
Henry Sandon: *op.cit.* Plate 81.

The Worcester blue scale ground nearly always
bears a factory mark, most often a fretted square
but occasionally a crescent or script W.

114 A Vase & Cover *c.*1765–68

decorated with Japanese flowers, foliage and
birds, edged with gilt scrolls, within mirror-
shaped panels, upon a blue scale ground.

Height: 9 inches

Mark: Fretted square

Provenance
Marshall Field & Co., Chicago

116

117

116 A Mug *c.*1768

of cylindrical form, with a grooved handle, painted with large bouquets of flowers within asymmetrical panels, edged with gilt scrolls upon a blue scale ground.

Height: 4¾ inches

Mark: Fretted square

Provenance
T. Leonard Crow

Literature
H. Rissik Marshall: *op.cit.* Plate 13, No.239.
Henry Sandon: *op.cit.* Plate 81.

This standard cylindrical mug form, issued in several sizes, first appeared at Worcester in about 1758 and continued, unaltered in shape, into the middle 1770s.

Cf. No.149 for a slightly later example of this shape.

117 A Mug *c.*1768–70

of cylindrical form, with a grooved handle, painted with Chinese ladies within gilt-edged asymmetrical panels upon a blue scale ground.

Height: 3½ inches

Mark: Fretted square

Provenance
The Goldblatt Collection
Sotheby's 1 May 1956

Literature
H. Rissik Marshall: *op.cit.* Plate 47, No.970, and Plate 53, No.1086.

Chinese figure decoration is rare in conjunction with a blue scale ground. A similar mug, larger in size, is in the Victoria and Albert Museum.

118

118 A leaf-shaped Dish *c.*1768–70

with a twig handle, painted with exotic birds in landscapes, within mirror-shaped reserved panels, edged with gilt, upon a blue scale ground.

Length: 7 inches

Mark: Fretted square

Provenance
Marshall Field & Co., Chicago

Literature
Simon Spero: *op.cit.* Page 86, illustrates a dish of similar shape with flowers upon a blue scale ground.

This form of leaf-shaped dish also occurs with underglaze blue decoration, both transfer-printed and hand-painted. The shape, derived from a Meissen original, was also used at Chelsea. It was introduced at Worcester in the late 1760s.

119

119 A Plate *c.*1770

with a scalloped edge, painted with exotic birds within mirror-shaped panels, edged with gilt scrolls, upon a blue scale ground.

Diameter: $7\frac{1}{2}$ inches

Mark: Fretted square

Provenance
T. Leonard Crow

Literature
Simon Spero: *op.cit.* Page 92, illustrates a similar plate with flowers, upon a blue scale ground.

120

120 A Plate *c.*1772–75

painted with bouquets of flowers within mirror-
and vase-shaped panels, edged with gilt, upon a
blue scale ground.

Diameter: 8¾ inches

Mark: Crescent

Provenance
T. Leonard Crow

Literature
H. Rissik Marshall: *op.cit.* Plate 23, No.452.

This shape of Worcester plate tends to be a little
later in period than the slightly smaller scalloped
form (No.119). Examples often exhibit the deterioration in the paste that occurred in the middle 1770s.

121

121 An openwork Basket c.1768

of circular form with a scalloped rim, painted in the centre with a star-shaped bouquet of flowers, within a blue scale border edged with gilt scrolls. The rim is decorated with an outer blue scale border, enriched in gilt, and the pierced sides are painted with garlands of flowers.

Diameter: $8\frac{1}{2}$ inches

Mark: Fretted square

Provenance
T. Leonard Crow

Literature
Albert Amor Ltd: *Dr. John Wall, 1708–1776,*
Exhibition Catalogue, No.62.
R.L. Hobson: *op.cit.* Plate 67, No.321.

Cf. Nos 154 & 156 for the looser treatment of the central floral bouquet at the Giles atelier.

122

123

122 A Dish *c.*1768

of rectangular shape with indented corners, painted with bouquets of flowers within mirror- and vase-shaped panels, edged with gilt, upon a blue scale ground.

Length: 16½ inches

Mark: Fretted square

Provenance
T. Leonard Crow

Literature
R.L. Hobson: *op.cit*. Plate 66, No.315.

Dishes of this size are rare.

The blue scale ground was occasionally used at Bow, often in conjunction with the fretted square mark. This decoration was also employed at Christian's Liverpool factory where the blue was applied over the glaze.

COLOUR PLATE 31

123 A Teabowl, Coffee Cup & Saucer *c.*1768

painted with figures in Chinese costume, playing musical instruments, after Watteau, seated in front of rococo trelliswork within mirror-shaped panels edged in gilt, divided by exotic birds and insects within vase-shaped panels, all upon a clearly defined blue scale ground enriched with gilt scroll borders.

Diameter of saucer: 5 inches

Mark: Fretted square

Provenance
T. Leonard Crow (Cf. letter No.35)

Literature
R.L. Hobson: *op.cit*. Plate 79, No.355.
F. Severne MacKenna: *op.cit*. Plate 49, No.99.

This rare and ambitious form of decoration occurs principally on tea and coffee services, two-handled cups and saucers and vases. Several different patterns are known, almost invariably in conjunction with an especially well-defined blue scale ground.

Several examples of this decoration are in the Victoria and Albert Museum and a two-handled chocolate cup and saucer are in the Untermyer Collection in the Metropolitan Museum, New York.

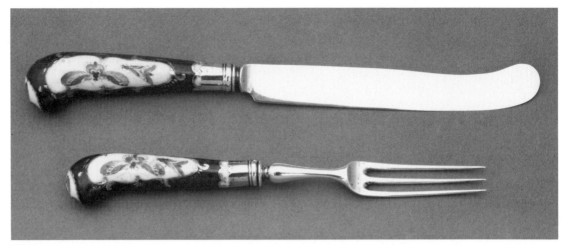

124

125

124 A Knife & Fork *c.*1768–70

with pistol-shaped handles, painted with butterflies and insects within panels edged in gilt, upon a blue scale ground. The blade, prongs and hilts are of silver. The 'Archbishop Cobbe' service.

Length of knife: 8¼ inches

Length of fork: 6¾ inches

Provenance
T. Leonard Crow (Cf. letter No.10)

Literature
Albert Amor Ltd: *Worcester Porcelain 1751–1784,* Exhibition Catalogue, No.49.
H. Rissik Marshall: *op.cit.* Plate 14, No.253.

This service, comprised solely of cutlery, is reputed to have been made for Archbishop Cobbe of Dublin. Charles Cobbe was born in 1687, educated at Winchester and graduated from Trinity College, Oxford in 1709. He went to Ireland in 1717 as Chaplain to Charles, Duke of Bolton, the Lord Lieutenant. He became Archbishop of Dublin in 1742 and died whilst in office in 1765. His connection with the service of cutlery is traditional but should be treated with caution as the porcelain appears slightly to post-date the Archbishop's death. It is more likely that the service was made for the Archbishop's son, Thomas Cobbe.

Coloured specimens of Worcester cutlery are scarce. In addition to the 'Cobbe' service, Marshall illustrates in his book an armorial pair (No.769), an apple-green pair (Colour Plate 23) and a less rare white moulded pair (No.910). Knives and forks painted in underglaze blue occur in five different patterns, all of which are unmoulded. Several overglaze 'dry blue' specimens are known.

In addition to these examples from the First Period, there are also some pieces of cutlery decorated in a similar style to that of the 'Cobbe' service, but made at Chamberlain's factory, probably in the late 1780s.

COLOUR PLATE 33

125 A Teapot & Cover *c.*1765

of globular form painted with 'agitated' birds within fan-shaped reserved panels and butterflies and insects within circular panels, edged with gilding, all upon an even powder blue ground, with sprays of gilt flowers and foliage.

Height: 6½ inches

Mark: None

Provenance
T. Leonard Crow (Cf. letter No.37)

Literature
F. Severne MacKenna: *op.cit.* Plate 42, No.85.

Though basically of the same globular form, this is a significantly earlier teapot than the blue scale example (No.113) or the gros bleu specimen (No.128). The 'agitated' bird decoration resembles that on the pair of salts (No.68). The deep rose pink on the handle, spout and finial is a colour seldom employed at the Giles atelier and can be regarded as a strong indication of Factory decoration.

126 A Teacup & Saucer *c.*1768

painted with exotic birds within fan-shaped reserved panels and insects within circular panels edged in gilt, upon a dark powder blue ground with sprays of gilt flowers and foliage.

Diameter of saucer: 5¼ inches

Mark: None

Provenance
T. Leonard Crow

A slightly later example of the powder blue ground than the teapot (No.125) which has a lighter-coloured, more 'powdery' tone of underglaze blue.

Where the 'powder blue' ground occurs in association with coloured decoration, underglaze blue marks were not used, but a crescent, painted in red, is sometimes present.

126

127

127 A Sucrier & Cover *c.*1768

painted in the Japanese taste with flowers in fan-shaped reserved panels and formalised chrysanthemums in circular panels, upon a dark powder blue ground.

Diameter: 4 inches

Mark: None

Provenance
T. Leonard Crow

Literature
H. Rissik Marshall: *op.cit.* Plate 9, No.145, illustrates a teabowl and saucer with similar decoration.

Powder blue decoration on Worcester porcelain invariably occurs in conjunction with fan-shaped reserved panels, a feature which has its origins in the Chinese designs from which it was derived. The 'open' flower finial was introduced in the mid-1760s, replacing the earlier 'closed' floral finial (Nos 38 & 176) of the 1758–65 period.

Prior to about 1770, sucriers tend to have relatively flat covers and flanges which overhang the sides. Thereafter, covers are generally more domed in outline and flanges are more flush with the rim of the bowl.

128

128 A Teapot & Cover *c.*1768–70

of globular form, painted with Chinese figures in
a landscape with buildings, with oval gilt-edged
reserved panels, upon a gros bleu ground with gilt
flower sprays.

Height: 6½ inches

Mark: Fretted square

(Cf. letter No.20)

Literature
Albert Amor Ltd: *Dr. John Wall, 1708–1776,*
Exhibition Catalogue, No.45, illustrates a teapot
stand, identically decorated but marked with a
crescent.
H. Rissik Marshall: *op.cit.* Plate 26, No.588,
illustrates a spoontray also bearing a crescent mark.

The combination of oriental figures and a solid
blue ground is rare.

129 A Teacaddy & Cover *c.*1772–75

of slightly flared cylindrical form, painted with
plump exotic birds in landscapes, within four gilt-
bordered panels, upon a gros bleu ground with
gilt sprays. The 'Duchess of Kent' pattern.

Height: 4¾ inches

Mark: Crescent

Provenance
The Eckstein Collection (Cf. letters Nos 13 & 14)
Sotheby's 29 March 1949
Formerly in the Thomas Berners and Robert
Drane Collections

Literature
R.L. Hobson: *op.cit.* Plate 62, No.295, illustrates a
teabowl and saucer from this service.
H. Rissik Marshall: *op.cit.* Plate 38, No.814,
illustrates a saucerdish and Plate 39, No.829, the
teapot.

The service is reputed to have belonged to the
Duchess of Kent, mother of Queen Victoria. She
was born in 1786, married the Duke of Kent in
1818 and died in 1861.

The shapes are not of conventional form, the
teabowls being of an almost straight-sided bucket
shape and this teacaddy resembling that of the
'Stormont' service (No.67) in its outline. These are
relatively late Worcester forms.

Another teacaddy, with apparently identical
decoration, is in the Dyson Perrins Museum.

129

130

131 A Butter Tub & Stand *c.*1770

painted with long-legged exotic birds in
landscapes, within reserved panels edged in gilt,
upon a gros bleu ground with gilt scrolls. The
'Marchioness of Ely' pattern.

Diameter of stand: 6¼ inches
Diameter of dish: 5 inches

Mark: Fretted square

Literature
R.L. Hobson: *op.cit.* Plate 62, No.292.
H. Rissik Marshall: *op.cit.* Plate 48, No.983.

This service was sold at Christie's on 26 March
1908, as the property of Caroline, Marchioness of
Ely, the widow of the 4th Marquess. A pair of
almost identical butter tubs but with slightly
different gilding is in the British Museum. The bird
painting is executed in a style reminiscent of that
on Tournai porcelain.

Butter tubs of this shape, more commonly found in
underglaze blue, were also made at Caughley and,
less often, at Lowestoft and Bow. The form was
introduced at Worcester in the 1765–68 period.

COLOUR PLATE 32

130 A Spoontray *c.*1772–75

of hexagonal shape, with fluted sides, painted
with plump exotic birds in landscapes, within four
gilt-bordered panels and with two plums within
an oval cartouche, all upon a gros bleu ground
with gilt sprays. The 'Duchess of Kent' pattern.

Length: 6⅛ inches

Mark: Crescent

Provenance
The Eckstein Collection (Cf. letters Nos 13 & 14)
Sotheby's 29 March 1949
Formerly in the Thomas Berners and Robert
Drane Collections

Literature
R.L. Hobson: *op.cit.* Plate 62, No.295, illustrates a
teabowl and saucer from this service.
H. Rissik Marshall: *op.cit.* Plate 38, No.814,
illustrates a saucerdish and Plate 39, No.829, the
teapot.

The gros bleu ground at Worcester is usually
accompanied by a factory mark generally either a
fretted square or a crescent, but occasionally a
script W.

A slightly earlier version of this orthodox Worcester shape is No.62 in this Collection.

For a direct comparison with the style and palette
of Giles bird decoration upon a blue ground, cf.
No.154 in this Catalogue, Colour Plate 44.

132 An openwork Basket *c.*1768–70

of circular form, with green twig handles, painted
in the Kakiemon taste, with a long-tailed bird
perched upon a turquoise rock, among flowering
plants, within a circular reserved panel edged in
gilt, upon a gros bleu ground with flowers and
foliage in gilt. The 'Sir Joshua Reynolds' pattern.

Diameter: 8½ inches

Mark: Crescent

Provenance
T. Leonard Crow (Cf. letter No.1)
The Esperance Collection

Literature
H. Rissik Marshall: *op.cit.* Plate 8, No.140,
illustrates a lozenge-shaped dish in this pattern.

The central portion of this decoration is associated
with Sir Joshua Reynolds, who lived from 1723 to
1792, but the nature of the connection with this
design is obscure. It occurs on Worcester from the
mid-1750s onwards, on a white ground, on a gros
bleu ground and with panels of underglaze blue.
The 'ho-ho' bird and the flowering foliage are
derived from a Japanese version of a Chinese
design. This is possibly the 'fine old japan pheasant
pattern' listed in Christie's 1769 Sale.

131

132

133

134

133 A Plate *c.*1770

with a scalloped edge, painted with stylised flowers and fern-like leaves in gilt, upon a solid gros bleu ground.

Diameter: 8¼ inches

Mark: None

Provenance
T. Leonard Crow (Cf. letter No.56)

Literature
H. Rissik Marshall: *op.cit.* Plate 24, No.538.

The pattern is derived from a Chinese K'ang Hsi original. A similar plate is in the Dyson Perrins Museum at Worcester.

134 A Plate *c.*1770

with a scalloped edge painted with swags of flowers and smaller sprays, within mirror-shaped panels, edged in gilt, upon a gros bleu ground. The 'Burdett Coutts' service.

Diameter: 8½ inches

Mark: Fretted square

Provenance
T. Leonard Crow (Cf. letter No.5)

Literature
Albert Amor Ltd: *Dr. John Wall, 1708–1776*, Exhibition Catalogue, No.63.
R.L. Hobson: *op.cit.* Plate 69, No.331.
H. Rissik Marshall: *op.cit.* Plate 39, No.826.

A service with this distinctive decoration belonged to Angela Georgina, Baroness Burdett Coutts. She lived from 1814 until 1906 and was the first woman to be created a Baroness in her own right. According to Severne MacKenna, the service was Lot 79 of the Burdett Coutts Sale on 9 May 1922 and sold for the considerable sum, at that time, of £556 10*s.* It comprised four oval baskets, two tureens, stands and ladles, fourteen dishes and twenty-five plates.

This is an especially fine and successful example of the Sèvres bleu lapis, as interpreted at Worcester, giving a brilliant effect similar to that of the finest Chelsea mazarine blue ground.

The floral sprays on this plate are tightly composed, a typical Factory characteristic which is quite unlike the freer style associated with Giles's floral decoration. Cf. Nos. 150 & 154.

COLOUR PLATE 31
A Teabowl, Coffee Cup & Saucer *c*.1768 (No.123)

COLOUR PLATE 32
A Spoontray *c*.1772–75 (No.130)

COLOUR PLATE 33
A Teapot & Cover *c*.1765 (No.125)

COLOUR PLATE 34
A Teapot & Cover *c*.1768–70 (No.128)

COLOUR PLATE 35
A Butter Tub & Stand *c.*1770 (No.131)

COLOUR PLATE 36
A Plate *c.*1770 (No.136)

COLOUR PLATE 37
A Dish *c.*1770–72 (No.140)

COLOUR PLATE 38
A Plate *c.*1770–72 (No.142)

135

136

135 A Plate *c.*1770

with a scalloped edge, painted with a bouquet of flowers in a large circular panel with an elaborate gilt border, upon a gros bleu ground.

Diameter: 8¼ inches

Mark: Crescent

Provenance
T. Leonard Crow

Literature
George Savage: *op.cit.* Plate 102(a)
Simon Spero: *op.cit.* Page 93.

This pattern seems to have been a popular one as it was continued into the 1780s.

Although this 'solid blue' ground is principally associated with Worcester, it was used with success at Chelsea, where it was known as 'mazarine blue' and introduced during the late 1750s, at Derby, where it was first used in about 1760, and at Bow, where it was introduced in the late 1760s. A blue ground was also utilised in conjunction with overglaze colours at the Liverpool factories of Philip Christian and Seth Pennington, at West Pans, and more rarely, at Bristol.

COLOUR PLATE 36

136 A Plate *c.*1770

with a scalloped edge, painted by Jefferyes Hamett O'Neale with the fable of 'The Eagle and the Tortoise', enclosed within a circular panel with a gilt scroll and latticework border, upon a gros bleu ground.

Diameter: 7½ inches

Mark: Fretted square

Provenance
The James MacHarg Collection (Cf. letter No.25)

Literature
English Ceramic Circle: Exhibition Catalogue 1948, No.439.
H. Rissik Marshall: *op.cit.* Plate 14, No.26.

In Chapter 4 of Part I of *Coloured Worcester Porcelain of the First Period*, Rissik Marshall describes the life and work of J.H. O'Neale and summarises his style. The present plate was Lot 26 of the Heathcote Sale on 21 February 1947, when it was sold for £94 10*s*. The subject, taken from Francis Barlow's fable *110*, is quoted in full by Marshall on Page 58.

137

It is sometimes suggested that O'Neale's work was done at the London atelier of James Giles. However, an examination of gilding on this plate reveals it to be in a completely different style to that of the Giles atelier, neither is the palette in any way typical of Giles.

This fable is also known on Chelsea porcelain.

137 A two-handled Cup & Saucer
*c.*1770

of double ogee shape, painted with large bouquets of flowers, enclosed within panels edged with gilt scrollwork, upon a gros bleu ground bordered in gilt.

Diameter of saucer: $5\frac{7}{8}$ inches

Mark on cup: Fretted square
Mark on saucer: Crescent

Provenance
T. Leonard Crow (Cf. letter No.34)

Literature
Albert Amor Ltd: *Worcester Porcelain 1751–1784*, Exhibition Catalogue, No.47, illustrates an example complete with its cover.
H. Rissik Marshall: *op.cit.* Plate 14, No.244.

This is probably a caudle cup and saucer of the type listed in Christie's Sale of December 1769 in Lot 69 on the fifth day, and described as 'Six caudle-cups covers and plates'. A number of caudle cups and saucers were listed in the catalogue of this six-day Sale and although this is the only specific reference to 'covers', it does suggest that at least some of the *two-handled* examples of this shape were intended to be complete with covers. An identical shape was made during the same period with a single handle and this may have been intended as a breakfast (or chocolate) cup and saucer and would therefore not have had a cover. This ogee form occurs also in overglaze transfer-printed decoration and in underglaze blue. It was introduced in about 1765.

138

138 A pair of small Mugs *c.1765–68*

of thistle shape, with scroll handles, painted in 'Japan' style with alternate panels of flowering plants and vertical underglaze blue panels, each containing a single red mons.

Height: 2¾ inches

Mark: Fretted squares

Literature
Albert Amor Ltd: *Dr. John Wall, 1708–1776,* Exhibition Catalogue, No.41.
H. Rissik Marshall: *op.cit.* Plate 14, No.246.

These small mugs or cups were possibly intended for toddy and the shape was probably derived from a silver original. Silver mugs of this basic shape dating from about 1700, were known as thistle cups.

139 A Cider Jug *c.1770–72*

of pear shape with a scroll handle and masked lip, painted with a large circular medallion containing an extensive river landscape with a turquoise husk border, flanked by two clusters of fruit and with royal blue borders, above and below, elaborately gilded.

Height: 8½ inches

Mark: Crescent

Literature
Franklin A. Barrett: *op.cit.* Plate 55.

The pattern has sometimes been associated with the Earl Dalhousie who at one time owned a service with similar decoration.

This graceful pear-shaped jug was a form first introduced at Worcester, without the additional ornamentation of the mask, in about 1754 and the same basic outline remained in production until the early 1770s.

A representative selection of this style of decoration on dishes, plates, tureens, teaware, mugs and a cider jug, can be seen at the Dyson Perrins Museum at Worcester.

139

140

141

COLOUR PLATE 37

140 A Dish *c.*1770–72

of kidney shape, painted with an extensive river landscape within a turquoise husk border, surrounded by clusters of fruit and flying birds within a royal blue border, gilded with cable and trellis patterns. The 'Lord Henry Thynne' pattern.

Length: 10½ inches

Mark: Crescent

Literature
R.L. Hobson: *op.cit.* Plate 41, No.203.
Henry Sandon: *op.cit.* Plate 121.

This pattern is popularly associated with the name of Lord Henry Thynne, although the exact personage in question and the nature of his association with the pattern, are not clear. One candidate of that name lived from 1797 until 1837 and was the second son of the 2nd Marquess of Bath. Another Lord Henry Thynne was the second son of the 3rd Marquess, born in 1832, died in 1904.

The painting of the fruit and especially the birds, outside the central panel, is in the style of Sèvres.

142

141 A Dish *c.*1772–75

of lozenge shape, painted with an extensive landscape depicting a windmill on a hill, overlooking an estuary, enclosed within a turquoise husk border, surrounded by clusters of fruit and flying birds within a royal blue border, gilded with cable and trellis patterns.

Length: 12 inches

Mark: Crescent

Literature
R.L. Hobson: *op.cit.* Plate 41, No.203.
Henry Sandon: *op.cit.* Plate 121.

Some of the river landscapes depicted on these dessert dishes have been identified as scenes on the River Severn.

The crescent mark first appears on Worcester porcelain only in conjunction with underglaze blue decoration and was introduced in about 1760–62. It was not until ten years later (*c.*1770–72) that the crescent was used in association with purely overglaze decoration.

COLOUR PLATE 38

142 A Plate *c.*1770–72

with a scalloped edge, painted with two long-legged pheasant-like birds in an extensive watery landscape with other birds in flight, within a narrow royal blue border, edged with gilt scrolls.

Diameter: 8½ inches

Mark: Crescent

Provenance
T. Leonard Crow

Literature
Franklin A. Barrett: *op.cit.* Plate 52B.
H. Rissik Marshall: *op.cit.* Plate 16, No.277.

A service with this decoration was at one time in the possession of Admiral Lord Rodney.

The style of bird decoration was derived from Sèvres where it is associated with the painters Evans, Aloncle and Chappuis. The birds are characterised by their brightly coloured plumage, usually incorporating a vivid blue, and by their long spindly legs which give the appearance of being unlikely to support the weight of their bodies. By comparison with the Sèvres decoration which inspired this style, the Worcester birds are more flamboyant and the landscapes less realistic. A similar style of bird painting occurs on Plymouth vases.

143

144 A Coffee Cup & Saucer *c.*1772–75

of fluted form, painted with a central circular medallion with a landscape, with a turquoise husk border, surrounded by insects and bouquets of flowers, all within a royal blue border with a chain-link pattern in gilding.

Diameter of saucer: $5\frac{1}{4}$ inches

Mark: Crescent

Provenance
T. Leonard Crow (Cf. letter No.26)

Literature
H. Rissik Marshall: *op.cit.* Plate 23, No.466.

A variant of this same basic style of decoration has clusters of fruit and flying birds in the place of the insects and bouquets of flowers.

145 A Teacup & Saucer *c.*1772

of fluted form, painted with three bouquets of flowers, entwined around the emblems of Cupid, a bow and an arrow, below a royal blue border, gilded with chains. The 'Royal Marriage' pattern.

Diameter of saucer: $5\frac{1}{4}$ inches

Mark: Crescent

The Worcester patterns with royal blue borders do not always bear a factory mark. When they do so, it is most often a crescent, but occasionally a script W. The fretted square does not occur in conjunction with this style of decoration and is principally found in association with patterns that include underglaze blue painting.

143 A Saucerdish *c.*1772–75

of fluted form, painted with garlands of flowers entwined around gilt scrolls pendent from a royal blue rim, edged with C-scrolls in gilt, the inner decoration with a turquoise caillouté border enclosing a floral sprig.

Diameter: 7 inches

Mark: Crescent

Provenance
T. Leonard Crow (Cf. letter No.25)

Literature
F. Severne MacKenna: *op.cit.* Plate 37, No.74, illustrates a kidney-shaped dish in this pattern.
H. Rissik Marshall: *op.cit.* Plate 23, No.481, illustrates a teacup and saucer.

A similar service, formerly in the possession of Mr Roland Worth of Stourport, was presented by the Borough of Cheltenham, in 1948, to H.R.H. Princess Elizabeth, as a marriage gift.

144

145

146

146 (interior)

146 A Teacup *c.*1772-75

of fluted form, painted with three bouquets of flowers concealing a bow, arrow and quiver, below a royal blue border edged with C-scrolls in gilt, and in the interior of the cup, an urn inscribed : KEW.

Diameter: $3\frac{1}{4}$ inches

Mark: Crescent

Literature
R.L. Hobson: *op.cit.* Plate 43, No.209.
H. Rissik Marshall: *op.cit.* Plate 30, No.671A.

From a service reputed to have been made for use in Kew House, which was leased by the Royal Family in about 1730 and ultimately purchased by George III in 1781.

Chapter VI

Outside Decoration

A news-sheet advertisement in the Public Advertiser on Thursday, 17 December 1767, under the heading 'WORCESTER CHINA', refers to a warehouse which had recently opened at the Arts Museum in Cockspur Street. The second paragraph begins: 'As the Enamelling Branch is performed in London under the immediate Direction of the Proprietor who has followed that Profession many Years...'. A further advertisement, on 8 January 1768, using very much the same wording, disclosed the identity of the proprietor: J. Giles.

James Giles was an independent decorator who had a workshop with its own kiln in Kentish Town, before moving in 1763, to 82 Berwick Street, Soho, where he remained for the next thirteen years. In 1767, he entered into an arrangement with the Worcester factory who undertook to supply white porcelain for him to enamel. For the next four years, until the termination of this arrangement in 1771, the Giles atelier was quite literally, the 'Enamelling Branch' of the Worcester factory. Whilst the factory concentrated on overglaze transfer-printing, underglaze blue patterns, simple floral designs and underglaze blue grounds, some of which were sent to London for enamel decoration, the Giles atelier was responsible for most of the more ambitious and prestigious forms of polychrome decoration, including the majority of the coloured grounds. Indeed, it has been estimated that during the last ten years of its existence, from 1767 until 1776, the atelier undertook more coloured decoration than the factory itself.

Our knowledge of the nature and full extent of Giles's achievements as an independent decorator, has been greatly extended by the researches of W.B. Honey, Robert Charlston and, more recently, Gerald Coke.[1] The identification of Giles's decoration in contrast to that of the factory is based primarily upon six pieces believed to have been painted by Giles himself and upon the catalogue of a Sale held at Christie's in March 1774 of 'the Elegant Porcelaine of English and Foreign Manufacture, Part of the STOCK in TRADE of Mr. JAMES GILES, CHINAMAN and ENAMELLER...'.

In 1935, Mrs Dora Edgell Grubbe, a direct descendant of Giles, presented four plates to the Victoria and Albert Museum. It is generally accepted that these plates were painted by Giles and they, together with two teacaddies, one of which is now in the Ashmolean Museum in Oxford, represent a starting point in the attempt to identify the decoration carried out at the Giles atelier.[2] Most of the decorative clues relating to Giles's work emanate from aspects of the painting on these six pieces.

Sometimes Giles's decoration is immediately obvious, but more often it is detected by interconnecting links in an expanding chain of identification. The clue is often found in a

[1] Gerald Coke: *In Search of James Giles*.

[2] The four 'Grubbe' plates, together with one of the teacaddies are described and illustrated in colour by Rissik Marshall in his definitive work: *Coloured Worcester Porcelain of the First Period*. These five pieces are also illustrated, in monochrome, by Franklin A. Barrett in *Worcester Porcelain*.

subsidiary part of the decoration, perhaps in a simple sprig or floral spray which relates to part of the border decoration on one of the 'Grubbe' plates. The style of gilding tended to be freer and less restrained than that of the factory and sometimes it was of the most superb quality. Characteristic Giles motifs found on the 'Grubbe' plates include cut fruit, a spray of auriculas, a tulip with reflexed (divergent) petals and tiny floral sprigs, often in carmine. Once linked in this way with a 'Grubbe' plate, a piece can afford other clues in its decoration, which identify further pieces. However, as Gerald Coke has observed in his illuminating and lucid monograph *In Search of James Giles*, we have still much to learn about Giles's work. No attribution to him should be accepted without question and it is quite possible that subsequent research will throw doubt upon some of our present conclusions.

In this chapter the Giles pieces are grouped together with others, not necessarily decorated at his atelier, but untypical of Factory decoration. It should be remembered that there were many other independent decorators besides Giles, about whom almost nothing is known, and one should be wary of ascribing all 'outside decoration' to the Giles atelier.

The Klepser Collection does not contain a large representation of this category of Worcester porcelain, but it does include some outstanding pieces. The carmine landscape plate (No.147) and the bleu céleste bordered plate with the cut fruit (No.151) each relate directly to a 'Grubbe' plate. The delightful landscape plate (No.148) is identified by the dark puce sprigs around its rim and from this it becomes a key piece in recognising Giles landscape decoration.

The small mug (No.149) is a good example of the atelier's figure painting in the style of Teniers, whilst the 'sea-green' cup and saucer (No.152) illustrates the strong Meissen influence evident in so much of Giles's decoration. The quality of the atelier's finest ciselé gilding can be seen in the 'Lady Wortley Montagu' plate (No.154) and the beautiful teabowl and saucer from the 'Lord Dudley' service (No.157), both of which contrast vividly with the less sophisticated decoration on the bell-shaped mug (No.162), which is probably an example of his earlier style.

The twenty-three items in this section of the Catalogue give a clear impression of the quality and range of styles in the decoration on Worcester porcelain undertaken outside the factory. Some pieces successfully aspire to the highest standards, whilst others are directed at a more humble market. But anyone doubting the contribution of James Giles to the decoration on eighteenth-century English porcelain should direct their gaze to the magnificent two-handled cup and saucer (No.159); for me, at any rate, this embodies all that is best in the work of James Giles.

147

148

147 A Plate *c.*1770

painted in the atelier of James Giles, in carmine, in the style of Tournai, with an equestrian figure, accompanied by a sheep in the foreground, flanked by an urn, set upon a pedestal and, in the background, a drive leading up past a barn towards a large house. The border is edged in gilt, below which are five carmine flower sprays, including a tulip with divergent petals.

Diameter: 9 inches

Mark: None

Provenance
The Rissik Marshall Collection
Sotheby's 27 January 1953
Literature
Franklin A. Barrett: *op.cit.* Plates 62, 63, 64 and 65, illustrates the four 'Grubbe' plates.
Gerald Coke: *In Search of James Giles*, Plate 32(a).
H. Rissik Marshall: *op.cit.* Part I, Colour Plate 6.
Soil de Moriamé and Delplace: *Porcelaine de Tournay*, Colour Plate 33.

Many similarities link this plate with the 'Grubbe' plate, painted in carmine, in the Victoria and Albert Museum. The figure painting, the treatment of the branches of the trees and the overall composition are all features in common with the 'Grubbe' plate but, as so often with the Giles atelier, it is the floral decoration that offers the strongest clues. In this instance two of the flower sprays, which resemble anemones, are virtually identical to those on the carmine 'Grubbe' plate, and a third spray, the divergent petalled tulip, is a recurring floral motif in Giles's decoration.

148 A Plate *c.*1770

painted in the atelier of James Giles with an extensive landscape scene incorporating a windmill and houses, flanked by trees in the foreground and a town and church across a river in the wooded background. The border is edged in gilt, below which are five scattered sprays of flowers painted in dark puce.

Diameter: 9 inches

Mark: None

Provenance
The Rissik Marshall Collection
Sotheby's 27 January 1953

149

149 A Mug *c.*1775

of cylindrical form, painted in the atelier of James Giles, in the manner of David Teniers, with a mother and child seated upon a rock, in a wooded landscape, within a pink scale border outlined with gilt scrolls.

Height: $3\frac{1}{4}$ inches

Mark: None

Literature
Gerald Coke: *op.cit.* Colour Plate XIX, illustrates a pink scale coffee cup and saucer by the same hand.
Henry Sandon: *op.cit.* Plate 63, illustrates a pink scale mug of a slightly earlier date.

Lot 51, on the second day of Christie's Sale in March 1774, devoted entirely to Giles's porcelain, reads: 'a pair of jonquil jars in figures after Tenier [sic], fine crimson ground'.

This is a relatively late example of the atelier's figure painting. The attribution to Giles is partially based upon the two blue scale teacaddies sold in 1952 by Miss M.J.M. Grubbe, a descendant of Giles. It is most likely that he painted the tea-caddies, and their decoration, which includes a figure of a child, painted in the Teniers style, links them to a series of mugs and teaware painted with Teniers subjects.

The pink scale ground was derived from Meissen and was first used by Giles, only later being adopted by the factory. This ground colour occurs not only on Worcester porcelain decorated in the atelier, but also on Caughley and Neale porcelain of the mid-1770s, at a time when Giles was presumably having difficulty in obtaining Worcester to enamel.

By comparison with the slightly earlier cylindrical mugs in the Collection: Nos 47, 115–117, 185 & 202, this example has a slightly wider handle with a lower handle terminal set further down the body.

A display of pieces decorated in this style is in the Lady Ludlow Collection at Luton Hoo.

Literature
Albert Amor Ltd: *James Giles, China Painter 1718–1780*, Exhibition Catalogue, No.6, illustrates the companion plate.
Franklin A. Barrett: *op.cit.* Plate 60.
W.B. Honey: *Old English Porcelain*, Plate 93 fig(c).
H. Rissik Marshall: *op.cit.* Part I, Plate 7(d).

Lot 46, on the first day of a Sale at Christie's, Monday, 21 March 1774, devoted to 'Part of the STOCK in TRADE of Mr. JAMES GILES, CHINAMAN and ENAMELLER', reads: 'twelve plates painted with different landscapes in colours'.

The scattered sprigs and flower sprays around the border afford a crucial clue to the attribution to Giles of many other pieces.

Two plates decorated with landscapes are in the Dyson Perrins Museum at Worcester, together with a further plate, painted with a landscape in carmine.

150

151

COLOUR PLATE 41

150 A Saucerdish *c.*1772–75

of deep form, painted in the atelier of James Giles, with a large bouquet of flowers within a curving purple scale border incorporating three pendant cornucopiae, outlined with narrow gilt scrolls, below which hang sprays of garden flowers.

Diameter: 7½ inches

Mark: None

Literature
Gerald Coke: *op.cit.* Colour Plate XXIII.

Like the pink scale ground (No.149), the purple scale was a Giles rather than a Factory colour, and it is listed in the advertisement for the Burnsall Sale in May 1769, at a time when Giles was working as the 'Enamelling Branch'. Both the border pattern and the distinctive floral decoration were inspired by Meissen.

This deep form of saucerdish was introduced in the early 1770s and occurs also at Bristol, Derby and elsewhere. Prior to this date, saucerdishes tended to be shallower and less 'bowled'.

A two-handled cup and saucer, painted by the same hand, is No.159 in this Collection.

COLOUR PLATE 42

151 A Plate *c.*1770–72

painted in the atelier of James Giles, with a central group of fruit and flowers, including a cut lemon and a plum surrounded by smaller sprays of flowers, within a wide bleu céleste cornucopia-shaped border with flowers in ciselé gilding.

Diameter: 8⅞ inches

Mark: None

Provenance
The Darcy Taylor Collection
Sotheby's 9 April 1957

Literature
Gerald Coke: *op.cit.* Colour Plate VI, illustrates a similar lozenge-shaped dish.
H. Rissik Marshall: *op.cit.* Part I, Colour Plate 7, illustrates the 'Grubbe' plate No.3.

152

The 'Grubbe' plate No.3, in the Victoria and Albert Museum, decorated with scales of grey, puce and gilt, has an arrangement of fruit and flowers which is almost identical to the composition on this bleu céleste bordered plate.

The 'cut fruit' is a recurring Giles motif, derived from Meissen, possibly by way of Chelsea, and the ciselé gilding is also indicative of an attribution to the atelier. The cornucopia-shaped border which is so distinctive a feature of the Worcester coloured grounds, originated at Vincennes.

Three plates with similar decoration are in the Dyson Perrins Museum at Worcester.

COLOUR PLATE 43

152 A Teacup & Saucer *c.*1768–70

painted in the atelier of James Giles with semi-naturalistic birds placed in three sections, within a sea-green ground gilded with floral sprays.

Diameter of saucer: 5 inches

Mark: Crossed swords and numeral 9

Provenance
T. Leonard Crow (Cf. letter No.50)

Literature
Albert Amor Ltd: *James Giles; China Painter 1718–1780*, Exhibition Catalogue, No.23, illustrates a teapot and stand.
Gerald Coke: *op.cit.* Colour Plate XII(a) illustrates a bowl.

This is almost certainly the 'sea green' of the advertisement for the May 1769 Sale and is solely a Giles colour, not appearing on Factory decoration. The relatively naturalistic bird decoration was derived from Meissen, which was also the inspiration for the ground colour. However it is the style and composition of the gilded decoration which most readily identifies this as emanating from the atelier.

The shape of the teacup was derived from Meissen and it is this which accounts for the presence of the crossed swords mark.

153

153 A Coffee Cup & Saucer
*c.*1772–75

of fluted form with entwined branch handle, painted in the atelier of James Giles with alternate radiating panels of bleu céleste and claret, with festoons of flowers in ciselé gilding.

Diameter of saucer: $5\frac{1}{4}$ inches

Mark: Fretted square

Provenance
T. Leonard Crow (Cf. letters Nos 3 & 13)

Literature:
Gerald Coke: *op.cit.* (Plate 61(a)).
R.L. Hobson: *op.cit.* Plate 45, No.214, illustrates a teapot.
H. Rissik Marshall: *op.cit.* Plate 21, No.402, illustrates a teacaddy.

Lot 75 on the second day of Christie's Sale in March 1774, reads 'a pair ditto [caudle cups] to a beautiful stripe fancy pattern'.

During the 1760s, the predominant decorative influences at the Giles atelier were those of Meissen and Chelsea and it was not until the early 1770s that the more formalised patterns derived from Sèvres, such as can be seen on this cup and saucer, were absorbed into the atelier's style.

A milkjug and cover with this decoration are in the Dyson Perrins Museum at Worcester.

COLOUR PLATE 44

154 A Plate *c.*1772–74

painted in the atelier of James Giles, with dishevelled birds and foliage within mirror-shaped panels, flanked by gilt trelliswork and flower sprays, upon a blue scale ground, the white central circular panel painted with a bouquet of flowers. The 'Lady Mary Wortley Montagu' service, No.2.

Diameter: 9 inches

Mark: Fretted square

Provenance
T. Leonard Crow (Cf. letter No.5)

Literature
Franklin A. Barrett: *op.cit.* Plate 72.
Gerald Coke: *op.cit.* Plates 38(a), 38(b), 39(a) illustrates four of the seven variations of this pattern.
J. Emerson: *op.cit.* No.93, Colour Plate, illustrates this plate.
Henry Sandon: *op.cit.* Plate 80.

Lady Mary Wortley Montagu (1689–1762) was a well-known literary figure in the eighteenth century, as well as being celebrated for her beauty and wit. Her husband was for a time the Ambassador to Turkey and she is credited with the introduction of the practice of innoculation against smallpox into

154

155

England. The nature of her connection with the pattern that bears her name is obscure as she died at least ten years before the design appeared.

Lot 64 on the fourth day of Christie's Sale in March 1774, reads: 'a desert [sic] service of the fine mazareen blue enrich'd with chased and burnished gold, painted with birds and flowers'.

As Gerald Coke has pointed out, Giles's apprenticeship to a jeweller in the 1730s contributed to his skill as a gilder and the superb quality of much of his ciselé gilding was an important factor during his years of prosperity. The style of gilding used on his coloured grounds is very distinctive and quite unlike the Factory's, as is evident from an examination of this plate, by comparison with Nos 117 to 121 in Chapter V.

An example of the Worcester blue scale ground at its most clearly defined.

155 A Plate *c.*1770–72

painted in the atelier of James Giles, with a neo-classical urn garlanded with flowers in the centre, within a gros bleu ground, gilt with a border of fruiting vines.

Diameter: 8½ inches

Mark: Script W

Provenance
T. Leonard Crow

Literature
Gerald Coke: *op.cit.* Plate 47(a).
H. Rissik Marshall: *op.cit.* Plate 23, No.497.

Lot 57 on the fifth day of the 1774 Sale reads: 'a desert [sic] service elegantly painted with different vases and an ultramarine blue border, enriched with chased and burnished gold . . .'.

This neo-classical design, which also occurs on Derby porcelain decorated at the Giles atelier was derived from Sèvres. As with all Giles's blue ground patterns, the underglaze blue ground was applied at the Worcester factory.

COLOUR PLATE 39
A Plate *c.*1770 (No.147)

COLOUR PLATE 40
A Plate *c.*1770 (No.148)

COLOUR PLATE 4I
A Saucerdish *c*.1772–75 (No.150)
A Mug *c*.1775 (No.149)

COLOUR PLATE 42
A Plate *c.*1770–72 (No.151)

COLOUR PLATE 43
A Teacup & Saucer *c.*1768–70 (No.152)

COLOUR PLATE 44
A Plate *c.*1772–74 (No.154)

COLOUR PLATE 45
A Teabowl & Saucer *c.*1767–68 (No.157)

COLOUR PLATE 46
A two-handled Cup & Saucer *c.*1770–72 (No.159)

COLOUR PLATE 47
A Plate *c.*1768–70 (No.160)

COLOUR PLATE 48
A Plate *c.*1768–70 (No.161)

COLOUR PLATE 49
A Saucer *c*.1772–75 (No.167)

156

156 A Plate *c.*1768–70

painted in the atelier of James Giles with landscapes and buildings in rouge de fer, within mirror-shaped reserved panels upon a well-defined blue scale ground.

Diameter: 9 inches

Mark: Crescent

Provenance
T. Leonard Crow (Cf. letter No.41)

Literature:
Franklin A. Barrett: *op.cit.* Plate 67A.
Gerald Coke: *op.cit.* Plate 43(a).
H. Rissik Marshall: *op.cit.* Part I, Plate 7b.

These primitive scenes, delft-like in their simplicity, are possibly an early example of the atelier's landscape decoration, although it is difficult to believe that the same hand was responsible for the fluent painting on No.148 in this Collection. A surer clue to an attribution to Giles lies in the floral decoration which, even allowing for the slightly unusual monochrome colour, shows strong similarities with the typical Giles bouquets and scattered sprays.

The absence of gilding emphasises the heaviness of

the blue scale ground and is a reminder of how helpful the style of gilding is in identifying Giles's work.

The loosely composed floral bouquet in the central circular panel (and in that of No.154) contrasts strongly with the tightly bunched bouquets so typical of Factory decoration: Nos 121, 122 & 135.

COLOUR PLATE 45

157 A Teabowl & Saucer *c.*1767–68

painted in the atelier of James Giles, with European figures playing musical instruments, in the style of Watteau, enclosed within fan-shaped reserves and circular panels containing butterflies, insects and cherries, all upon a powder blue ground, gilded with flower sprays in ciselé gilding. The 'Lord Dudley' service.

Diameter of saucer: 4½ inches

Mark: None

Literature
Albert Amor Ltd: *James Giles: China Painter 1718–1780*, Exhibition Catalogue, No.50.
Franklin A. Barrett: *op.cit.* Plate 74A.
Gerald Coke: *op.cit.* Plate 45(a), illustrates a bowl.
H. Rissik Marshall: *op.cit.* Plate 19, No.352, illustrates a sucrier and cover.

This service was at one time in the possession of the Earl of Dudley.

Lot 84 on the fourth day of the 1774 Sale is described as follows: 'a complete set of tea china, 40 pieces, mazareen blue with chased and burnished gold enamel'd in compartments with figures grotesque'. This seems a reasonably convincing description of the 'Lord Dudley' service, although from an examination of its paste and glaze, the porcelain itself cannot be dated at later than 1768. The *overglaze* decoration, however, could well be of the early 1770s. The style of decoration occurs on gold anchor period Chelsea, another link between the Giles atelier and artists from the Chelsea factory. An example of Factory decoration in this style is No.123 in this Collection.

The 'Lord Dudley' service is an excellent example of Giles's gilding at its finest and most opulent. The use of gilding on the foot of the teabowl is an elaboration typical of the atelier and seldom encountered on Factory decoration. This was a feature, like so many associated with the atelier, which was inspired by the Meissen factory.

157

158

159

158 A Teabowl & Saucer *c.*1765–68

painted in the atelier of James Giles with Chinese
figures, one of whom is standing in a jar, within
mirror-shaped panels, divided by small vase-
shaped panels enclosing floral sprays, all outlined
with gilt scrolls, upon a clearly defined blue scale
ground. The 'Bodenham' service.

Diameter of saucer: 4½ inches

Mark: None

Provenance
T. Leonard Crow (Cf. letter No.1)

Literature
Albert Amor Ltd: *The Elegant Porcelain of James
Giles*, Exhibition Catalogue, No.35, illustrates a
coffee cup.
Gerald Coke: *op.cit.* Plate 42(a) illustrates a
spoontray.
H. Rissik Marshall: *op.cit.* Plate 9, No.148,
illustrates a spoontray.

The name is derived from the Sale of the
Bodenham Collection, in 1872, which included a
service of this pattern. However, two teapots in the
pattern are extant, suggesting that more than one
service may have been made.

This pattern, which seldom bears a mark of any
kind, has recently been attributed by Gerald Coke
to the Giles atelier. It is certainly an un-Worcester-
like combination of Chinese figures and a blue scale
ground, and both the palette and the floral sprays
might more reasonably be associated with Giles.

COLOUR PLATE 46

159 A two-handled Cup & Saucer
*c.*1770–72

of double-ogee form, with pierced gilt handles,
painted in the atelier of James Giles with large
bouquets and sprays of flowers including dahlias
in the style of Meissen.

Diameter of saucer: 5½ inches

Mark: None

Provenance
The Rissik Marshall Collection
Sotheby's 27 January 1953

Literature
Albert Amor Ltd: *James Giles, China Painter
1718–1780*, Exhibition Catalogue, No.73.
Franklin A. Barrett: *op.cit.* Plate 66.
H. Rissik Marshall: *op.cit.* Part I, Colour Plate 8,
illustrates the companion cup and saucer, now in
the Marshall Collection at the Ashmolean
Museum, Oxford.

The majority of Giles's floral decoration was
inspired by Meissen and in the case of this fine
example, the shape too shows the influence of the
German factory. The flower painting can be linked
with the border decoration on two of the 'Grubbe'
plates and is by the same hand as the purple scale
saucer dish, No.150, in this Collection.

The ochre yellow, pale burgundy and russet red
are characteristic of the Giles palette.

160

161

COLOUR PLATE 47

160 A Plate *c.*1768—70

painted in the atelier of James Giles, with a central cluster of fruit, including a peach or nectarine surrounded by cherries, 'grapes', a plum and two insects.

Diameter: 9 inches

Mark: None

Provenance
T. Leonard Crow (Cf. letter No.54)

Literature
Gerald Coke: *op.cit.* Plate 14(a).
H. Rissik Marshall: *op.cit.* Plate 36, No.785.

Lot 47 on the first day of the 1774 Sale is described as follows: 'a complete desart [sic] service enamel'd in fruit and insects, viz. 2 dozen plates and 20 compoteers different sizes'.

This decoration was derived from Chelsea and many examples, especially plates, bear an anchor mark in brown. The palette tends to be brighter than on the Chelsea examples, giving the decoration a more vivacious appearance. The expansiveness with which the decoration is laid out, contrasts with the tighter treatment of comparable subjects in Factory decoration, cf. No.97 (Colour Plate 28).

COLOUR PLATE 48

161 A Plate *c.*1768—70

painted in the atelier of James Giles, with a large exotic bird standing upon a rock, among trees and foliage, flanked by two smaller birds on branches.

Diameter: $7\frac{5}{8}$ inches

Mark: None

Provenance
T. Leonard Crow

Literature
Franklin A. Barrett: *op.cit.* Plate 71.
Gerald Coke: *op.cit.* Colour Plate III, illustrates a Worcester teapot, together with a Chinese saucer.
F. Severne MacKenna: *op.cit.* Plate 31, No.63.

A Worcester advertisement of 1768 quoted by Nightingale: 'Contributions towards the History of Early English Porcelain', 1881, refers to 'Curious Patterns that are wanted will be made in a short time not to be distinguished from the original, as the Proprieters [sic] have engaged the best painters from Chelsea . . .'.

This pattern is an adaptation of a Chelsea design. The Giles colours, especially the greens and blues, are far brighter than on Chelsea, and the Giles birds have a far more 'agitated' appearance with their prominent head feathers and sharp beaks which are often open. In place of the relatively realistically drawn rocks, upon which the Chelsea birds stand, the Giles birds perch upon far more stylised yellowish promontories, which have been aptly likened to slices of cheese. In consequence, though the Worcester plates follow the overall composition of their Chelsea counterparts fairly accurately, the artistic effect could hardly be more different.

The use of two shades of green in foliage or in floral decoration is a recurring feature in the Giles palette.

162 A Mug c.1765–68

of bell shape painted in the atelier of James Giles, with a bird standing beside flowering plants, within a large reserved panel outlined in brown and black, flanked by bouquets and sprays of flowers.

Height: 3¼ inches

Mark: None

Literature
H. Rissik Marshall: *op.cit.* Part I, Plate 6(a), Part II, Plate 31, No.682.

162

This style of bird painting also appears on Chinese porcelain decorated in London and this mug may be an example of the early exotic bird painting at the Giles atelier, before the beginning of the arrangement with the Worcester factory in 1767. An examination of the paste and glaze suggests a date consistent with this theory and the palette of the mug is also indicative of Giles's early work.

A strongly reminiscent style of bird painting also occurs on Bow porcelain of the 1768–70 period. This is generally found in conjunction with the anchor and dagger mark and often in association with a blue ground. Cf. Anton Gabszewicz and Geoffrey Freeman: *Bow Porcelain*, No.177.

In general, the Giles birds have a more vivacious and alert appearance than their plumper, un-ruffled and somewhat stylised Factory counterparts.

163 A Teabowl & Saucer c.1767–70

painted in the atelier of James Giles, with two birds, one large and one smaller, within a panel of purple C-scrolls and scattered sprays in carmine.

Diameter of saucer: 4⅞ inches

Mark: None

Provenance
The Goldblatt Collection

Literature
R.L. Hobson: *op.cit.* Plate 21, No.115, illustrates a teapot with identical decoration.
H. Rissik Marshall: *op.cit.* Plate 32, No.699.

The bird decoration, in the style of Meissen, may be the forerunner of the more familiar and the more sophisticated birds (Nos 154 & 161 in this Collection), although this teabowl and saucer seem slightly later in date than the bell-shaped mug (No.162).

As so often with Giles's decoration, it is the secondary motifs that furnish the useful clues to his work. Here, the five small floral sprays in carmine provide a far surer and more convincing indication of the Giles atelier, than would the bird decoration alone. It is perhaps significant that the stand accompanying the teapot in the British Museum, illustrated by R.L. Hobson in the *Catalogue of the Frank Lloyd Collection* (Plate 21, No.115), has a fire crack which is concealed by a spray of flowers in carmine. As Gerald Coke has pointed out, flawed pieces were unlikely to have been painted at the factory and they are a useful, though not infallible, indication of Giles's decoration.

163

164

165

164 A Dish *c.*1768–70

of lozenge shape, probably decorated in the
atelier of James Giles, in Japanese taste with
fantastic birds, flowering plants and banded
wheat-sheaves within narrow borders of rouge de
fer and gilt and latticework diaper. The 'Phoenix'
pattern.

Diameter: 10¼ inches

Mark: None

Provenance
T. Leonard Crow

Literature
Gerald Coke: *op.cit.* Plates 25(a) and 25(b),
illustrates both the factory and the Giles versions.
H. Rissik Marshall: *op.cit.* Plate 10, No.173.

By comparison with the Factory version of this
design, the one attributed by Gerald Coke to the
Giles atelier is more fully decorated and more
confused in its visual effect. In this case, the Factory
version is more faithful to the Meissen version of the
Japanese original than is that of Giles.

165 A Teapot & Cover *c.*1765–68

of globular shape, probably decorated in the
atelier of James Giles with alternating panels of
oriental flowering plants and narrower orange
panels painted with gilt trelliswork and each
containing a mons.

Height: 5⅛ inches

Mark: None

Literature
Gerald Coke: *op.cit.* Plate 56(b), illustrates a bowl
painted with oriental figures in the Giles atelier.
Klaber & Klaber: *op.cit.* Plates 12, 12a, 13 and
13a, illustrate a teapot with Giles decoration and
a bell-shaped mug with the Factory version of this
pattern, together with their Chinese prototypes.
H. Rissik Marshall: *op.cit.* Plate 42, No.887,
illustrates a milkjug and cover painted with the
Factory version.

It has been suggested that this is the colour
described in the advertisement for the May 1769
Christie's Sale as 'Scarlet', a colour that has
otherwise not been conclusively identified on
Worcester porcelain. Lot 66, on the second day of
the December 1769 Sale, was a 'fine old scarlet
japan pattern'. The majority of overglaze ground
colours occur mainly in conjunction with
European decoration, whereas orange panels are
principally associated with oriental patterns. In
the light of this, 'orange' becomes an increasingly
convincing identification for the 'scarlet' of the
1769 catalogue.

A number of orange panel designs are known, some
with oriental figures alternating with foliage.
Several of these are Factory versions and others,
including the earlier examples, were probably
decorated at the Giles atelier. The latter often have
a distinctive 'soft' low-fired gilding which occurs on
much outside-decorated Worcester and which is
much more prone to wear than the characteristic
Giles gilding. The style of decoration, the palette
and the type of gilding, clearly indicate that this
teapot was not decorated at the factory, but there
must be a slight element of doubt in ascribing it to
the Giles atelier. A very similar pattern with the
same gilding is found on Chinese porcelain decorated in England.

An identical pattern, with the same gilding, occurs
on Chaffers' Liverpool porcelain of about 1765.

166

167

166 A Bowl *c.*1767–70

with a scalloped rim, probably painted in the atelier of James Giles with two quails pencilled in black and a large flowering plant and rockwork, with a scroll border in rouge de fer and gilt. The 'Quail' pattern.

Diameter: 6 inches

Mark: None

Provenance
T. Leonard Crow (Cf. letter No.40)

Literature
Franklin A. Barrett: *op.cit.* Plate 31A, illustrates a teapot.
Klaber & Klaber: *op.cit.* Plates 22 and 22a, illustrate a teapot, together with a Chinese teabowl of the same pattern.
H. Rissik Marshall: *op.cit.* Plate 32, No.697, illustrates a 'Chelsea ewer' creamboat.

Unlike the majority of the 'Quail' patterns on Worcester, this version is derived from Chinese rather than Japanese porcelain. The palette, especially the dark green and the slate blue, and the soft gilding, indicate that this was decorated outside the Worcester factory and like Nos 162, 163 & 165 is probably a fairly early example of the Giles atelier.

A similar bowl, together with a teapot, is in the Dyson Perrins Museum at Worcester.

COLOUR PLATE 49

167 A Saucer *c.*1772–75

probably painted by Fidelle Duvivier, with a shepherdess seated upon a rock beside two sheep in a landscape with trees, rocks and foliage, within a plain, narrow gilt border.

Diameter: 5 inches

Mark: None

Provenance
T. Leonard Crow

A documentary teapot in the Ashmolean Museum in Oxford, illustrated by Rissik Marshall, *op.cit.* Colour Plate 29, is inscribed within the decoration: 'F in [venit] ins [cripsit] Duvivier 1772'. The teapot is painted on one side with a boy and a girl and a recumbent sheep in a wooded landscape with ruins, and on the reverse with another couple, seated beside an urn on a pedestal, upon which the inscription is written. There are several similarities

168

linking the decoration on this saucer to the teapot: the treatment of the sheep, the shepherdess's clothing, much of the foliage and, in particular, the hazily painted tree in the background.

Fidelle Duvivier was trained at Tournai and his style can be said to have originated there. Scenes of figures, together with domestic animals, are not uncommon on Tournai porcelain and figures are occasionally painted from behind, a curious and distinctive feature seldom encountered elsewhere. Figures, sometimes children, often painted in conjunction with animals, occur on Newhall porcelain attributed with reasonable certainty to Fidelle Duvivier and although the subject on this Worcester saucer does not appear on Newhall, there are several elements in the decoration that strongly resemble his work there.

Duvivier signed a contract with William Duesbury of Derby on 31 October 1769 which expired 31 October 1773 but, from the inscription on the Worcester teapot, it is apparent that he did not honour this agreement in full. Whilst there seems little obvious justification in linking the painting on this saucer to the Giles atelier, an examination of the gilded decoration on the handle, spout and, especially, the cover of the Duvivier signed teapot,

reveals it to be very much in the distinctive Giles style. If this is the case, it is reasonable to assume that the saucer too emanates from the atelier.

The identification of Duvivier's work on Worcester porcelain is discussed by Franklin A. Barrett, *op.cit.* Pages 54–56.

168 A Teapot & Cover *c.*1770–72

of globular form, painted in underglaze blue with a figure standing beside a fence, flanked by flowering shrubs and overpainted in rouge de fer and green.

Height: 6¼ inches

Mark: Script W

Provenance
T. Leonard Crow

Literature
L. Branyan, N. French and J. Sandon: *Worcester Blue and White Porcelain 1751–1790*, IA b., illustrate a bowl.
H. Rissik Marshall: *op.cit.* Plate 24, No.542, illustrates a creamjug, also with additional overglaze decoration.

The overglaze decoration is an 'embellishment' to a well-known underglaze blue pattern. It is not absolutely certain whether this 'clobbering' was carried out at the factory or done elsewhere, but the presence of similar overglaze decoration on Chinese pieces is indicative of outside decoration. The underglaze blue design spans a period from about 1765–75 and also occurs on Caughley porcelain.

A creamjug with similar decoration is in the Dyson Perrins Museum at Worcester.

169 A Dish *c.*1775–78

of fluted lobed form, painted with dishevelled birds within four mirror-shaped panels edged in gilt, upon an elaborately gilded claret ground.

Diameter: $7\frac{1}{4}$ inches

Mark: None

Provenance
The Eckstein Collection
Sotheby's 29 March 1949
T. Leonard Crow (Cf. letter No.32)

Literature
Gerald Coke: *op.cit.* Plate 53(b) illustrates a similar dish.
H. Rissik Marshall: *op.cit.* Plate 34, No.732, illustrates a tureen and cover with similar decoration and gilding.

This dish has been tentatively attributed to the atelier of James Giles on the basis of the style of gilding, which bears a superficial resemblance to that on the 'Lady Mary Wortley Montagu' plate (No.154) and also on the 'cheese-like' rocks upon which the birds stand. However, the birds themselves are by no means typical of Giles's style and the gilding lacks the quality and the richness normally associated with the atelier. Some doubt must therefore attend the genuineness of this dish.

169

Chapter VII

'Pencilled' and Transfer-printed Decoration

The term 'pencilling' refers to a form of decoration on Worcester porcelain whereby the artist achieved his effect in one colour, most often black, by using a very fine, lightly charged brush. This technique was derived from Chinese porcelain and indeed is invariably found in conjunction with decoration in the oriental style. The vogue for this decoration lasted for no more than ten years, from about 1756 to 1765 and only a handful of standard patterns were used.

The Klepser Collection contains six examples of 'pencilling' and they readily convey the delicate and detailed effects which were so skilfully obtained, with such economy of colour. The outstanding piece is undoubtedly the wonderful saucerdish (No.170). The pattern has been laid out in such a way as to emphasise the unusual and exuberant outline of this dish and the painting itself is of the finest quality.

The development of transfer-printing was one of the very few original contributions made in England, during the eighteenth century, to the decoration of ceramics. The tragic irony of this achievement was that, in its very effectiveness, it represented a terrible threat to the livelihood of the porcelain painters and ultimately resulted in a lowering of standards in hand-painted decoration. A single design, engraved on a copper plate, could be used repeatedly and detailed designs could be transferred on to the porcelain using only a small number of skilled workmen. An affidavit records that on 27 July 1756 Sadler and Green of Liverpool 'did within the space of six hours . . . print upwards of twelve hundred earthenware tiles of different patterns'.[1] It is hardly to be wondered at that by the early 1770s it was generally only the most simple and basic of the landscapes and Chinese designs that were hand-painted.

The technique of transfer-printing over the glaze was first used by John Brooks on enamels, at Birmingham, before he went to Battersea in 1753.[2] The earliest Worcester examples date from about 1753–54 and are associated with the designer L.P. Boitard and several prints bear his signature. These early prints are known as 'smokey primitives', a description reflecting their characteristically 'smudged' appearance, caused by imperfect printing, but lending them a refreshingly experimental quality. This is enhanced by the almost eggshell thinness of the potting of such pieces as the creamjug (No.178) and the teabowl and saucer (No.179), both of which belong to this early class.

Whilst other porcelain factories, notably at Bow and Liverpool, also undertook overglaze transfer-printing, the Worcester factory was unequalled in its mastery of the technique, in terms of quantity, quality, clarity and aesthetic effect. The guiding spirit behind this important achievement was Robert Hancock, who was eventually to become a full partner in the factory from 1772 to 1774. From the mid-1750s until the early 1770s

[1] William Turner: *Transfer-Printing on Enamels, Porcelain and Pottery* (1907). Page 6.

[2] Bernard Watney and Robert Charlston: 'Petitions for Patents'. *E.C.C. Transactions*, Volume 6, Part 2 (1966).

147

the output of transfer-printed wares was enormous and only in the last few years of this period did the consistently high standards of printing and potting begin to deteriorate.

Unlike the majority of underglaze blue decoration carried out during the same period, many of these transfer-printed designs were of European and even English scenes, inspired by prints which were in turn derived from paintings, usually of Continental origin. Another fertile source of inspiration were the contemporary drawing books, the most celebrated of which was *The Ladies Amusement, or the Whole Art of Japanning made Easy*, first published by Robert Sayer in about 1760. Among the notable contributors to this were J. June, Charles Fenn and Robert Hancock himself.

Much of Hancock's finest work was derived from paintings by Boucher, Watteau, Lancret and the Italian artist Jacopo Amiconi. The enchanting chinoiserie scenes of chalets, fantastic bridges and oriental figures (Nos 181 & 189) were principally taken from *Livre de Chinois*, a book of engravings by P.C. Canot, from designs by Jean Pillement, published in 1758. These have the fantasy quality which imbued so much of the painted decoration at Worcester in the early 1750s. Pillement was also the inspiration for many of the designs on printed textiles, an industry which also flourished at this time.

Rococo design at Worcester is seldom more pronounced than on this class of printed wares and the asymmetrical scrolls which embellish the saucerdish No.184 are echoed on such diverse items as chimneypieces, mirrors, embroideries and even trade cards. Likewise, the chinoiserie vignettes derived from Pillement are ornamental developments which find parallels in the architectural designs of Matthew Darly and George Edwards and the silver epergnes of Thomas Pitts. Most of the overglaze transfer prints at Worcester were in 'jet enamel', a fine, strong black colour, but some prints occur in a reddish-brown and others in dark lilac. In certain instances, the printed design has been 'embellished' with the addition of overglaze colours and gilding, and it is possible that this decoration was carried out in the Giles atelier.

Two fine teapots, one printed in 'jet enamel' with 'L'Amour' (No.176) and the other in a brownish sepia tone, with a scene from the Italian Comedy (No.177), illustrate the stylistic differences between Robert Hancock's work and that of John Sadler of Liverpool. Bird decoration is represented by two fingerbowl stands, printed with river scenes (Nos 182 & 183) and they are among the most successful of all Hancock's transfer-printed subjects.

Perhaps the foremost piece in this section of the Klepser Collection is the bowl, No.180. This is printed with 'Earth' and 'Fire' from the Four Elements, but the third subject, 'Water', has not previously been recorded. These three printed subjects, the first two derived from Boucher, embody much of what is best in overglaze transfer-printed decoration. The symbolism is clear, and yet absorbed naturally into the composition. It is doubtful if either the clarity or the detail of this effect could have been attained in polychrome or underglaze blue painting.

170

170 A Saucerdish *c*.1756–58

with a scalloped rim, 'pencilled' in black with a
Chinese boy riding a buffalo towards a river,
flanked by a tall pine tree with overhanging
branches, two sampans and rocks. The 'Boy on a
Buffalo' pattern.

Diameter: 7¾ inches

Mark: None

Cf. letter No.15

Literature
Franklin A. Barrett: *op.cit.* Plate 35A, illustrates
another saucerdish.
Klaber & Klaber: *op.cit.* Nos 61 & 61A, illustrate
a Worcester creamjug together with a Chinese jug
painted 'en grisaille' with a similar pattern.

This shape of dish appears to be unrecorded in
eighteenth-century English porcelain. The 'Boy on
a Buffalo' is found principally on teaware but it
occasionally occurs on mugs.

171

171 A Teabowl & Saucer *c.*1756–58

'pencilled' in black with a Chinese boy riding a buffalo towards a river, flanked by a tall pine tree with overhanging branches, two sampans and rocks. The 'Boy on a Buffalo' pattern.

Diameter of saucer: $4\frac{5}{8}$ inches

Mark: Painter's mark

Literature
H. Rissik Marshall: *op.cit.* Plate 10, No.172.

This well-known Worcester pattern, derived from Chinese porcelain, is mainly confined to the second half of the 1750s, but a few examples are known that date from the 1760–65 period. The teabowls and saucers tend to be especially thinly potted.

172 A Saucer *c.*1756–58

'pencilled' in black with an extensive Chinese landscape incorporating a formation of rocks in the foreground, two conversing Chinese figures and a church surmounted by a cross, with another church in the distance.

Diameter: $4\frac{3}{4}$ inches

Mark: None

Provenance
T. Leonard Crow

Literature
H. Rissik Marshall: *op.cit.* Plate 50, No.1012.

This pattern, which occurs only on teaware, is in a style somewhat reminiscent of the so-called 'Jesuit' decoration on Chinese porcelain. It is a rarer 'pencilled' design than Nos 171 & 173.

172

173

173 A Bowl *c.*1756–58

'pencilled' in black with a chinoiserie scene depicting an oriental figure holding a bird and a parasol, standing in a fenced garden, beside a pine tree, the rim with a border of scrolls.

Diameter: 6¼ inches

Mark: None

Provenance
T. Leonard Crow (Cf. letter No.28)

Literature
Franklin A. Barrett: *op.cit.* Plate 34, illustrates a saucerdish.
H. Rissik Marshall: *op.cit.* Plate 10, No.165, illustrates a teabowl and saucer.

The exact source of this pattern is unknown, but it evokes the atmosphere of the earliest chinoiserie pattern books and, in particular, of Darly and Edward's *A New Book of Chinese Designs, Calculated to Improve the present Taste*, published in 1754.

This pattern is confined to the second half of the 1750s.

A rare variant of this design has a second Chinese figure, leaning upon a fence, just to the right of the pine tree. An example can be seen on a saucerdish in the Loan Collection in the Bristol Art Gallery.

A teapot, creamjug and teabowl and saucer in this pattern are in the Dyson Perrins Museum at Worcester.

174 A Bowl *c.*1756–58

with an indented rim, 'pencilled' in lilac camaïeu with Chinese figures outside a pavilion, in a landscape with a fence, trees and a sampan in the background.

Diameter: 6⅛ inches

Mark: None

Provenance
T. Leonard Crow (Cf. letter No.41)

Literature
Franklin A. Barrett: *op.cit.* Plate 31B, illustrates a 'Blind Earl' sweetmeat dish.
H. Rissik Marshall: *op.cit.* Plate 6, No.102, illustrates a teabowl and saucer.
Henry Sandon: *op.cit.* Plate 52, illustrates a coffee cup and saucer.

174

175

This pattern appears on a wide variety of shapes including teaware, sweetmeat dishes, leaf-moulded dishes, tall 'Chelsea Ewer' creamjugs and moulded creamboats. One rare teaware version has a moulded rim. The monochrome colour varies from shades of lilac (sometimes described as mauve or purple) to a carmine or rose pink colour. The pattern ranges in date from about 1756–65, the carmine examples tending to date from the 1760s. It also occurs on Derby porcelain of about 1756–58.

175 A Bowl *c.*1760

'pencilled' in black with flowers, butterflies and foliage and with a border of tendrils embellished with touches of gilding.

Diameter: 6 inches

Mark: None

Literature
H. Rissik Marshall: *op.cit.* Plate 52, No.1066, illustrates a spoontray.
The Art Institute of Chicago: *The Stieglitz Collection of Dr. Wall Worcester Porcelain*, No.30, illustrates a fluted teabowl and saucer.

A spoontray painted in this pattern, derived from Chinese porcelain, is in the Victoria and Albert Museum.

176

177

176 A Teapot & Cover *c.*1760–62

of inverted pear shape, with a faceted spout, transfer-printed in black by Robert Hancock with 'L'Amour' and on the reverse with the 'Minuet'.

Height: 5 inches.

Mark: R H Worcester with anchor

Literature
Franklin A. Barrett: *op.cit.* Plate 40A, illustrates a milkjug and cover, with 'L'Amour'.
Cyril Cook: *The Life and Work of Robert Hancock*, Item 2 illustrates a spoontray with 'L'Amour', and Item 75, a teapot with the 'Minuet'.

'L'Amour' is, together with the 'Teaparty' and the 'Milkmaids', one of the three most common of Hancock's transfer prints and it occurs principally on teaware. It is found, with minor variations, on Bow, where it was first introduced; on Chinese porcelain, Battersea and Staffordshire enamels and also on wallpaper. On Worcester porcelain it ranges in date from about 1758–72. The 'Minuet' is often found in tandem with 'L'Amour'.

A precisely similar teapot is in the F.C. Dykes Collection in the Manchester City Art Gallery.

177 A Teapot & Cover *c.*1762

of inverted pear shape, with a faceted spout, transfer-printed in sepia by John Sadler, with Harlequin and Columbine, from the Italian Comedy, seated on chairs, whilst Pierrot observes them from behind a bush. On the reverse are trees, buildings and sheep.

Height: 6 inches

Mark: None

Provenance
T. Leonard Crow (Cf. letter No.40)

This is one of a small group of subjects, printed by Sadler in Liverpool, which appears on Worcester porcelain, mainly on teaware and mugs. This particular print also occurs on Wedgwood creamware. Sadler prints can be distinguished from those of Hancock both in their style and in their brownish sepia tone, as opposed to the 'jet enamel' associated with Hancock.

A coffeepot of this pattern is in the Victoria and Albert Museum and a teabowl and saucer are in the F.C. Dykes Collection in the Manchester City Art Gallery.

178

178 A Creamjug *c*.1754–55

of pear shape, with a grooved handle, transfer-printed in black possibly by Robert Hancock, after L.P. Boitard, with the 'Haymakers'.

Height: 3½ inches

Mark: None

Provenance
T. Leonard Crow

Literature
Cyril Cook: *op.cit.* Item 51, illustrates a sucrier and cover dating from about 1778, with a modified version of this design.

Versions of this subject occur on Worcester, engraved by Robert Hancock, on Leeds creamware and Staffordshire enamels. A creamware teapot, transfer-printed with this subject in the Liverpool Museum, is signed: 'T. Rothwell Delin et Sculp'.

It is sometimes asserted that the first use of transfer printing on English porcelain was undertaken at Bow. However, whereas the earliest 'smokey primitives' at Worcester date from about 1753–54, no examples of printing on Bow can realistically be ascribed to before about 1755–56.

179 A Teabowl & Saucer *c*.1754–55

transfer-printed in black, possibly by Robert Hancock, after Boitard with the 'Flute Lesson'.

Diameter of saucer: 4½ inches

Mark: None

Provenance
T. Leonard Crow

Literature
Cyril Cook: *op.cit.* Item 36.

This subject also occurs on Battersea enamels and upon Chinese porcelain printed in England. On Worcester porcelain it is found principally on teaware and 'ivy leaf' pickle trays. The design is based on a painting by Nicholas Lancret entitled 'Le Maître Galant (La leçon de flûte)'.

Teabowls of this early period often have a characteristically flared outline and are invariably thinly potted.

179

180 Earth

180 Fire

180 Water

180 A Bowl *c.*1756

transfer-printed in black by Robert Hancock, with 'Earth', 'Fire' and 'Water'.

Diameter: 5¾ inches

Mark: None

Literature
Cyril Cook: *op.cit.* Item 35, illustrates a mug with 'Fire' and, Item 108, another mug with 'Earth'.

'Water' is a subject which has not been previously recorded.

'Fire' and 'Earth' were engraved by P. Aveline from a set of 'The Four Elements' by François Boucher, illustrated in *La Peinture Décorative du XVIIIe Siècle*, Plate v; 'Earth' and 'Fire' appear on Bow and the former also occurs on Champion's Bristol porcelain. 'Water' seems to have been derived from a different source.

The fourth Element 'Air', not on this bowl, has not hitherto been recognised, but it is more accurately revealed, masquerading under the title 'L'Oiseau Chinois' (Cook: Item 76) and like 'Earth' and 'Fire', it is derived from the painting by Boucher.

181

182

181 A Finger Bowl *c*.1760–62

with an indented rim, transfer-printed in black by
Robert Hancock with 'Le Chalet des Palmes'
and, on the reverse, 'Le Chalet Double'.

Diameter: 3½ inches

Mark: None

Provenance
T. Leonard Crow (Cf. letter No.43)

Literature
Cyril Cook: *op.cit*. Items 21 and 22.

Both subjects are designs after Jean Pillement and
appear in the second and third editions of *The
Ladies Amusement*.

Worcester finger bowls were issued in three sizes of
which this middle size is the most common.

A spoontray transfer-printed with 'Le Chalet
Double' is in the F.C. Dykes Collection in the
Manchester City Art Gallery.

182 A Stand *c*.1760–62

for a finger bowl, with a scalloped rim, transfer-
printed in black by Robert Hancock, with a river
scene including swans, wild duck, overhanging
trees and, in the distance, a standing heron.

Diameter: 5⅞ inches

Mark: None

Literature
Cyril Cook: *op.cit*. Item 93.
Henry Sandon: *op.cit*. Plate 31, illustrates a
similar stand, together with its finger bowl.

Hancock's river scenes and bird subjects occur
mainly on Worcester of the 1756–65 period.

A selection of finger bowls and stands, some printed
with aquatic birds, is in the Dyson Perrins Museum
at Worcester.

183

184

183 A Stand *c.*1760–62

for a finger bowl, with an indented rim, transfer-printed in black by Robert Hancock, with a river scene including swans, wild duck and overhanging trees.

Diameter: 5¼ inches

Mark: None

Literature
Cyril Cook: *op.cit.* Item 93.
Henry Sandon: *op.cit.* Plate 31, illustrates a similar stand together with its finger bowl.

Finger bowls and stands occur both with indented rims or with plain ones, as in No.200 in this Collection.

184 A Saucerdish *c.*1760–62

'feather moulded' and transfer-printed in black by Robert Hancock, with a river scene within a circular panel, surrounded by a frame of rococo scrollwork and trees.

Diameter: 6½ inches

Mark: None

Literature
Cyril Cook: *op.cit.* Item 60, Fig 2.

This moulding is found more often in conjunction with underglaze blue decoration. An example of this moulding on a saucerdish, with a different transfer print, is in the Dyson Perrins Museum at Worcester.

The framework of rococo scrolls is reminiscent of the printed textiles and wallpapers of the period.

185 Rural Lovers

185 May Day

185 A Mug *c.*1762

of cylindrical form, transfer-printed in black by Robert Hancock, with 'May Day' and, on the reverse, the 'Rural Lovers'.

Height: 3⅜ inches

Mark: None

Provenance
The Martin Hutchins Collection
T. Leonard Crow (Cf. letter No.23)

Literature
Cyril Cook: *op.cit.* Items 68 & 69.
Henry Sandon: *op.cit.* Plate 33, illustrates a cabbage-leaf masked jug.

'May Day' was adapted from a painting by Francis Hayman, one of a series commissioned in the 1730s to decorate the Pleasure Gardens of Vauxhall. The design appears in the third edition of *The Ladies Amusement*.

The 'Rural Lovers' was copied from an engraving by Francis Vivares published in 1760, after the painting by Thomas Gainsborough. An underglaze blue version of this subject was utilised on Liverpool porcelain at Philip Christian's factory, in the early 1770s.

186 A Teabowl & Saucer *c.*1768

transfer-printed in black by Robert Hancock with the 'Tea Party, No.2' and, on the reverse of the teabowl, with 'Maid and Page, No.1'.

Diameter of saucer: 4⅝ inches

Mark: R H Worcester with anchor

Provenance
T. Leonard Crow

Literature
Cyril Cook: *op.cit.* Item 105, illustrates a saucer and, Item 63, a bowl with the 'Maid and Page, No.1'.
H. Rissik Marshall: *op.cit.* Plate 12, No.215, illustrates a masked jug.

This subject is found in three separate versions and also occurs on Bow, on Chinese porcelain, on Birmingham enamels and on creamware. The 'Tea Party' first appears on Worcester in about 1758–60 and was utilised for nearly twenty years. A further version of this subject, by John Sadler, is found on Liverpool porcelain and Wedgwood creamware.

The 'Maid and Page, No.1' usually occurs as a subsidiary print in tandem with the second and third versions of the 'Tea Party'.

186

187

187 A Vase *c*.1765

of ovoid shape, transfer-printed in dark lilac by
Robert Hancock with scenes of Classical ruins.

Height: 7¼ inches

Mark: None

Provenance
T. Leonard Crow

Literature
Cyril Cook: *Supplement to The Life and Works of
Robert Hancock*, Item 167, illustrates a mug.

Classical ruins were a very popular subject on
Hancock's transfer-printed designs of the 1760s.
This design was taken from an engraving by J.S.
Muller, after Panini, dated 1753, in the British
Museum. This discovery, made by Joseph Hand-
ley, is discussed by him in a paper in the *English
Ceramic Circle Transactions*, Volume II, Part 2, 1982,
'Robert Hancock and G.P. Panini'.

188

188 A Plate *c.*1768

transfer-printed in dark lilac by Robert Hancock
with Classical ruins and with a gilt rim.

Diameter: 8¾ inches

Mark: None

Provenance
T. Leonard Crow

A representation of dishes, plates and teaware,
transfer-printed in shades of lilac, is in the Dyson
Perrins Museum at Worcester.

189

189 A Creamjug *c.*1760–62

of 'sparrow beak' form, transfer-printed in lilac by Robert Hancock and enamelled in colours, with 'Les Garçons Chinois'.

Height: 3 inches

Mark: None

Provenance
T. Leonard Crow

Literature
Cyril Cook: *op.cit.* Item 44.
H. Rissik Marshall: *op.cit.* Plate 11, No.190, illustrates a bowl and, Plate 12, No.219, a coffeepot.

This subject, in the style of the French painter Jean Pillement, also occurs in a plain black print, although the majority of examples are enamelled. The design was used on a range of objects which include teaware, mugs, large vases and small hexagonal bottle-shaped vases, and spans the period from about 1756–65. The pattern is also known in underglaze blue, although only two examples have so far been recorded, both of them on mugs. The original copper plate for this design is in the Worcester Works Museum.

A teapot in this design is in the Victoria and Albert Museum, and a coffeepot and a sucrier and cover are in the Dyson Perrins Museum at Worcester.

190 A Teabowl & Saucer *c.*1762–65

transfer-printed in black and painted in enamel colours with the 'Red Bull' pattern.

Diameter of saucer: 4 inches

Mark: None

Provenance
T. Leonard Crow

Literature
H. Rissik Marshall: *op.cit.* Plate 24, No.522, illustrates a mustard pot.
Simon Spero: *op.cit.* Page 73, illustrates a creamjug.

This design always occurs with enamel colours and spans the period from about 1754–65. It appears on a wide range of forms including teaware, mugs, coffee cans, mustard pots, early hexagonal bowls, deep leaf-shaped dishes and finger bowls and stands.

A similar pattern, transfer-printed in underglaze blue, was done at Bow and at Derby.

An extensive representation of this design can be seen in the Dyson Perrins Museum at Worcester, including an early lobed teapot, a finger bowl, a foliate bowl and an octagonal saucer.

190

191

192

191 A Coffee Cup & Saucer *c.*1768

transfer-printed in black by Robert Hancock and picked out in colours, the saucer with two figures and a dog among ruins and the cup with a landscape scene.

Diameter of saucer: 5 inches

Mark: Crossed swords and numeral 9

Provenance
T. Leonard Crow

Literature
Gerald Coke: *op.cit.* Plate 62(a)

This type of enamelled decoration is sometimes attributed to the atelier of James Giles. This rather complicated issue is discussed by Gerald Coke, *op.cit.* Pages 92 and 93. A group of pieces decorated in this manner is in the Victoria and Albert Museum.

192 An oval Dish *c.*1768

transfer-printed by Robert Hancock and enamelled in colour with Classical ruins and figures, within panels edged with pink scrolls, upon a blue scale ground.

Width: 7¾ inches

Mark: Fretted square

Literature
H. Rissik Marshall: *op.cit.* Plate 11, No.192.

The palette suggests that this belongs to the same group as the coffee cup and saucer, No.191 in the Collection.

An identical dish is in the Dyson Perrins Museum at Worcester.

193 A Dish *c.*1758–60

of leaf shape, with twig handle, transfer-printed in black by Robert Hancock, with crested birds and wild duck outlined with a green border.

Length: 6½ inches

Mark: None

Literature
Albert Amor Ltd: *Dr. John Wall, 1708–1776,* Exhibition Catalogue, No.32, illustrates a similar dish printed with 'Tomtits'.

A small bell-shaped mug with a similar printed subject, but lacking the wild duck in flight, is illustrated by G.W. Capell: 'Rare Porcelain Decorated by Robert Hancock', *Connoisseur*, November, 1962.

A pair of similar dishes is in the Victoria and Albert Museum.

193

Chapter VIII

Underglaze Blue Decoration

Throughout the first three decades of the Worcester factory, from 1751 to 1780, a considerable proportion of the output was devoted to blue and white porcelain. This was relatively inexpensive to produce and could be sold cheaply enough to compete with the Chinese porcelain that was being imported into England at this period. It remained a staple part of their output, while other forms of decoration were subject to the whims of current fashion and, judging from the amount that has survived until today, Worcester produced a far greater quantity of blue and white porcelain than any other eighteenth-century factory.

For a brief period immediately after the 'unification' with the Bristol factory early in 1752, there were no 'set' patterns and designs were created in an almost haphazard manner, consisting of Chinese landscapes, figures and random motifs, some of which were partially incorporated into other 'patterns'. No two pieces from this early period seem to be quite alike and they have a distinctive vitality in their decoration, borne of this lack of repetition. This small group of pieces is generally decorated with Chinese landscapes, often forming a continuous design around cylindrical objects, such as the rare and slightly primitive-looking mustard pot (No. 197), painted with a hitherto unrecorded pattern.

From 1753–54 onwards, patterns became fully standardised and, for the next six or seven years, some of the finest and most visually satisfying of all European blue and white porcelain was produced. Its strictly utilitarian nature is embodied in the beautifully potted, sensibly designed, practical forms that came from the factory at this time. Potting shapes were often derived from silver but, until about 1768, the main decorative influence was Chinese, probably absorbed through the medium of English delftware. Underglaze blue painting on porcelain was still in its infancy in England and it is likely that many of the pioneers of this technique had learnt their expertise by painting on tin-glazed earthenware. The allure of early Worcester blue and white is the result of the harmonious understanding between potter and painter, the one complementing and embellishing the achievement of the other. But the commercial success attained so swiftly at the factory was based upon practical considerations rather more than aesthetic insights. The durability of the Worcester glaze, able to withstand the impact of boiling water, rendered the porcelain, however thinly potted, ideal for teaware. This technical mastery of paste and glaze, allied to well-designed shapes, subtly painted in a well-controlled tone of underglaze blue, was a formidable achievement, as much appreciated by the collectors of today as by the eighteenth-century households.

Three teapots (Nos 194–196) differing in their shape, period and decorative inspiration, illustrate the variety of styles and tones of underglaze blue, though the simple loop handle remains a constant factor in each. The heavily moulded example (No.194), painted in the pale, greyish tone of blue characteristic of the mid-1750s, typifies the

164

harmonious alliance of a basically European shape with oriental decoration. The smaller teapot, painted with birds, shows a Meissen influence which is uncommon on blue and white porcelain of this period. Fine-quality moulding is exemplified by the two-handled sauceboat (No.199) and the rare hexagonal creamboat (No.198). One of the most arresting standard designs of the mid-1750s, the 'Cormorant' pattern, is represented on the finger bowl (No.200).

As the 1760s progressed, an element of stylisation becomes increasingly evident in the painted designs. Many patterns were copied directly from Chinese porcelain and these can appear static and literal by comparison with the fluidly drawn chinoiserie landscapes of the 1750s. An exception to this trend is the utterly delightful 'Eloping Bride' pattern (No.203), derived from Chinese porcelain but painted with vitality and humour. Another pleasing design of the later 1760s is the 'cracked ice' ground, also inspired by Chinese porcelain and represented in the Klepser Collection by a set of three mugs in graduated sizes (No.202).

By 1770, the Worcester painted designs had become less ambitious, principally due to the increased use of underglaze blue transfer-printing. This technique had been introduced in about 1758 but it was not until nearly ten years later that it became established as a major form of decoration. As a consequence, the china painters were inevitably relegated to the more simple forms of decoration or even deprived of work altogether. A strike among some of the artists in 1770, protesting against the printing press, could not deflect the march of commercial progress and its failure probably resulted in a number of painters leaving for the newly established Plymouth factory.

Alongside the development of transfer-printing, the Worcester factory at last succeeded in the large-scale manufacture of flatware, an area of production in which they had hitherto been deficient. By 1770, dessert services, junket dishes, baskets and the like had become the mainstay of their underglaze blue production, the majority printed, most often with the 'Pine Cone' pattern (No.211).

From 1752 until about 1760–62, the majority of blue and white Worcester bears painters' marks: numerals or workmen's symbols, the significance of which has not yet been discovered. From the early 1760s onwards, the crescent mark was used; open on hand-painted pieces and hatched where the decoration was transfer-printed. The W mark occurs far less often and ranges in date from about 1762–78, the more elaborate script W tending to occur on the later examples.

The Collection contains only a small representation of blue and white Worcester, but this should not be seen as reflecting Mr Klepser's lack of interest in this form of decoration. Indeed, when he first began collecting in the early 1940s, it was upon blue and white that he concentrated and by the mid-1950s, shortly before the publication of his original catalogue, he had amassed a collection of well over one hundred pieces. At this point, he reluctantly took the step of culling his blue and white porcelain, in order to give himself more space, a decision which he came to regret in later years but which, even in retrospect, was probably necessary in the circumstances.

Within the framework of what is essentially a collection of polychrome Worcester, the proportion of blue and white seems to strike very much the correct balance, complementing the main emphasis of the Collection, without in any way competing with it.

194 A Teapot & Cover *c.*1754

of globular shape, moulded in relief with mirror-shaped panels enclosing Chinese landscapes with figures in fishing scenes painted in underglaze blue, and with flowering prunus sprays around the shoulder and upon the spout.

Height: 6 inches

Mark: A cross

Literature
L. Branyan, N. French and J. Sandon: *op.cit.* I B 22.
Bernard Watney: *op.cit.* Plate 32A.

Early moulded Worcester teapots painted with Chinese fishing scenes in underglaze blue occur in three slightly differing shapes: a plain globular, as illustrated here, a lobed form and a slightly later globular shape with a faceted spout. This form of moulding on teaware spans the period from about 1754–58 and is generally characterised by its thinness of potting. It occurs also on coffee cans but no teapot stand, spoontray or coffeepot has so far been recorded. This moulding occurs as well in association with coloured decoration and, occasionally, with overglaze transfer prints.

A similar teapot is in the Victoria and Albert Museum and another example is in the Dyson Perrins Museum at Worcester.

194

195

195 A Teapot & Cover *c.*1758–60

of inverted pear shape, with a faceted spout and loop handle, painted in underglaze blue with three birds perching in the branches of a tree and, on the reverse, with a bouquet and sprays of flowers.

Height: 4 inches

Mark: Painter's mark

Literature
L. Branyan, N. French and J. Sandon: *op.cit.*
I C 25.

This style of bird painting, derived from Meissen, seems confined primarily to teapots, and no tea-bowls, saucers, coffee cups or creamjugs are known to match with them. The bird painting is some-times associated with the artist James Rogers, but by comparison with his distinctive style (No.53 in this Collection) this attribution is unconvincing. The underglaze blue on this pattern is invariably a dark tone.

A similar teapot is in the Dyson Perrins Museum at Worcester.

196

196 A Teapot & Cover *c.*1765–68

of barrel shape, with a flat cover and floral knop, moulded in relief with an arrangement of floral sprays and painted in underglaze blue with a cell pattern border, above and below.

Height: 4¼ inches

Mark: Crescent

Provenance
T. Leonard Crow

Literature
Henry Sandon: *op.cit.* Plate 28, illustrates a slightly earlier example with differing painted decoration, together with two biscuit wasters.

A slightly earlier polychrome example of this shape is No.39 in this Collection.

197 (reverse side)   197

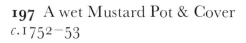

197 A wet Mustard Pot & Cover *c*.1752–53

of cylindrical form, painted in underglaze blue with a continuous scene incorporating a Chinese landscape with trees, houses, two Chinese figures and a third figure fishing from a boat.

Height: 3¼ inches

Mark: None

Provenance
T. Leonard Crow

Literature
H. Rissik Marshall: *op.cit.* Plate 24, No.522, illustrates a coloured example of a similar shape, but two years or so later in date.

This pattern is unrecorded. It dates from the 1752–53 period, before the Worcester underglaze blue designs had become fully developed. Among its early features are: the shape with its sloping shoulders, the angular handle which normally occurs on early creamboats, the fluid style of painting and the continuous manner in which the landscape is arranged, extending to either side of the handle. Another blue and white mustard pot of the same period has the numerals 56 incised into the cover, but the significance of this is not clear.

Blue and white mustard pots of the 1750s are scarce and it was not until the late 1760s that they appeared with any frequency. An early polychrome mustard pot is No.9 in this Collection.

198 A Creamboat *c*.1754

of hexagonal form with a scroll handle, moulded in relief with a continuous oriental mountain landscape of palm trees, pagodas, terraced gardens and birds, the interior painted in underglaze blue with meandering floral sprays.

Length: 4½ inches

Mark: None

Provenance
T. Leonard Crow (Cf. letter No.18)

Literature
Henry Sandon: *op.cit.* Plate 5, illustrates a similar creamboat but from a different mould, together with a biscuit waster from the site of the factory.

S.M. Clarke of Chicago has categorised these moulded creamboats in a paper in *The American Ceramic Circle Bulletin, Number 3*. He has designated this as Type A of the six different moulded designs which he has noted. All of the recorded blue and white creamboats of this type have underglaze blue painting only on the interior, with the sole exception of an example in the Loan Collection at the Bristol City Art Gallery. In this solitary instance, the moulded decoration is picked out in underglaze blue. These moulded creamboats were probably produced for only a short period between about 1752–54.

A coloured example is No.21 in this Collection.

198 (reverse side)

198

199

199 A two-handled Sauceboat
*c.*1755–56

with shell-moulded lips and scroll handles,
painted in underglaze blue in the interior with a
Chinese river landscape, the lips with diaper
panels. The exterior is moulded, each side having
two reserved panels containing miniature Chinese
scenes.

Length: 7¼ inches

Mark: Painter's mark

Provenance
T. Leonard Crow

Literature
L. Branyan, N. French and J. Sandon: *op.cit.*
I B 32.
Simon Spero: *op.cit.* Page 123.
Bernard Watney: *op.cit.* Plate 30B.

200

Two-handled sauceboats were made in three sizes and range in date from about 1754–58. They occur in conjunction with three different thumb-rest forms; flat pads, curved scrolls (as illustrated here) and monkey heads. The latter are confined to the largest size of sauceboat and can be seen on the coloured example (No.42) in this Collection.

Most blue and white examples bear this standard pattern but there are three two-handled sauce-boats extant, all in private collections, with the design known as the 'Fisherman with a Net'.

The Christie's Sale of Worcester porcelain in December 1769 contained a small amount of blue and white porcelain, among which were listed in the catalogue: 'two double handled Sauceboats'. This entry suggests that a certain amount of old stock was being disposed of, as this form of sauce-boat had not been produced for ten years or so.

200 A Finger Bowl *c.*1755–56

painted in underglaze blue with a large cormorant standing on a rock above a Chinese figure fishing from a boat, and a large flowering tree peony. The 'Cormorant' pattern.

Diameter: $3\frac{1}{2}$ inches

Mark: **T** monogram

Provenance
T. Leonard Crow (Cf. letter No.24)

Literature
L. Branyan, N. French and J. Sandon: *op.cit.* I B 28, illustrate two stands.
Henry Sandon: *op.cit.* Plate 20, illustrates a stand, together with a glazed waster found on the factory site.
Bernard Watney: *op.cit.* Plate 26c, illustrates a group of 'Cormorant' pieces including a finger bowl and a stand.

The 'Cormorant' pattern ranges in date from about 1754–56 and is found principally on tea-ware, bowls, mugs, coffee cans, round butter tubs and finger bowls and stands. The latter tend to be painted in a darker tone of blue than most of the teaware and mugs, perhaps indicating a slightly later date. Glost wasters of this pattern were found on the factory site.

Blue and white Worcester finger bowls are con-fined to the 1750s and occur mainly in conjunction with either the 'Cormorant' or the early version of the 'Mansfield' pattern, although two further designs are known in this shape.

201 A pair of Wall Pockets *c.*1758–60

of cornucopia shape, spirally-moulded and painted in underglaze blue with flowering branches, sprays and a bird.

Length: $11\frac{3}{4}$ inches

Marks: Crossed swords

Provenance
T. Leonard Crow (Cf. letter No.2)

Literature
Franklin A. Barrett: *op.cit.* Plate 45B.
Stanley Fisher: *English Blue and White Porcelain of the Eighteenth Century*, Plate 19 (Colour).

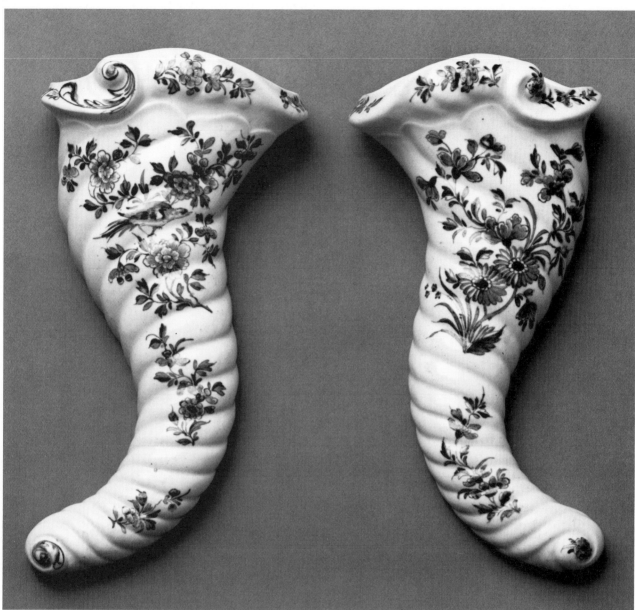

201

Worcester wall pockets occur in three basic moulded shapes and are sometimes found bearing up to five separate painter's marks. They range in date from about 1756–62 and were issued in a variety of floral patterns. Polychrome examples are known but they are rare. The listed wholesale price during the late 1750s for 'two sizes of cornucopia' was 2s 3d and 2s 6d per dozen, according to size.

202

202 (reverse side)

203

202 A set of three Mugs *c.*1765–68

of cylindrical form, in graduated sizes, painted in underglaze blue with an oriental lady flanked by flowering rockwork and a fence, within a foliate panel and, on the reverse, with an oriental lady seated upon a formation of barrel-like rocks, all upon a 'cracked ice' ground, enriched with hawthorn pattern.

Heights: $5\frac{7}{8}$ inches; $4\frac{7}{8}$ inches; $3\frac{7}{8}$ inches

Marks: Crescents in each case

Provenance
T. Leonard Crow (Cf. letter No.10)

Literature
L. Branyan, N. French and J. Sandon: *op.cit.*
I A 14, illustrate a bell-shaped mug.
Henry Sandon: *op.cit.* Plate 96, also illustrates a bell-shaped mug.

The 'cracked ice' ground, derived from Chinese porcelain, was particularly successful in its adaptation at Worcester. It seems to appear only upon cylindrical and bell-shaped mugs and generally is seen to its best effect on the larger sizes. The pattern ranges in date from about 1765–70. A large mug of this design is in the Victoria and Albert Museum, and three further examples are in the Dyson Perrins Museum at Worcester.

203 A Teabowl & Saucer *c.*1765

painted in underglaze blue with a bride and bridegroom seated on a galloping dappled horse, pursued by sundry figures bearing canopies and lances and with a further figure in a circular panel. The 'Eloping Bride' pattern.

Diameter of saucer: $4\frac{1}{2}$ inches

Mark: Pseudo-Chinese symbol

Provenance
T. Leonard Crow (Cf. letter No.10)

Literature
Franklin A.Barrett: *op.cit.* Plate 43B, illustrates a saucerdish.
L. Branyan, N. French and J. Sandon: *op.cit.*
I A 20, illustrate a bowl.
Bernard Watney: *op.cit.* Plate 35D, illustrates a teapot.

This celebrated Worcester pattern was adapted from a Chinese K'ang Hsi original and occurs only on teaware. The teabowls and saucers are invariably of a smaller size than usual for this period. The pattern spans the period from about 1765–70 and is normally painted with great precision and clarity.

204

204 A Saucer *c.*1765

together with a Chinese teabowl, painted in underglaze blue with radiating petal-shaped panels of 'Long Eliza' Chinese figures divided by similar panels of flower sprays, surrounding a central floral medallion. The 'Arcade' pattern.

Diameter of saucer: $4\frac{1}{8}$ inches

Mark: Pseudo-Chinese symbol

Provenance
T. Leonard Crow

Literature
L. Branyan, N. French and J. Sandon: *op.cit.*
I A 7, illustrate a saucer.
Bernard Watney: *op.cit.* Plate 35B, illustrates a coffee cup and saucer.

As with the 'Eloping Bride' teabowl and saucer (No.203), this pattern was adapted from a Chinese K'ang Hsi original and it occurs only on teaware of a smaller size than usual, perhaps echoing the size of the Chinese prototype. The pattern ranges in period from about 1765–70.

205 A Spoon *c.*1768–70

of Chinese rice-spoon form, with a tapering oval pierced bowl and straight handle, painted with a central flowerhead surrounded by scrolling foliage and with an applied moulded flowerhead on top of the handle.

Length: $5\frac{1}{2}$ inches

Mark: None

Provenance
T. Leonard Crow

Literature
L. Branyan, N. French and J. Sandon: *op.cit.*
I F I.
Simon Spero: *op.cit.* Page 148.

This shape, derived from a Chinese original, occurs in three distinct patterns and ranges in period from about 1765–80. A version of the pattern illustrated above appears on the much rarer Lowestoft spoons but these can be distinguished by their bluer glaze, lighter tone of underglaze blue and by the applied florette on the handle, which resembles a face. This shape of spoon was also made at Bow, although not in this pattern.

205

206

206 A Sucrier & Cover *c.*1768–70

painted in underglaze blue with a large peony and meandering floral sprays with a scrollwork border. The 'Mansfield' pattern.

Height: 5¼ inches

Mark: Crescent

Literature
L. Branyan, N. French and J. Sandon: *op.cit.* I E I.
Henry Sandon: *op.cit.* Plate 108.

The 'Mansfield' pattern appears upon a wide range of shapes including teaware, mustard pots, coffee cans, pickle leaves, mugs, butter tubs and finger bowls and stands. It spans one of the longest periods of any underglaze blue design from about 1758–80. Many other factories used a version of this pattern and it occurs on Lowestoft, Plymouth, Bow, Derby, the Liverpool factories of Chaffers' and Christian and on Caughley. In the latter case, a transfer-printed version was sometimes used.

207

207 A Bowl *c.*1770

painted in underglaze blue with two quails flanked by trees in a landscape setting. The 'Quail' pattern.

Diameter: 6¼ inches

Mark: Crescent

Provenance
T. Leonard Crow (Cf. letter No.40)

Literature
L. Branyan, N. French and J. Sandon: *op.cit.* 1 C 15, illustrate a saucer.
Henry Sandon: *op.cit.* Plate 94, illustrates a coffee cup and saucer, together with a fragment of a glazed waster bowl found on the factory site.
Bernard Watney: *op.cit.* Plate 35C, illustrates a teabowl and saucer.

This is a relatively late pattern in its underglaze blue form, ranging from about 1770–75 and it is principally confined to teaware. A version used at Bow was very much closer to the Chinese original and a transfer-printed design occurs on Pennington's Liverpool.

208 A Plate *c.*1770–72

painted in underglaze blue with Chinese fishing scenes in circular and fan-shaped reserved panels and floral medallions all upon a powder blue ground.

Diameter: 6½ inches

Mark: Pseudo-Chinese symbol

Literature
L. Branyan, N. French and J. Sandon: *op.cit.* 1 B 27, illustrate a plate of a differing form.

The 'powder blue' ground was derived from Chinese K'ang Hsi porcelain. It was introduced at Worcester in about 1760 but does not occur on dessert ware until about 1770. This pattern was copied fairly accurately from Bow, where it first appeared in the late 1750s, but the Worcester ground tends to lack the richness and depth of the Bow version. Powder blue grounds were also used at Lowestoft during the mid 1760s, at Derby in the 1770s, at Longton Hall in the early 1750s and, more commonly, at Caughley during the late 1770s.

208

209

209 A Junket Dish *c.*1765–68

of deep form, with a barbed and curved rim, moulded with three scallop shells, each painted in underglaze blue with flowers and shrubs and a central moulded petal-shaped motif, picked out in blue.

Diameter: 10 inches

Mark: Crescent

Literature
L. Branyan, N. French and J. Sandon: *op.cit.*
I E 35.
Henry Sandon: *op.cit.* Plate 95, illustrates wasters from the factory site of three different forms of junket dish.

Junket dishes were produced in several different moulded patterns, some of which were painted and others transfer-printed. They range in period from about 1760–78. Lowestoft copied the Worcester 'Pine Cone' transfer-printed version and the example illustrated here was imitated on Chinese porcelain. In each case the crescent mark was used.

210

210 A Chestnut Basket, Cover & Stand *c.*1770

with twig handles, each quatrefoil lobed piece moulded with florets and painted in underglaze blue, the interior printed with fruit sprays.

Length of stand: 10¾ inches
Length of basket: 9 inches

Mark: Hatched crescent

Literature
Henry Sandon: *op.cit.* Plate 122, illustrates a chestnut basket and cover, together with an unglazed waster of similar form.

This model ranges in date from about 1770–75 and was copied at Lowestoft and Caughley. The form also occurs at Worcester in various polychrome designs.

The first use of underglaze blue transfer prints on English porcelain occurred at Worcester in about 1758, but the technique was not fully developed until the late 1760s.

211

211 A pierced Basket *c.*1770–72

of oval shape, with entwined twig handles with floral terminals, transfer-printed in the interior with the 'Pine Cone' pattern.

Length: 8¼ inches

Mark: Hatched crescent

Literature
Geoffrey Godden: *Caughley and Worcester Porcelains 1775–1800*, Plate 90, illustrates the Caughley version of this shape.
Simon Spero: *op.cit.* Page 307, illustrates the Lowestoft version.

The 'Pine Cone' pattern was used on a wide range of Worcester shapes during the 1770s, including plates, dishes, tureens, round and oval baskets, vases, bottles and junket dishes. The main design is transfer-printed but the border is hand-painted. The pattern was also used at Lowestoft and Caughley, the former also 'borrowing' the crescent mark.

A similar basket bears the incised date: 1772. Cf. Appendix B.

A coloured basket of this shape is No.73 in this Collection.

Appendix A

'Bristoll'-marked pieces

The embossed 'Bristoll' mark, sometimes spelt 'Bristol', is recorded on nine moulded figures representing Lu Tung-Pin, the Chinese Immortal. It also occurs on sauceboats and creamboats and, in all, twenty-three of these have been recorded. They fall into four categories:

Nine Sauceboats of silver form, with elaborate high two-piece scroll handles. They are on oval pedestal bases and moulded in relief with cornucopia swags of ribbons and flowers. They resemble No.23 in this Catalogue in their moulding and overall form, but have higher, more elaborate handles. Seven examples are coloured and the remaining two, white.

Seven Sauceboats of low-footed moulded form, all painted in underglaze blue. They are approximately similar to No.26 in this Catalogue.

Five Creamboats of hexagonal form, with moulded scrollwork and panels containing Chinese scenes. All are painted in underglaze blue.

Two Creamboats of fluted form, supported on four pad feet; one is blue and white and the other, a coloured example, is No.20 in this Catalogue. This is the only coloured 'Bristoll'-marked creamboat recorded.

In all, eight of the above pieces are decorated in colour but it is not clear whether the decoration was applied at Bristol or at Worcester. Indeed it is not certain whether *any* coloured decoration was undertaken at Benjamin Lund's Bristol Factory.

Of these eight examples, the embossed 'Bristoll' mark has been painted over in green, in every case but one. The exception is a high-handled sauceboat, formerly in the Wallace Elliot Collection and now in the Victoria and Albert Museum. The obscuring of the embossed mark strongly suggests that the decoration was carried out at Worcester rather than at Bristol and an examination of the palette, by comparison with that found on the earliest Worcester wares, largely supports this contention.

It is not clear however, whether the sauceboats themselves were made at Bristol or whether they were made at Worcester utilising moulds brought from Bristol at the time of the unification of the two factories in 1752. The latter possibility cannot be discounted but it seems more likely that they are of Bristol manufacture, part of the 'stock, utensils and effects . . .' moved up the River Severn to Worcester.

A close examination of the paste and glaze of these 'Bristoll'-marked pieces enables one to make a start in separating the products of Lund's Bristol factory from those of the earliest period at Worcester. The presence of Benjamin Lund, 'china maker', in Worcester in February 1753 underlines the complexity of this task, but Dr Bernard Watney and others have isolated a small corpus of blue and white wares, forming a coherent group, that can be ascribed to the Bristol factory with a reasonable degree of confidence. After all, the Lund's factory was in production for some three years, and it is surely reasonable to presume that at least some few score pieces have survived the ravages of time.

Appendix B

Problems in dating Worcester porcelain

It is no coincidence that the majority of the standard reference books on eighteenth-century coloured Worcester porcelain, published during the past thirty-five years, have adopted a uniformly cautious attitude in the dating of Worcester porcelain. Such distinguished writers as Severne MacKenna, Cyril Cook, Rissik Marshall and, most recently, Gerald Coke, have deliberately avoided assigning dates to pieces and Henry Sandon has pointed out the problems and difficulties of attempting to date a piece closely.

The wisdom of this approach is not hard to discern. After a brief period of experimentation, in the early 1750s, the Worcester body and the glaze which covered it showed very little change or variation until the deterioration which became evident in the middle 1770s. Thus, at a stroke, the two factors that are so crucial in the dating of eighteenth-century porcelain are removed, or at any rate, much reduced in significance. Dating by style of decoration can be hazardous as these styles tended to overlap and it is likely that at any one time from 1755 onwards several different styles of decoration were being carried out simultaneously. The Worcester shapes provide a surer chronological guide but, by the nature of their gradual evolution, it is only a very general one.

The excavations at the site of the Worcester factory, far from affording assistance in the question of dating, seem to add to its complexity. Biscuit wasters of shapes, presumed to be of differing periods, have been found on the same level, implying that they were in fact contemporary. However, it should be borne in mind that establishing date by stratum may be as full of pitfalls as the precise dating of the porcelain itself. A level tentatively ascribed to one particular date may contain wasters from several years either side.

In endeavouring to assess the date of a piece of coloured Worcester porcelain from its decoration alone, a further problem arises. It is clear from contemporary advertisements, that stocks of porcelain were sometimes left in the white, for decoration at a later date. The practice was especially true of the Giles atelier. Hence, the teabowl and saucer from the 'Lord Dudley' service (No.157), which appears to have been manufactured in about 1768, may not have been decorated until several years later and was possibly not sold until the Christie's Sale of March 1774.

Furthermore, even the dated or documentary pieces, which might be expected to afford a reliable framework for the dating of similar pieces, cannot always be accepted at face value. Apart from the case of the 'Henry Cook 1761' creamjug, mentioned below, I would also cite the instance of the teapot, now in the British Museum, which is similar to No.113 in this Catalogue. The inscription 'No.45' under the spout, alludes to John Wilkes and Number 45 of his paper *The North Briton*, published on 23 April 1763. From this, some writers have deduced that this teapot was made and decorated in 1763, thereby providing a crucial date by which time the blue scale ground had been firmly established at Worcester. However, at this point, the political history of the 1760s intrudes into this academic exercise. Issue No.45 did not come to widespread public attention until the Middlesex Elections of 1768 and the ceramics commemorating this celebrated issue date from 1768 rather than 1763.

All the foregoing observations refer to coloured decoration, applied over the glaze. With regard to underglaze blue, we are on firmer ground and the dated pieces are altogether less likely to be misleading. Indeed writers on blue and white Worcester have shown a far greater willingness to assign precise dates to each piece. This may be partly because they have the evidence of unglazed wasters found during excavations. These sometimes bear underglaze blue designs whereas no coloured biscuit wasters exist, as enamel decoration was an overglaze process.

However, it seems to me that this additional evidence, denied to the student of coloured porcelain, does not fully account for the constrasting attitudes towards dating between writers on coloured and blue and white porcelain. Perhaps the study of blue and white, fraught with its own particular hazards and challenges, attracts a more analytical and clinical approach to the subject.

At any event, I have taken the view that, despite its evident pitfalls, it is worth attempting to suggest a reasonably precise date for each item in this Catalogue. In putting forward one particular date, I am not implying that the piece was necessarily made in that year. For example, 'c.1755' is intended to suggest a span of 1754 to 1756 as a probable date of manufacture. It follows from this that in assigning a piece to 1770–72, I am giving it a span of some five years.

My criterion for undertaking this task has been a combination of many different clues and guidelines. I have deduced as much as possible from an examination of the paste and glaze of each piece, a factor more helpful in the 1750–55 and post-1775 periods, than in the intervening years. I have considered the evidence of overall shapes, together with such important facets as handle forms and footrims. The available dated specimens of Worcester, listed below, have in certain cases been of great assistance, and the various Sale advertisements and the surviving Sale catalogues have afforded some general guidelines on dating. I have also endeavoured to relate our understanding of the chronology of underglaze blue decoration and shapes, to comparable coloured pieces.

Inscribed and dated pieces of English porcelain are justly prized by collectors and students alike. In most cases they make a valuable contribution to our knowledge of the porcelain factories and, in particular, to the chronology of the changing shapes and styles of decoration. The Lowestoft factory made a speciality of inscribed pieces and over two hundred dated examples have been recorded. Three comprehensive lists of the known specimens have been published, by A.J.B. Kiddell in 1931, George Levine in 1968 and Geoffrey Godden a year later. In 1982, Anton Gabszewicz incorporated into his excellent book, *Bow Porcelain*, a list of the thirty-six recorded pieces of dated Bow.

Most recently, Dr Nigel Cooke has published a compilation of all the known pieces of dated blue and white Worcester.[1] He has kindly allowed me access to all his information on the subject and to it I have added details of all the dated pieces of coloured Worcester that I have been able to discover. The list is probably not complete, as there are likely to be other dated pieces in museum vaults and private collections, but it is at least a foundation upon which one can build.

A group of dated pieces serves as a framework from which other similar items can be identified, classified and given an approximate date. Where a sufficient body of dated pieces exist, it is sometimes possible to build up a picture, through them, of changes in pastes, glazes, shapes and styles of decoration. In the case of Worcester there are several crucial periods which are very sparsely represented.

For instance, in the first six years of the factory's existence, from 1751 to 1756, we have only one blue and white coffee cup (D2) and three more-or-less identical mugs (D3 a, b and c) from which anything can be learnt of this early period. In the following three years, there is a small group of coloured mugs and jugs with high-quality, although somewhat untypical decoration, together with two miniature blue and white pieces.

The following period, from 1760 to 1766, is represented by a single coffee cup (D10) together with an atypical teapot in the Lady Ludlow Collection (D9). These years, in the early 1760s, are arguably the period from which dated pieces would be most valuable; many of the early decorative styles were falling out of favour and yet the colourful Imari and blue ground patterns had yet to appear. The exact nature of the predominating styles is not clear. It is possible that some of the chinoiserie designs (e.g. No.48) and some of the Meissen-style floral patterns (e.g. No.49) date from this period, rather than from the late 1750s. Similarly, the 1760–65 period is something of a 'no man's land' as regards underglaze blue decoration. It is presumed, on very

---

[1] 'Dated Blue and White Worcester Porcelain: 1751–1780; A Checklist'. *Antique Collecting*, October 1984.

little evidence, that the use of painter's marks had been discontinued by 1760 and yet very few of the crescent-marked pieces seem to fall into the immediate post-1760 category.

Dated pieces, by their very nature, are likely to be commemorative and may therefore be untypical in their decoration. This adds to their interest in one sense, but it also tends to lessen their documentary value. The teapot and the teabowl and saucer (D12 and 13), both decorated with the 'Cannonball' pattern, are important because they provide a date for a standard (though long-lived) pattern and, from the presence of their crescent marks, a firm date by which the mark was in use. Several other examples are helpful in establishing the chronology of shapes, but for evidence relating to other typical decorative styles, one has to look to the saucer (D20) and the bowl (D25). Thus it is the mundane pieces which add most to our knowledge of Worcester porcelain, rather than the more spectacular but less typical specimens.

Dated pieces of first-period Worcester

1751

D 1 **A Tureen**, moulded, but otherwise undecorated, bearing the date: 1751 in underglaze blue on the base. Despite some doubt as to whether this piece is Worcester or Bow, it is included here for completeness, as it has been referred to in a number of books on English porcelain.

Whereabouts unknown

1753

D 2 **A Coffee Cup**, painted in underglaze blue with a continuous Chinese landscape scene and inscribed on the base: 'T B 1753'.

Height: $2\frac{3}{4}$ inches. Mark: None.

Illustrated
L. Branyan, N. French and J. Sandon: *op.cit*: I B 1.
Bernard Watney: *op.cit*: Plate 26B.

British Museum

1754

D 3A **A Tankard** of bell shape, painted in early colours with a long-tailed bird, perched upon the branch of a tree, leaning forward to peck at a snail, and inscribed on the base: 'E × L 1754'.

Height: $4\frac{5}{8}$ inches. Mark: Incised cross in footrim.

Illustrated
English Ceramic Circle: Exhibition Catalogue 1948, No.370

Victoria and Albert Museum

D 3B **A Tankard** of bell shape, exactly similar to the above.

D 3C **A Tankard** of bell shape, exactly similar to the above.

1757

D 4 **A Mug** of bell shape, painted with a pheasant-like bird standing on a mound, flanked by other birds, both perched and in flight and inscribed on the base in black enamel: 'I Rogers Pinxit 1757'.

Height: $3\frac{1}{3}$ inches. Mark: None.

Illustrated
Franklin A. Barrett: *op.cit*. Plate 14A.
Hugh Tait: *Connoisseur*, April 1963, Colour Plate.

British Museum

D 5 **A large Jug** of moulded form, painted with the coat-of-arms of the City of Worcester, flanked by the seated figures of Commerce and Justice and inscribed upon a bale in one section of the decoration, with a W monogram and the date: 1757. The calligraphy appears to correspond exactly to that on the dated 'Rogers' mug.

Height: 11 inches. Mark: None.

Illustrated
Severne MacKenna: *op.cit*. Plate 68, No.139.
Hugh Tait: *op.cit*. Figs 3 and 4.

In the possession of the Corporation of the City of Worcester

1758

D 6A **A miniature Teabowl & Saucer**, painted in underglaze blue with the 'Prunus Root' pattern and both inscribed upon the base: 'C S 1758'. Part of a 'toy' tea service reputed to have been made for Charlotte Sherriff of Upton-on-Severn, Worcestershire.

Diameter of saucer: $3\frac{1}{4}$ inches. Marks: None.

Dyson Perrins Museum, Worcester

D 6B **A miniature Saucer**, painted in underglaze blue with the 'Prunus Root' pattern and inscribed on the base: 'c s 1758'.

Diameter of saucer: 3¼ inches. Mark: Painter's.

Illustrated
Albert Amor: *Worcester Porcelain: The First Decade 1751–1761*, Exhibition Catalogue, No.92.
F. Severne MacKenna: *op.cit.* Plate 12, Nos 24 & 25.

Private Collection

1759

D 7 **A Mug** of bell shape, painted in enamel colours with a gentleman in a frock coat and tricorn hat, accompanied by his dog, within an extensive European landscape background, enclosed within a scrollwork cartouche and inscribed on the base: 'Lord and Lady Sandy's health. T G 1759'.

Height: 4½ inches. Mark: None.

Illustrated
Franklin A. Barrett: *op.cit.* Colour Plate A.
R.L. Hobson: *op.cit.* Plate 81, No.384.
H. Rissik Marshall: *op.cit.* Plate 47, No.961.
Hugh Tait: *op.cit.* Fig 15.

British Museum

D 8 **A Cider Jug** of pear shape, painted in enamel colours with the arms of Chalmers, flanked by a European landscape incorporating a coastline with a church and other buildings and on the reverse ships in full sail, with the motto: 'SPIRO', beneath the crest and inscribed under the handle: 'A C 1759'.

Height: 5¾ inches. Mark: None.

Illustrated
Franklin A. Barrett: *op.cit.* Plate 24.
R.L. Hobson: *op.cit.* Plate 82, No.386.
H. Rissik Marshall: *op.cit.* Plate 47, No.957.
Hugh Tait: *op.cit.* Fig 17.

British Museum

1760

D 9 **A Teapot & Cover**, pierced with a broad band of arabesque foliage, transfer-printed with a portrait of George II and dated 1760. The shoulder and cover are decorated with arabesques in red and gold.

From the Humphrey Cook Collection. The Lady Ludlow Collection

1764

D 10 **A Coffee Cup**, painted in colours with 'Japan' flowers on either side of the handle and, within a central cartouche, the inscription in black enamel: 'Nancy, Squier, 1764'.

Height: 2½ inches. Mark: None.

Illustrated
R.L. Hobson: *op.cit.* Plate 12, No.73.
H. Rissik Marshall: *op.cit.* Plate 47, No.960.
Hugh Tait: *op.cit.* fig 5.

British Museum

D 11 **A fragment of a Mug**, undecorated, found on the factory site during the excavation, incised: 'P.W. 1764'.

Dyson Perrins Museum, Worcester

1766

D 12 **A Teapot & Cover**, painted in underglaze blue with the 'Cannonball' pattern and inscribed on the base: 'W × M 1766', enclosed within an elaborate ring border.

Height: 5 inches. Mark: Crescent.

Illustrated
L. Branyan, N. French and J. Sandon: *op.cit.* I D 6.
Henry Sandon: *op.cit.* Plate 91.

Dyson Perrins Museum, Worcester

D 13 **A Teabowl & Saucer**, painted in underglaze blue with the 'Cannonball' pattern and inscribed on the base of the saucer: 'W × M 1766', enclosed within an elaborate ring border.

Diameter of saucer: 4¾ inches.
Mark: Crescent.

British Museum

1767

D 14 **A Teapot & Cover** of globular form, painted with floral bouquets within large irregular cushion-shaped panels, upon a yellow ground, and inscribed in a small cartouche, below the spout: 'N C 1767'.

Height: 5½ inches. Mark None.

Illustrated
The Catalogue of the Robert Drane Collection, No.819.

Now in the Lady Ludlow Collection

1769

D 15 **A Vase** of baluster form with trumpet mouth, painted with Aeneas fleeing from Troy with his father Anchises within a reserved panel upon a dark-blue ground. Signed in the foreground: 'O'NEALE 1769'.

Height: 15½ inches.
Mark: fretted square.

Illustrated
Franklin A. Barrett: *op.cit.* Page 79.
H. Rissik Marshall: *op.cit.* Plate 27, No.602.

Dyson Perrins Museum, Worcester

D 16 **A small Mug** of bell shape (lacking its handle), painted in underglaze blue and inscribed within an elaborate cartouche: 'Peter Taylor 1769'.

Height: 2½ inches. Mark: None.

Dyson Perrins Museum, Worcester

1770

D 17A A pair of mugs of cylindrical form, painted in
D 17B underglaze blue and inscribed: 'FRANCIS JAMES – 1770'.

Height: 2¼ inches. Marks: None.

Dyson Perrins Museum, Worcester
Private Collection

D 18A **A pair of mugs**, painted in colours with a shield
D 18B bearing the arms of Martindale of Cumberland, flanked by a cherub and bouquets and sprays of flowers, decorated in the atelier of James Giles and inscribed on the base in gold: 'I M April 5th 1770'.

Height: 5⅞ inches. Mark: None.

Victoria and Albert Museum

1771

D 19 **A Mug** of bell shape, painted in underglaze blue with the arms of the Foresters' Company within a large elaborate cartouche inscribed with mottoes and the words: 'Saml SHERIFF IN UPTON 1771'.

Height: 4¾ inches. Mark: None.

Sold at Sotheby's 14 May 1957
Ownership now unknown

D 20 **A Saucer**, painted with isolated sprigs in green camaïeu, outlined in black with a gilt dentil border and inscribed within the footrim in black enamel: 'THO^S HAMPTON pinxt 1771'.

Mark: None.

Dyson Perrins Museum, Worcester

1772

D 21 **An openwork Basket** of oval form with entwined twig handles and floral terminals, transfer-printed in underglaze blue with the 'Pine cone' pattern and incised on the base: 1772.

Formerly in a Spanish private collection

D 22 **A Teapot & Cover**, painted in enamel colours with landscape scenes on each side, depicting two figures, a boy and a girl and an urn bearing the inscription: 'F in(venit) ins(cripsit) Duvivier 1772'.

Height: 6 inches. Mark: None.

Illustrated
Franklin A. Barrett: *op.cit.* Plate 69B
H. Rissik Marshall: *op.cit.* Colour Plate 29 & Plate 19, No.345.

1773

D 23 **A Mug** of cylindrical form, painted in underglaze blue with an elaborate version of the 'Cannonball' pattern and inscribed on the base: 'T ·∴· A 1773'.

Height: 4½ inches. Mark: None.

Illustrated
L. Branyan, N. French and J. Sandon: *op.cit.* I B 35.

Dyson Perrins Museum, Worcester

D 24 **A Mug** of cylindrical form, transfer-printed in underglaze blue with flowers and incised upon the base 'July 31st 1773'.

Victoria and Albert Museum

D 25 **A Bowl**, painted in colour with sprays of flowers, inscribed on the base in overglaze red, within a double circle: 'John Evans Feb 11 1773'.

Mark: None.

The Museum of Fine Arts, Houston, Texas

1776

D 26 **A Mug** of cylindrical form and of enormous size, painted in underglaze blue and inscribed within a cartouche: 'S + B 1776'.

Height: 6 inches.
Mark: Painted crescent.

The Dyson Perrins Museum, Worcester

D 27 **An Inkwell**, painted in underglaze blue with floral sprays and inscribed under the base: 'I R 1776', in script.

Height: 3 inches. Diameter: 4 inches. Mark: None.

Private Collection.

D 28 **A Mug** of cylindrical form, painted in underglaze blue with the inscription: 'W B 1776'.

Mark: Painted crescent.

Private Collection.

D 29 **Four Mugs** of cylindrical shape, painted in underglaze blue with St George and the Dragon and inscribed: '1776', under the handle.

D 29A Height: 4½ inches.
Mark: Painted crescent.

Illustrated
L. Branyan, N. French and J. Sandon; *op.cit.* I A 34.

The Dyson Perrins Museum, Worcester

D 29B Inscribed: 'A DUNN BIRMINGHAM 1776', near the base.

Height: 4½ inches.

The Willett Collection, No.1404
Brighton Museum and Art Gallery

D 29C Inscribed: 'ANN DUNN BIR^m 1776' (5?), near the base.

Height: 4½ inches. Mark: None.

Messrs. Winifred Williams

D 29D Inscribed: 'ANN DUNN BIR^m 1776', near the base.

Height: 4½ inches.

Private Collection

1780

D 30 **Three Mugs** of cylindrical shape, transfer-printed in underglaze blue with 'La Pêche' and 'La Promenade Chinoise'

D 30A Inscribed: 'IOHN IZOD STRATFORD 1780'., under the handle.

Mark: Hatched crescent.

Private Collection

D 30B Inscribed: 'IOHN IZOD STRATFORD 1780', under the handle.

Illustrated

Geoffrey Godden: *Godden's Guide to English Porcelain*, Page 140.

Geoffrey Godden Reference Collection

D 30C Inscribed 'IOHN IZOD STRATFORD 1780', under the handle.

Godden of Worthing

I have excluded from this list the following four pieces:

1759

A Cylindrical Mug, painted with a silhouette of a man, in a white reserve panel and inscribed 'J.W. 1759', all upon a yellow ground.

Illustrated

The Catalogue of the Robert Drane Collection, No.802

The Lady Ludlow Collection

Although this mug has a fine pedigree, formerly being in the Robert Drane and Wallace Elliot Collections, the decoration cannot be considered contemporary with the porcelain and it therefore has no significance as a documentary piece. Furthermore, 1759 is an improbably early date for an English silhouette.

1766

An octagonal teacaddy with a floral finial on the cover, inscribed: 'Fine Tea. 1766'.

Ownership unknown

From an examination of a photograph of this teacaddy, it seems extremely unlikely that it is a Worcester piece. Neither the painted decoration, nor the overall style are consistent with an attribution to Worcester, and it is more probable that it is of Derby or possibly of Lowestoft manufacture.

1761

A Creamjug, painted in a dark pink with a pink scale border, inscribed within a rococo cartouche: 'Henry Cook, 1761'.

Height: 3½ inches. Mark: None.

Illustrated

H. Rissik Marshall: *op.cit*. Plate 18, No.315.

The Dyson Perrins Museum, Worcester

This creamjug is cited in many standard reference books on Worcester Porcelain as clear evidence that the pink scale ground was in use at Worcester by 1761. However, an examination of this creamjug reveals it to be of a later period than the inscription suggests. Its shape somewhat resembles No.77 in this Catalogue and the poor quality of the porcelain body indicates a date in the mid-1770s. The decoration itself is more likely to be from the Giles atelier than to have been painted at the Factory.

1772

A bell-shaped Mug, painted with exotic birds in panels, upon an apple-green ground and 'signed' in red: 'Mr. Benga^n Giles May ye 16, 1772'.

Height: 4¾ inches. Mark: None.

Illustrated

Apollo, February 1935.

H. Rissik Marshall: *op.cit*. Plate 34, No.744.

Formerly in the Berners and Eckstein Collections

Despite its illustrious provenance, this mug cannot be attributed to the Worcester Factory or the Giles atelier with confidence. The decoration seems very much later than the inscription implies and the signature itself is unconvincing. Furthermore, the painting bears no resemblance to that of a Giles artist, nor is the gilded decoration in the style of the Giles atelier.

Introduction to the Crow Letters

The correspondence between Kenneth Klepser and T. Leonard Crow began in the autumn of 1944, when Mr Klepser wrote inquiring about a piece of Worcester in a magazine advertisement, and continued for almost sixteen years, until Mr Crow's death in 1960. At first, Mr Crow's letters were not preserved, but their distinctive flavour was soon recognised by Mr and Mrs Klepser and from March 1948 onwards, the whole of Mr Crow's side of the correspondence was carefully filed. Unfortunately, none of Mr Klepser's letters has survived, but the sentiments and opinions which he expressed in them are not difficult to perceive from Mr Crow's responses.

The letters throw a revealing light upon the manner in which a large collection of Worcester porcelain was formed, six thousand miles distant from the main source of supply, and upon the developing friendship between the collector and the dealer so crucial in the assembling of the collection. The letters also present a picture of two men, separated by different backgrounds and cultures, and yet united by a common interest in travel, politics and porcelain. Their friendship and mutual respect were sustained almost entirely through their correspondence. They met only twice, at the Bi-Centenary Exhibition of the Royal Worcester Porcelain Company in Mayfair, during Mr and Mrs Klepser's visit to London in 1951, and at Tewkesbury in June of the same year, when Mr Crow was in hospital. In a wider context, the letters are illustrative of the working life of a country antique dealer, nearly 40 years ago; of his attitudes, problems and priorities and, not least, of the prices which prevailed at the time for early Worcester porcelain, and the knowledge and tastes of those who collected it.

Kenneth Klepser needed less advice and guidance than many collectors, but the encouragement and interest which Mr Crow conveyed in his letters were of enormous value to a man who was of necessity far removed from the salerooms and antique shops of England. Mr Crow, on the other hand, was on the most friendly terms with many of the eminent collectors and experts of that time and his letters are full of the opinions and views expressed by Dr Severne MacKenna, Rissik Marshall, Cyril Cook, A.J.B. Kiddell and others. The anecdotes told by and about these scholarly collectors, united by their love and understanding of Worcester porcelain, enabled Mr Klepser to gain a fascinating insight into the porcelain-collecting world from which he was so geographically remote. Mr Crow was also on excellent terms with many of his business colleagues and the names of John Perkins, David Manheim and Frank Tilley recur with illuminating frequency. His letters, which were regularly five or six pages, are full of information about recent or forthcoming auctions, collections which he had seen, rare items for sale in shops, as well as the opinions and theories current among his collector friends. In obtaining for Mr Klepser over half of the pieces which eventually made up his collection, Mr Crow demonstrably made an important contribution to its formation, but the exchange of ideas and information conveyed through these letters provided a source of stimulation for Mr Klepser which was fully of equal value.

Leonard Crow was, in many respects, typical of an English country antique dealer during the 1940s and 1950s. His business, established in the town of Tewkesbury, in the Cotswolds, in 1940, included a fairly extensive stock of general antiques, especially silver, pictures, glass and furniture but it was with English porcelain that Mr Crow was chiefly associated. He stocked a full range of eighteenth-century English porcelain and pottery and prided himself on his Swansea and Nantgarw, but his main speciality was 'Old Worcester Porcelain'.

His earlier business enterprises, in Devon, in Surrey and later in London, had not been entirely successful and those post-war years at Tewkesbury were the most settled and prosperous of his life. Like so many antique dealers, both at that time and today, he was an individualist, and the day-to-day running of the business, the buying, the selling, the packing and despatching of parcels, the bookwork and correspondence were all undertaken with the sole assistance of his wife. As is the case today, both the strength and the weakness of so idiosyncratic a 'one-man' business lay in its dependence upon the knowledge, experience, integrity and personality of its proprietor. As they unfold, these letters afford a revealing glimpse into the vicissitudes of the life of the country antique dealer soon after the war, with his problems, his little triumphs, his relationships with his customers and with his fellow dealers. In a broad sense, surprisingly little has changed, yet one cannot resist the impression that we are looking back on a way of life which is in the process of disappearing.

Naturally, the most crucial facet of a business of this kind was the buying of the stock. Where the porcelain was concerned, Mr Crow purchased from four main sources; from collectors, from other dealers, through his 'scouts' (see letter No.6) and, to a lesser extent, from the London and provincial salerooms. From time to time he was able to supplement these purchases, when invited to private houses whose owners wished to dispose of certain pieces. He was totally absorbed in his business and especially enjoyed 'la chasse'. His buying trips, a central feature of the antique dealer's life at that time, were gradually curtailed, due to his failing health and subsequent lack of mobility. His frustration at being unable to get 'on the warpath', as he termed it, is often evident.

Then, as now, the purchasing of stock required knowledge and taste and where capital was limited, careful planning too. As regards porcelain, the supply was plentiful by today's standards but, as is apparent from his letters, Mr Crow did not always find it easy to purchase the good pieces which he sought. There were certainly collectors with the knowledge, taste and funds to make significant purchases, but they were relatively few in number and it was mainly for the finer pieces that there existed a ready market. This partly accounts for the importance which Mr Crow placed upon his American clients and for the pride and satisfaction which he took in selling porcelain to them.

Like Mr Klepser, Leonard Crow was a man of strong convictions, and he was not backward in expressing them. This is reflected in his political opinions and his keen involvement on the committee of the British Antique Dealers' Association. His distaste for socialism and, in particular, for the post-war Labour Government, made him sympathetic to Mr Klepser's parallel situation, as a lifelong Republican, in a country that was experiencing twenty unbroken years of Democratic Administrations. This common ground, undoubtedly contributed to the respect and understanding which grew between the two men; shared exasperation proved a strong bond. From this mutual frustration, the two men became increasingly fascinated with the politics of one another's countries. America was only just emerging from two decades of isolationism, and there was little knowledge or awareness in England of the political climate on the far side of the Atlantic ocean.

Mr Crow was not in a position to indulge his love of travel, but his letters convey the interest and curiosity with which he followed Mr and Mrs Klepser's various travels throughout the world. Yet, whilst openly envying these extended journeys, Mr Crow's enduring affection for and pride in the English countryside are always vividly apparent.

Much of Mr Crow's character and personality emerges from the letters. His love of his country, his pride, his humour, his industry and his generosity, a likeable capacity for self-mockery and his courage and fortitude in adversity, are all evident alongside a certain irrascible obstinacy, a readiness to criticise and an unwillingness to tolerate fools gladly. His family background was intensely nonconformist and much of his youth was spent campaigning in the West Country for the Temperance Movement. He was a man of great energy; a keen enough walker to have hiked the whole coastline of Devon and Cornwall. He had a strong and persuasive personality, great charm and an enormous facility for friendship. Whilst he seldom disguised his criticism or even scorn for the shortcomings of others, he always remained steadfast in his affection and admiration for Mr Klepser.

His persistence, a necessary component of an antique dealer's character, is well illustrated by

T. LEONARD CROW

(ESTABLISHED 1908)

THE ANTIQUE SHOP
10 CHURCH STREET, TEWKESBURY

GLOS.

PHONE: TEWKESBURY 261

SPECIALITIES:—OLD PORCELAIN AND POTTERY OF THE WEST COUNTRY—WORCESTER, BRISTOL,
PLYMOUTH, SWANSEA AND NANTGARW. OLD BRISTOL AND NAILSEA GLASS.

ANTIQUE SILVER   OLD SHEFFIELD PLATE

The letterheading of T. Leonard Crow

the instance of the pair of oval moulded Worcester butter tubs (No.6). These are first mentioned on 14 November 1949 as having been sighted in Cambridge by Dr MacKenna and were subsequently missed by the narrow margin of three days. Mr Crow pursued these butter tubs with great tenacity and they are referred to on numerous occasions until being finally tracked down, brought to book and despatched to Seattle on 30 August 1950, an event recorded on 22 September, ten months and fourteen letters after their initial discovery. Extended stories of this kind, linking the letters, lend them their continuity and add an element of anticipation as we await each fresh episode.

As is evident from the correspondence, Mr Crow took a tremendous pride in his part in the formation of the Klepser Collection, and his pleasure in being asked to write the Foreword for the Exhibition Catalogue, published in the spring of 1955, is especially poignant in the light of their diminishing business association at that time. Mr Klepser's invitation to write this Foreword was more than merely a gesture from a loyal and sensitive man towards an old and valued friend; it was an affirmation of his affection and respect. He regarded Mr Crow as a man of honour and trusted him accordingly. In return, Mr Crow had given him no reason to doubt the wisdom of that trust.

The correspondence includes some seventy letters and in editing these into a manageable format I have tried to encapsulate the spirit of the man, his attitudes and prejudices and his business and personal relationship with Mr Klepser. I have included a number of the very detailed descriptions of items which Mr Crow offered for sale, together with their prices. The descriptions afford an interesting insight into the current state of knowledge at that time, of early Worcester porcelain. Considering that the great majority of the standard reference books on Worcester, which we use today, were written after 1953, one can only marvel at the scholarship of the collectors of the 1940s and the relative accuracy of Mr Crow's descriptions. The prices have a certain historical relevance, and many readers may be surprised at how high they were at a time when the middle bracket of incomes were measured in hundreds, rather than thousands of pounds a year. The implication might be that the Worcester collector of the time was of greater means than his contemporary counterpart.

Yet the business aspect of these letters often seems almost incidental. On a personal and purely human level, the correspondence traces the last thirteen years of Mr Crow's life as glimpsed through his relationship with one client. Through these letters we can discern his absorbing interest in his work, his love of porcelain, his energy and enthusiasm in tracking down rare pieces, his curiosity about life in America and his refusal to submit to physical handicaps.

At the beginning of the correspondence in the autumn of 1944, Mr Crow was aged 61 and Mr Klepser 48, though the difference in their ages often seems far greater. At first the letters were exchanged with great frequency often separated by only a week or so and reflecting an almost continuous level of business activity. Soon, in late 1948, there are the first intimations that all is not well with Mr Crow and that he is considering retirement. At first this seems not to impinge upon the regularity of their correspondence, nor upon the extent of Mr Klepser's purchases. Yet gradually, from the end of 1950 onwards, the letters become more infrequent as Mr Crow's health begins to deteriorate, necessitating a series of major operations. Thereafter, although several of the letters are long and cheerful, others are tinged with nostalgia and resignation. By the autumn of 1954, failing health had severely disrupted his business activities and the letters had become intermittent, sometimes separated by up to a year. The references to the fine pieces of Worcester that Mr Klepser had purchased elsewhere have a poignant quality in the context of the more ordinary items which were all that Mr Crow could now offer for sale. The closure of the Tewkesbury shop, together with his physical handicaps, had severely diminished his business activities. Then, just as the clouds seem to be gathering ominously, we read the letter of 24 November 1954, referring to the invitation to write the Foreword for the Catalogue of the Klepser Collection. This proposal seems to have had a most stimulating effect on Mr Crow and its repercussions are evident in the renewed frequency of the correspondence over the ensuing months. The final few letters, however, have undertones of sadness.

The following extracts form only a small portion of the correspondence. I have endeavoured to allow the letters to speak for themselves, only incorporating comments (in italics) where I feel they might be helpful to the reader.

Letter No.1   6th March 1948

Kenneth C. Klepser Esq.,
Seattle, 99, Washington, U.S.A.

Dear Sir,

Further to my letter of 27th February, I now have pleasure in sending for your kind perusal and consideration, a selection of photographs of various pieces of Old Worcester Porcelain now in my stock, including three of the items detailed on your list. I was hoping to have been able to include a piece from the 'Bishop Sumner' service but have not been able to track any down to date. As you probably realise you have included some items in your list which are very rare and difficult to trace. This applies especially to the 'Bodenham', the 'Hope Edwardes' and 'Eloping Bride' patterns. The first and last-named I already have, but they are necessarily costly because of their scarcity. The 'Hope Edwardes' if it can be found will be expensive. Single plates now realise anything from £100 to £150. Dishes more still. About a year ago I had two plates from the 'Duke of Gloucester' service, which I sold at £60 each, but the price will now be considerably more than that, if they can be found.

I shall be pleased, if you so desire, to continue searching for all pieces listed by you in your letter of Feb 1st, and to notify you from time to time of any such pieces coming into my possession.

Turning now to the enclosed photographs, descriptions and prices are as follows:

Saucer 5¼ inches diameter. Painted in blue underglaze with the Eloping Bride pattern. Mark on back, in blue underglaze, one of the pseudo-Chinese symbols, enclosed in a double ring. Perfect condition. Price: £17.10.0.

Dish from the 'Sir Joshua Reynolds' Service. Length 8½ inches (Inclusive of handles). Width 6½ inches. Painted in colours and gold. Wide border of Royal Blue, relieved with foliage sprays in gold. Oval panel in centre, decorated with long-tailed bird on tree-stump with flowering branches, and with dragon flies. At each end a rustic handle, with encrusted flowers at finials. Mark, a fretted square in blue underglaze. Perfect condition. Price £12.10.0. (See Hobson pl.xxxiv, fig.2. Frank Lloyd pl.16, fig.96)   *Cat. No.132.*

A Tea-bowl (or handleless teacup) and Saucer, from the 'Bodenham' service. Painted in blue underglaze and with enamel colours and gold. With gold reserves on blue scale ground. The three largest reserves painted with Chinese figures and flowering plants. One with Chinese figure holding a long spear and standing in a vase. The smaller reserves painted with sprays of flowers. Outstanding feature of pieces in 'Bodenham' service is the clarity of the salmon-scale ground. Very rare. Price £52.10.0.   *Cat. No.158.*

A Coffee-pot & Cover. Overall height 10½ inches. Finely moulded body, of Silver shape, painted in enamel colours, with large bouquets of flowers on either side, smaller sprays around base, on spout and on handle.

Smaller floral bouquets on cover. Around the neck is a wreath of formal foliage in puce. Early period of Worcester, circa 1758. In mint condition throughout. Price £37.10.0.   *Cat. No.50.*

A Plate. Diameter 8½ inches. With fluted and escalloped border. Painted in enamel colours and gold, in the Imari manner, with panels of diaper and with Oriental flowers (Chrysanthemum, Prunus, etc.) and with Chinese Dragons. Marked on back with a Gold Crescent. In perfect condition. Price £20.0.0.   *Cat. No.79.*

The whole of the foregoing pieces guaranteed to be genuine Old Worcester Porcelain, of the Dr. Wall period, 1751–1783, and as described...

Trusting to receive your valued orders and assuring you of my best attention thereto, I remain, with Compliments,
                         Yours faithfully,
                         T. Leonard Crow

Letter No. 2   14th April 1948

Dear Mr. Klepser,

At long last I am able to reply fully to your letter of the 14th March, only regretting that it has been necessary to keep you waiting a whole month. My difficulty is that I have no staff of assistants in my employ. Under the present government there is no likelihood of my getting anyone. Over here are now both military and industrial conscription which practically bars anyone between the age of 18 to 45 from employment in what is termed non-essential business. So it falls to me to carry on as best I can quite alone, doing my own correspondence, packing, buying, selling and the thousand-and-one little details in management of the business. At the age of 65, that's not so easy.

With reference to the pieces of Worcester Porcelain which you have kindly purchased from me, these have been carefully packed in two strong wooden boxes, and were despatched to you per parcels post, insured to full value, on the 9th inst, and will, I trust reach you safely and in perfect condition.

A rare and interesting piece which I have just bought, and which I think might appeal to you (perhaps in place of the teapot) is an early Worcester or soft-paste Bristol (commonly known as Lowdin's) pear-shaped Jug, nicely painted in colours and gold with Chinese Figures – Long Elizas. The exact jug as to shape, but not decoration, is illustrated in the Schreiber catalogue, plate 68, fig 461. This jug is 7-inches high and is mint perfect. Of special interest is the mark viz that known as 'the scratched cross', i.e. a cross incised and under the glaze, close to the foot-rim. The Schreiber places date as at 1755, but I should put it earlier than that, viz 1748–52. Price of Jug is £27.10.0.   *Cat. No.30.*

Another item of more than usual interest, bought only this week, is a pair of Worcester Cornucopia, painted in underglaze blue on white with floral festoons in the Meissen manner. Each marked with the 'Crossed swords'. Overall length 11¾ inches, and in perfect condition. If you have a copy of 'English Blue and White Porcelain of the 18th C'y' by S.W. Fisher, and will turn to plate 19 (in colour), there you have an exact illustration of my pair of cornucopia. Price £32.10.0 *Cat. No.201.*

Tomorrow I am off up North to spend a few days in Edinburgh & Glasgow. Our British Antique Dealers' Ass'n is holding a week-end Conference in Glasgow, . . . (and as a member of the Council, I'm expected to put in an appearance!) I never know what I may come across on trips of this kind and it's quite possible that one or other of the pieces you seek may fall into my net.

Yours sincerely,
T. Leonard Crow

Letter No.3   26th May 1948

Dear Mr. Klepser,

Yesterday I was offered a very nice specimen of the Worcester Hope Edwardes service, with claret-ground cornucopia border and painted fruit and flowers, in a Milk Jug *(Cat. No. 97)*. I at once cabled you, and this morning have duly received your reply confirming purchase, for which I am much obliged.

I think I ought to mention to you, regarding one of the decorations you have asked for, viz: Teapot, with alternating stripes of Turquoise Blue and Claret, Frank Lloyd Plate 45, No.214, that recently the opinion has been expressed that this is not true Worcester decoration. My friend and client, Dr. Severne MacKenna[1], and likewise Mr. Leslie Perkins[2] (who is usually consulted on Ceramic matters by Her Majesty Queen Mary and who is considered one of the leading authorities on English Porcelain) both contend that this is what is known as 'redecorated'. That is that although the porcelain originated from the Worcester Factory in the period of Dr. Wall, it was decorated and refired much later.

[1] Dr F. Severne MacKenna, Collector and author of books on Worcester, Plymouth, Bristol and Chelsea. See letters Nos.8 & 11.
[2] Leslie Perkins was at that time proprietor of the firm Albert Amor Ltd.

The decoration 'with alternating stripes of Turquoise Blue and Claret' is in fact a Giles pattern and Mr Klepser eventually purchased a cup and saucer in this pattern, from Mr Crow.   Cat. No.153.

Letter No.4   8th June 1948

Dear Mr. Klepser,

In my last letter to you, I fear I displayed a woeful ignorance of American geography, when I commented upon the distance you would be travelling to British Columbia. I had been imagining Seattle to be on the East Coast of U.S.A., not so very far from New York! On reading the reports of the disastrous flooding of the Columbia and Fraser Rivers recently, I turned out my atlas to discover just where these are, and to my amazement spotted Seattle on the map right away there on the West Coast.

The list of the various pieces of Worcester for which you are seeking is constantly before me, and although at the moment of writing no further pieces have come to light, I confidently hope to be able to report fresh finds ere long. My efforts to obtain a piece of the 'Lord Henry Thynne' service from one of my customers, have not succeeded so-far but I've not given up hope yet!

Letter No.5   24th June 1948

Dear Mr. Klepser,

Last week I sent off to you by ordinary letter post, a copy of the handbook of the Antiques Fair, at Grosvenor House, London which closes down tomorrow.

I went up to London on the 10th inst and spent a day at the Fair, and greatly enjoyed meeting old friends and customers there, and of course was much interested by the fine goods displayed, although taking it all round I felt that it was not quite as fine a show this year as it was last.

Whilst I was there Her Majesty Queen Elizabeth arrived and went right round the Fair, and later in the day Their Royal Highnesses the Duke & Duchess of Gloucester visited. It was rather fine that these important personages were walking casually through this big exhibition and mingling with the people so freely. When I was a youth I several times saw Queen Victoria, but wherever she went she was always ringed round by armed police and detectives and the people had to keep their distance.

Thank-you very much for your letter of the 14th inst. I am so glad to know that you are pleased with the Bodenham pieces and with the transfer-printed ones, but I do feel so dreadfully concerned about the missing parcel, and hope with all my heart that it will be traced. It will be a thousand pities if that lovely Coffee Pot is lost, for apart from being a rare and first-rate specimen it was in such brilliant condition. *(Cat. No.50.)* Further more that was a piece which I was able to buy very reasonably, compared with the ruling market price for such bits. It will be very difficult to find another . . .

During your absence from Seattle, I have been successful in finding two more items on your list of Worcester porcelain.

(a) A Plate, diameter $8\frac{1}{2}$ inches, from the Baroness Burdett-Coutts Service. (Frank Lloyd, pl.69, No.331). Marked with a large open square in underglaze blue. Price £85.0.0.   *Cat. No.134.*

(b) A Plate, diameter 9 inches, from the Lady Mary Wortley Montagu Service. (Frank Lloyd, pl.55 No.268). Marked with a fretted square in underglaze blue. Price £110.0.0.   *Cat. No.154.*

Both pieces are in superb condition and perfect in every way, and I really think the Wortley Montagu decoration is certainly as beautiful, if not the most beautiful Worcester decoration I have ever had through my hands.

Today I had the sad and melancholy duty of attending the funeral of a very dear and valued friend, of many years standing, in the person of Mr. Conrad H. Tipping, who was widely-known as an authority on Ceramics. You may have read some of his articles in *Apollo* magazine, and you will find a reference to him in 'The Author's Preface' to Stanley Fisher's book on Blue and White Porcelain.[3] Tipping was a very fine man with a great store of knowledge of archaeological and antiquarian matters, and at the same time one of the most modest and unassuming, wholly lovable men one could wish to know. He was President of the Cheltenham Ceramic Circle and one of the advisers to whom the Cheltenham Museum Authorities constantly referred. We have lost a great personal friend whose memory will be ever dear to us, but immeasurably greater is the loss incurred by the Fine Art World, through the passing of Conrad H. Tipping, tho' alas, by the people of that World he may soon be forgotten.

In your letter you refer to the trip on which you were starting next day to Philadelphia, to attend the Republican National Convention when you hoped to see Senator Vandenburg nominated for President. If the news reported in our papers tonight is to be relied upon, it looks to me as tho' Senator Vandenburg was duly nominated but subsequently stood aside in favour of Governor Dewey of New York, and that in the third ballot Mr. Dewey was carried unanimously. I am not at all well-informed upon American politics, but I presume that the position now is that at the Presidential Election in November, there will be only the two candidates, Dewey and Truman in a straight fight. How thankful must you be that Socialism and Communism have not lifted their ugly heads to any extent in your political field! Heaven preserve the U.S.A. from Government – or rather Mis-Government – by such an unspeakable crowd of muddleheads as we have over here. I am no politician thank Goodness, but scarcely a day passes but I bubble over with wrath, as one or other of my personal liberties are infringed upon or taken away by this abominable set of mountebanks who masquerade as The British Government. No, Sir, I do not propose to inflict my feelings upon you further. Indeed I apologise for having said as much, though would add God speed your Republican Party, especially if, as I believe it to be, it is paramount to our Conservative Party over here.

[3] Stanley Fisher, a former schoolmaster, was the proprietor of an antique shop in Bewdley, near Worcester. He published a book *English Blue and White Porcelain of the Eighteenth Century* in 1947 and was a regular contributor to magazines on antiques

Mr Crow took a keen interest in politics but had little enthusiasm for the post-war Government which had come to power in 1945. President Truman, a Democrat, was standing for a second term of office. His opponent was the Republican Governor Thomas Dewey of New York. Kenneth Klepser shared Mr Crow's interest in politics and also his conservative views. As a staunch Republican in a country where the Democrats had been in office for nearly sixteen years, he was sympathetic to Mr Crow's unflattering opinion of the Labour Government, and deeply anxious that Governor Dewey should win the forthcoming Presidential Election. He had every reason to be optimistic about the result, as President Truman's popularity at this time, was at a very low ebb.

Letter No.6
Bank Holiday, 2nd August 1948

Your letter of the 29th June gave me the disturbing news that none of my shipments had so-far arrived, but this was contradicted by a letter the next day reporting, to my great relief, safe arrival of all three shipments.

. . . For the past 5 or 6 weeks I have been angling for a very nice Covered Sucrier painted with the 'Eloping Bride' decoration, which is in perfect condition. It belongs to a lady Collector who by extraordinary chance has two of these Sucriers in this very rare decoration, and is willing to part with one of them. But, the price she has asked me for it was in my opinion quite fantastic. Perhaps I was foolish, but I refused point-blank, and made her an offer which she, in turn is adamant in refusing! At her price this piece would cost you £65.0.0., whereas I consider £45.0.0., would be plenty. I may be able to conclude a deal with her eventually at somewhere between these figures but unfortunately the lady is now away on holiday, so the matter has to rest for a couple of weeks.

I am leaving no stone unturned in endeavouring to find pieces of the remaining services on your list. Apart from my own efforts, I have two 'scouts' (one in London and one in the Provinces) who are always on the look-out for stock for me, and I have provided them with descriptions of the pieces you want. To the list, I have now added the four services mentioned in your last letter viz: 'Kew', 'Cobbe', 'Stormont' and 'Sebright'. The first and last of these are illustrated in Frank Lloyd Catalogue (Plate 43 No 209, and Plate 9 No 57). The Stormont is described by Hobson, but not illustrated, nor do I remember seeing it illustrated anywhere. The Cobbe, as doubtless you have noticed, is only Knives and Forks with blue-scale handles, relieved by panels of insects. I had a pair of the latter about three years ago but have not seen any since. One never knows when some of the wanted pieces may turn up. The queer thing is that one good find often appears to herald another! That happened with this last parcel, the two plates came to light from different sources within a couple of hours, and then later on and just when arrangements were almost complete for the shipment of the plates, I was out in my car and, at Thame in Oxfordshire, spotted the Parrot cup and saucer; and the day after I got home from that trip my Provincial Scout turned up with the Horner Jug. *(Cat. No.77.)* That's the way it's done!

You made my mouth water, in describing the trips you've been taking with your Wife's Cousins. We have friends living out in British Columbia, and from what they tell me of the glorious country with which they are surrounded, I have had great longings to go out there.

Letter No.7   12th August 1948

Dear Mr. Klepser

Since my letter dated 2nd inst & posted on 4th inst, I have bought amongst other pieces of Worcester a really superb mug in mint condition. Painted with 'Long Eliza' decoration in brilliant enamel colours, I think this may possibly fill one of the items on the first list you sent me, dated Feb 1st. Since that I have had other pieces painted with Chinese figures, but none perfect, as is this one. I enclose photographs of this mug, taken in three positions to enable you to see the whole of the decoration. Height is $3\frac{1}{4}$ inches & diameter $2\frac{3}{4}$ inches, Price £23.10.0. *Cat. No.47.*

None other of the named services have come to light, but they will do, sooner or later. I'm sorry I've bungled my chances of securing that Eloping Bride Sucrier and Cover, mentioned in my last letter. If I don't succeed in getting it, I'll surely find another somewhere else.

Letter No.8   1st September 1948

For the past few weeks there seems to be a dearth of the goods I particularly want to find, and the pieces I want to find for you are in the same category. My two scouts have brought nothing in of late. In about ten days' time (provided my car, now under repair is back on the road again) I am arranging to get 'on the warpath' myself to see whether I can do better than they do. In fact 'I'll eat my hat' if I don't find at least one specimen of one of those 'named services'! The awkward part about this is that I do not wear a hat!!

I note that you enjoyed reading about my attempts to purchase a Sucrier of 'Eloping Bride' pattern from a lady collector. Well (although quite seriously I'm rather sorry to have lost this piece) you and Mrs. Klepser will perhaps be amused at hearing the sequel. The lady owner of this piece has now beaten me completely by moving away from her house and leaving no address. Now the lady has herself eloped with both her 'Eloping Bride' Sucriers, and has thus stymied me completely! Maybe she will communicate with, or come and see me, but otherwise I've lost her.

I don't know whether in a previous letter to you, I have mentioned that my friend Dr. F. Severne MacKenna, is now busily engaged in writing a book on 'Worcester Porcelain'. No book of any particular merit has been published on this subject since Hobson's book in 1910,[4] and there is real need for a new work embodying the results of research-work which has been carried out since that date. Dr. MacKenna is now recognised in this country as a leading authority on Ceramics, and his recently published books on 'Cookworthy's Plymouth' and 'Champion's Bristol' have been well received by Collectors. Each book was sold out within a few days of publication. Another of his books 'Chelsea Triangle and Raised Anchor Wares' is expected to be off the press any day now. His latest book, above-mentioned on Worcester, is not yet in the publisher's hands and quite probably will not be on sale inside another year but it will be well-worth securing. There will be some 160 illus-

trations in black-and-white, and others in colours, and he aims to illustrate as many pieces as he can which have not hitherto appeared in books, and he is not relying upon the various public museums to provide him with photographs.

[4] R.L. Hobson: *Worcester Porcelain*, Quaritch, 1910.

Letter No.9   25th September 1948

About a week ago I cabled you 'Have secured fine specimen from Stormont details follow air mail'. Ever since then I have been seeking an opportunity to write this letter. September is always one of my busy months, when hundreds of people visit my galleries wanting to be shown round. There is none here but myself to talk to these people, many of whom come from abroad, U.S.A. included.

To return however to Lord Stormont, and to the service of Worcester porcelain which bears his name. The piece which I have secured is a Tea Jar and Cover, the exact shape as one illustrated on Plate LXV, Fig. 1, in Hobson's 'Worcester Porcelain', and the decoration (of course) as illustrated in Herbert Allen Catalogue Plate 54, Fig 222. Height overall is $5\frac{1}{2}$ inches. Condition – absolutely perfect. Date is circa 1775. Price £45.   *Cat. No.67.*

Among many fine pieces which I brought back with me is a rare and fine Worcester Bowl, diameter $6\frac{1}{2}$ inches, matching a dish which is illustrated in colour in Hobson's book, Plate III, facing Page 8. As you will see this is similarly decorated to the Hope Edwardes Service, but with the cornucopia border in pale blue instead of claret. This bowl is a beautiful piece, mint perfect, and marked with the Crossed Swords and numeral 91 in underglaze blue. Date circa 1770. Price £55.0.0.   *Cat. No.98.*

Letter No.10   2nd November 1948

You will I am sure be pleased with the set of 3 'Hawthorn' Mugs *(Cat. No.202)*, though it is unfortunate that the middle size (i.e. 5 inch) is imperfect, but it would have been a pity I think to separate them. I understand that the largest one formerly belonged to the Actor, Mr. Fred Terry. Since my cable to you last week, I have been fortunate enough to find two more items from your list of pieces required, viz:

(i) A delightful specimen small teabowl and saucer with 'Eloping Bride' decoration, each perfect, and marked in underglaze blue with a pseudo-Chinese symbol, which I don't remember having had before. Price is £35.0.0. *Cat. No. 203.*

(ii) A quite unexpected find, viz a pair of Knife and Fork from the Cobbe Service! Worcester porcelain pistol-shaped handles, painted with butterflies and insects, in reserves on blue scale ground. Quite perfect. Price £45.0.0.   *Cat. No.124.*

Though it sounds like I'm 'counting my chickens before they are hatched', I am as certain as I am that DEWEY will be to-day's WINNER, that within the next week or 10 days I shall get hold of a piece of the service, decorated with alternate strips of Claret and Turquoise.

In one of my previous letters to you, I think I passed on an opinion, which had been expressed by Dr. MacKenna, that this decoration was not a Worcester original, but that it had all of it been re-decorated later. Subsequently I came to my own conclusion, that the Dr. must be under a delusion in expressing that opinion, and I have discussed it further with him: Now he has qualified his first statement by saying that this is one of the patterns which has frequently been adopted by the blighters who foist redecorations on to the market as genuine. That is, of course quite another story, and it behoves both Collectors and Dealers to be extra careful in their examination of such pieces.

I am so glad to know that you have made the aquaintance of my good friends, Mr. Kaufman[5] and Mr. Knouff. Though I have never met either of them other than by correspondence, I know what fine collections they have, Mr. Kaufman's mainly Chelsea and early Bow, and Mr. Knouff's more varied and including Chelsea, Derby, Worcester and Bow, also Bristol and Plymouth. Both have bought many pieces from me, and from time to time they send me photographs of other acquisitions, which I keep by me mounted in scrap-albums. The same day as I cabled you about the 3 mugs, I cabled Mr. Kaufman to tell him of a very rare and early Bow figure of Henry Woodward, as 'The Fine Gentleman' in Garrick's farce 'Lethe' and now have his cable back that he will buy same. There is also a letter from Mr. Kaufman telling me of his pleasure at your having called on him and expressing the hope that one day he may be able to get to Seattle to see you and your Collection. That same day a third cable went off from here to Chicago, reporting to our mutual friend Mr. Malcolm Franklin[6] on some pieces he was looking for, and which he too has cabled back to me for goods to be sent on to him. So you see the U.S.A. keeps me pretty busy apart from my collector-clients in the home country. My difficulty is in having to attend to every blessed thing with my one pair of hands. I just cannot find a competent assistant.

I find it very amusing to discover, from your letter, what a fine Delegate you are for sending to a Convention; and then spending the time at football matches, orchestral concerts and theatricals! Reminds me of an International Conference which I attended, as a delegate, some years ago in Lausanne – a whole week of meetings with sessions morning, afternoon and evening each day. I went to about two sessions, which were more than enough for me. Lausanne had many very much greater attractions!

Our Evening Paper has just come in, and in big head-lines on front page announces:'*Dewey is 15 to 1 odds-on Favourite*'. That looks good to me and I guess at this very moment you are all very excited over there. Let's hope that our people will have the good sense to follow America's example and, in 1950, return CHURCHILL to head our Government with a big majority.

Recently Mr. and Mrs. A.W.Tuke, kindly invited me to see their wonderful collection of Worcester Porcelain, including most, if not all, of the named services. They have a lovely house just off Bayswater, London, He, incidently is one of the Directors of Barclays Bank Ltd., and is a keen collector of many years' standing.

Great news in your letter is that you and Mrs. Klepser are planning to visit England in 1951. It's a long time to look forward to, but be very sure that my wife and I will be looking forward eagerly and with great pleasure to your visit. I hope it will be possible for you to spend a few days in Tewkesbury, as I shall want to drive you around the Cotswolds in my car (tho' it won't be on a par with your Rockies or any of the grand scenery in your country), and to arrange to introduce you firstly to my friend Mr. C.W. Dyson Perrins[7] who will, I know, very gladly show you his Collection, secondly Dr. F. Severne MacKenna at Droitwich, and his Collection; and, thirdly to Tom Burn[8] of Rous Lench Court, whose Collection is worth seeing. These folk are all living within 20 miles of Tewkesbury. However, that is nearly 3 years ahead yet and too soon to be making any detailed plans. I don't know what the Worcester factory have in their minds for celebrating their bi-centenary, but that they will do something spectacular may be taken as a certainty.

[5] M.G. Kaufman collected principally Chelsea porcelain of the triangle and raised anchor periods. His collection now forms the basis of the Chelsea Porcelain at Colonial Williamsburg in Virginia.

[6] Malcolm Franklin, the proprietor of an antique shop in Chicago specialising in English antiques.

[7] C.W.Dyson Perrins. A collector of Worcester porcelain of long standing and owner of the Royal Worcester Porcelain Company. See letter No.12.

[8] T.G. Burn of Rous Lench Court, near Evesham in Worcestershire, which houses his extensive collection of early English Pottery, Porcelain and Furniture.

The American Presidential Election of November 1948 was almost universally expected to be a triumph for the Republican Party. Such was the confidence in a win for Governor Dewey, that the 'Chicago Tribune' published headlines whilst the results were still coming in, actually announcing a Republican victory.

Letter No.11   31st December 1948

At long last I am able to make a start on this much overdue letter to you. There is so much to write about I scarce know where to begin, but first of all allow me to condone with you on your disappointment at the result of the Presidential Election. Over here everyone was confident of Dewey's victory, and when we had the news that Truman was at top of poll, it was an enormous surprise.

In my last letter I note that I wrote to you:– 'I am as certain as I am that DEWEY will be today's winner, that within the next week or ten days I shall get hold of a piece of the service, decorated with alternating stripes of Claret and Turquoise.'!

As it turned out I was as unlucky over that piece of Worcester as Dewey was at the poll, for I didn't get it after all. It was at auction and the price it realised was a great deal more than I felt justified in paying for a cup and saucer of that decoration. For a teapot which is what I really want, I would have paid more, but not for a cup and saucer.

Since October, I have been more or less on the sick list, however, whilst I was ill, Dr. MacKenna was putting the finishing touches to his book on Worcester Porcelain, and the manuscripts have now gone to the printers. All the various photographs I have sent him he has used as illustrations but has acknowledged them all to me in the book, whereas I particularly wished him to acknowledge to your name, the two or three of them which were pieces which you have bought from me. I am very sorry about this.

For some time I have felt that the time has come when I ought to retire from business, though for many many reasons I don't want to. Now, that decision has been made, under the urgent and insistent advice of my own regular doctor, backed by our great friend Dr. MacKenna (who, as you may perhaps not know is an eminent medical doctor in this country – the study and collecting of porcelain being just one of his hobbies) both of them tell me that it is imperative that I should rest. The Devil of that is that I don't like resting. I like, more than anything, working in my business, which has been the source of untold happiness to me. It is true to say that I really love my porcelain and my silver; and, since I've been on the Council of the British Antique Dealers' Ass'n, its work has been of absorbing interest to me. Now it all has to be thrown overboard! However, 'it's no good kicking against the pricks'. I suppose I've had my day. I have to realise that I'm a sick man, and that for my youthful years, only $65\frac{1}{2}$, I'm older than many others of my age. Anyway I can still smile! I think I've always had a sense of humour above the average, and believe me that's a great help in one's life . . . especially to a poor old antique dealer whose worries are galore!!

I mention this so that you will not be surprised at my advertisement which is to appear tomorrow in January *Apollo*. When my business is sold, my wife and I hope to settle down much nearer London, in a small house or flat which won't need so much keeping clean (my wife's dept.) as do my big premises here. I shall not want to stay idle for long, and may possibly want to do a bit of quiet dealing. One thing I'd much like to do – if quite agreeable to you – is to endeavour to complete your list of desired pieces.

Letter No.12   8th February 1949

I've never had the experience of selling, or trying to sell, a business before, but I find it has its interesting points, as well as irksome and annoying ones! Some folk seem to look upon it as a good opportunity to buy a good well-selected stock for about 75% less than it cost, but they soon discover that I'm not that sort of Juggins!

It may be quite a time ere the right man comes along, and meantime I'm not worrying, but am carrying on as usual. Now that, as I'm glad to report, I'm back to normal fitness again, I don't know that I'm so anxious to get out of it!

However, turning to your letter in which you mention 'tulip-shaped jugs'. Dr. MacKenna came to see me the other day and very kindly brought his Drane Catalogue[9] to show me Tulip Cream Jugs, Nos. 568–569, and now I have a sketch of them. It tickles me that they should be so described! The late Mr. Robert Drane, who lived at Cardiff, ought to have known better for in the fine gardens which surround the Cardiff City Hall they usually make a magnificent show of tulips in the bulb-season, so Mr. Drane ought to know what a tulip looks like! These pieces which he has christened 'Tulip Cream Jugs', are more like Mugs than Jugs, and in shape more thistle-like than tulip-like. In shape and decoration, are they not more curious than beautiful? However all this may be, you may rely upon me to do my best to find specimens of them.[10]

I've added this piece to my list of desired pieces, likewise Pencilled Wares (referred to in my last letter) and the 'Famille Verte' Teapot (Hobson, plate XXXIV, fig 5). This latter will be by no means easy to find, and I believe it is extremely rare. I don't remember ever having had a specimen of this decoration, yet I'm sure I've seen it somewhere – probably in the Victoria and Albert Museum. I don't think Mr Dyson Perrins has it even, but I will make a point of looking for it next time I go to his house. I should so like you and Mrs. Klepser to meet Mr. Dyson Perrins and to see his Collection, and I look forward to the pleasure of taking you both there in 1951. Mr. Perrins is one of the most charming, genial and kindly old gentlemen (he is over 80) one could wish to meet, and I think there is nothing he likes better than to talk about his collection, with people who are earnestly interested in and who have some knowledge of Worcester Porcelain.

He has no room whatever for the empty-headed sight-seer. His Collection is magnificent, and includes almost every known decoration of the Dr. Wall period. You will revel in it when you see it. Some years ago he handed it over to the City of Worcester, together with the Deeds of a plot of land in the City, and the wherewithal to build a Museum on the plot, for the housing of the Collection, the one condition being that the Collection should remain in Mr. Perrins' care during his lifetime. I have heard him tell his visitors 'This is not my collection. It belongs to the City of Worcester. I am only the caretaker'.

All this is rather taking up your time, and wandering away from business, but it is I think, interesting, and in a way gratifying, to know that this man is the present owner of the Royal Worcester Porcelain Company and is an undoubted authority upon Old Worcester Porcelain. His fortune derives however not so much from the Worcester Porcelain Works, but from 'Lea & Perrins' Worcester Sauce' which is known far and wide, probably all over the World. Next time you pour a little Worcester Sauce on the side of a plate of cold meat, think of Worcester Porcelain!

Reverting to your letter, and mention of 'Hop Trellis' decoration, I enclose a photograph of a Plate already in my stock, which has, what most folk consider to be the most attractive of the different versions of 'Hop Trellis'. In centre is a cluster of pink roses with green foliage, enclosed in a circle of gold. The S-shaped fancy scrolls which extend outwards from the gold circle, are of purple and gold, whilst the festoons of Hops are green with tiny berries, and the small alternating panels at the edge of the escalopped border are of pink diaper. A very beautiful plate in fine condition, price £35.0.0. *Cat. No.105.*

It's a wee bit doubtful whether this letter will reach you before you are off on your trip through the West Indies, but you say you start latter half of February, so I may be just in time to wish you and Mrs. Klepser a very happy and enjoyable trip. I wonder whether you'll discover any rare Wall, Worcester in Kingston or Havana! Do you travel all the way by sea, or overland to Florida or New Orleans, and thence by sea?

[9] Catalogue of the Drane Collection of Old Worcester Porcelain. Albert Amor Ltd, 1922.

[10] Mr Klepser eventually obtained a pair of these. *Cat. No.138.*

Letter No.13   26th February 1949

This is not to be a long letter, to worry you, whilst on holiday, but just a line to report that the identical Tea-jar and Cover, illustrated in colour in Hobson's book, from 'The Duchess of Kent's Service', together with a Spoon-tray from the same service, will be offered at auction in London on 25th March. I have actually seen the pieces which are in good order and are very delightful.

It is in the sale of the famous porcelain collection of the late Sir Bernard Eckstein.[11] For every Lot in this sale there is bound to be keen competition. The above two pieces (in one Lot) are pretty certain to make big money. Indeed it is difficult to prophesy what it may run to. I shall go to town on purpose to attend this sale, and I feel you ought not to lose the opportunity of securing these pieces from a Service, for which you have for so long been waiting.

If I do not hear from you to the contrary I shall go 'all out' and buy them for you, but I shall feel much happier if you could possibly cable me, from wherever you may be, either confirming that I may buy at any price, or stating what amount is the utmost limit of what you are prepared to pay.

In the meantime, I have secured a very nice Coffee Cup and Saucer, with alternating stripes of Claret and Turquoise overlaid with gilt swags and festoons, which I will hold until your return home.   *Cat. No.153.*

Anxiously awaiting your cabled message, and with kindest regards.

P.S. Re: the 2 pieces Duchess of Kent Service, I consider they should be bought inside £150, but there is no knowing. They may run to double that sum!

[11] Sir Bernard Eckstein Bt formed a varied collection of English ceramics including Chelsea, Bow, Worcester and early English pottery. He was especially interested in figures.

Letter No.14   1st April 1949

Before replying in detail to your letters of 11th Feb and 5th and 6th March, let me first give you some good news. I have secured the Tea-poy and Cover, and the Spoon-tray of the Worcester 'Duchess of Kent' service. The Tea-poy is the identical piece from which the coloured plate LXV was printed in Hobson's book. It bears the 'R. Drane' label, and was formerly in the Berners Collection, then in the Eckstein Collection. It is quite perfect, except for the flower knob of cover which has been repaired, also the Spoon-tray is perfect. The two pieces for £100. *Cat. Nos 129 and 130.*

Talking about blemished or faulty pieces in fine porcelain, it is no exaggeration to say that at least 75 to 80% of the Lots in the sale of the Eckstein Porcelain were in some way faulty. Cracked, chipped, or repaired and restored, many having parts made-up with composition, yet this appeared to make no difference to the high prices realised. Pair of Worcester figures of the Gardener and Companion figure, fetched £700. The well known Chelsea figure *'La Nourrice'* (Nurse with child) fetched £540. Chelsea all white head of a Baby Boy, a very beautiful piece of modelling and of potting fetched £640. With few exceptions the Worcester in this collection was comparatively poor, and it was the Chelsea which made the big money. A magnificent garniture of 3 claret ground vases was bought by Mr. Frank Partridge[12] for £880. They were of Chelsea gold anchor period. A very lovely pair of early Chelsea figures triangle period (1745-50) realised £650. The Bow also was fine, a pair of saucerdishes $7\frac{3}{4}$ inches diameter, realising £430, which is a high price for Bow.

Turning to your letters, I am grateful to you for calling my attention to those articles in *Apollo* for August & November 1945, and for pointing out that my plate, with Hop-trellis decoration belonged to the Earl Manvers Service. As soon as I turned up *Apollo*, I remembered the whole affair having particularly noticed and read, the correspondence between Mr. H.R. Marshall,[13] Mr. Antony Tuke and Dr. MacKenna, at the time it appeared. I had quite forgotten about it when this plate came into my possession. It is a real worry to me to find that my memory is failing so. They tell me nothing can be done about it and that it is one of the fruits of "anno domini'!

Incidentally, Mr. Tuke is a member of one of the very early Quaker families, and I know him in that connection quite apart from the fact that he collects Worcester Porcelain. He has an extremely fine collection, and at the rate he is going on with it may bid fair to rivalling Mr. Dyson Perrins' collection.

[12] Frank Partridge, the prominent London antique dealer.

[13] H. Rissik Marshall, collector and authority on Worcester porcelain and later, author of the standard reference work: *Coloured Worcester Porcelain of the First Period.* See letter No.24.

Letter No.15   10th May 1949

I am glad to see that you have secured that Worcester Saucer-dish with pencilled decoration. *Cat. No.170.* It is a very good piece and the wavy-edge is unusual. I blame myself for letting it go, because I had it earmarked for you. This came up at Sotheby's on 15th February, and I was the underbidder, but it was running up to a figure which I considered excessive and I let it go.

Congratulations too, on your acquisition of the Softpaste Bristol Helmet Cream-Jug and double-handled sauce boat, *Cat. No.3 and Cat. No.42,* both of which from your descriptions sound very attractive and desirable. There were several variations in the moulding of these S.P.B. double-handled sauceboats, but I don't recall having seen them with animal heads. Lewis[14] is a live-wire, and certainly does get hold of rare bits, tho' he pays hefty prices for them. Prices all round are still very high, and where fine rare pieces are concerned are unlikely to drop.

You may possibly wonder why I describe your so-called Lowdin's Worcester as Softpaste Bristol *(S.P.B.).* The products of this factory have been termed Lowdin's for as long as I can remember but to associate the name of Lowdin with porcelain is wholly erroneous; and an effort is now being made in porcelain circles to correct this error, by terming products, either 'Softpaste Bristol' or 'Bristol-Worcester', both of which are reasonably correct. The point is that Lowdin was a glass-maker in Bristol, long before porcelain was ever made in this country, and was dead before the production of porcelain ever started. As Mr. Dyson Perrins says it is therefore wholly absurd to talk about Lowdin Porcelain!

[14] Alex Lewis was a prominent antique dealer in London and New York, with a fine reputation for expertise.

Letter No.16   30th May 1949

Last week I was in London, mainly with the object of attending the Annual Meeting of the British Antique Dealers' Assoc'n, at Grosvenor House. In between-whiles, I had my usual prowl round the trade in search of anything special, without finding very much, though I did buy a couple of bits of apple-green Worcester, a Nantgarw cup and saucer which I think will interest our mutual friend Mr. Wells of Los Angeles, and an unusually fine old Staffordshire pottery 'Bull-baiting Group' for which I have a customer waiting.

Reverting to your letter, I quite agree with you that the term 'Bristol-Worcester' is the most sensible to apply to the soft-paste Bristol wares. It implies, what is really the fact viz Worcester porcelain made at Bristol, just as in the case of 'Chelsea-Derby' which refers to porcelain which was made at Chelsea after the works had been bought by Dewsbury of Derby, and which altho' made at Chelsea was in effect Derby porcelain.

Letter No.17   8th June 1949

Since my last letter to you I have learnt on good authority, that the Worcester 'Kew House' Service is now in the possession of Her Majesty Queen Mary. It may be that she hasn't quite the whole of it and that there are some stray pieces elsewhere, but if my information is correct we are probably 'crying for the moon' in trying to get a piece.[15]

There is just a possibility that I may be able to buy a complete tea-service of the 'Eloping Bride' decoration. Until I heard of this I would have said that such a thing didn't exist! It will cost me the earth but I shall buy it if I can. Would it interest you? I'll say more about it when it comes!

[15] Mr Klepser finally obtained an example from the 'Kew' service, a teacup, purchased in the 1970s. *Cat. No.146.*

A complete service of the 'Eloping Bride' pattern was offered for sale in an antiques shop in Cambridge at this time.

Letter No.18   30th July 1949

It seems a long time since I last corresponded with you, for which fact I am sorry. My last letter to you was dated 8th June, to which you very kindly replied from Lake Tahoe dated 16th June.

From 12th to 20th June I was away on a week's jaunt in my car looking around, calling on various people, to see what could be found in the way of fine porcelain. I made I suppose some 20 to 25 calls, some at private houses and some on little out-of-the-way country dealers, travelling nearly 700 miles, without finding much of any special interest. I could have brought back a car-load of more or less ordinary goods, the stuff I don't particularly want, but of the fine rare pieces which I seek there is a great dearth. However, I got some nice bits of Chelsea, Plymouth and Nantgarw, but those are not in your line. I picked up some very nice bits of Bristol-Worcester (so-called Lowdin's) and 2 Wall Worcester Plates, all of which in my mind I had earmarked for you. I am extremely sorry to say that I am not now in the position to offer them to you, though I believe you would have wanted to buy them all. Unfortunately, in one sense, they've been snapped up in the meantime by local collectors, who frequently look in to see anything fresh in my stock.

I had all these pieces photographed on purpose for sending prints to you, and although the pieces are no longer available I will enclose the photographs just the same as you may be interested in seeing them. One item is still available and will I think interest you. One of the earliest pieces of Worcester known. A moulded cream-boat, $4\frac{3}{8}$ inches long, from tip of spout to back of handle. This precisely matches the pair of creamboats, bearing the extremely rare mark 'Wigornia' in relief, sold at Sotheby's about two years ago for about £300.[16] Unfortunately this is unmarked. A similar creamboat with moulding picked out in colours, is in the Stieglitz collection, illustrated in the catalogue, Plate 1, Fig 3, exhibited Chicago May-November 1947. The body is moulded with a Chinese landscape, with pagodas and trees, and a figure holding an open sunshade passing over a bridge. All white. A border of flowers, painted in underglaze blue around top inside. Circa 1752. Price £20.0.0. *Cat. No.198.*

The other piece which would have most interested you, but which I'm afraid is now sold, is the extremely rare Bristol-Worcester Wine Funnel, painted in colours with Chinese figures (Long Elizas) in a garden scene. Circa 1748–52.

Turning now to your letter from Lake Tahoe, your descriptions of which fairly make my mouth water! Your references to Pine-covered Mountains surrounding an exquisite lake nestling high up at an altitude of 6200 feet enhances the vision of what must be a little 'Heaven on Earth'. We have nothing like it in this Country. Our highest point is Ben Nevis, in Scotland, 4406′. and Snowdon in Wales, 3540′. What a hateful contrast Reno must have seemed to you, with its gambling dens and rowdy highlife, of which one has heard before, after the beauty and peace of Tahoe. I can well imagine that one night was enough for you in Reno.

16 This creamboat, bearing the embossed 'Wigornia' mark, was subsequently sold at Sothebys in November 1973, for £20,000. It is now in the Dyson Perrins Museum in Worcester.

Letter No.19   15th August 1949

When I last wrote to you, I was fully expecting that within the next few days the name of my successor in the above business would be announced, but alas, the long negotiations which extended from early May, through June & July into August, fell through at the last moment.

Thank-you very much for addition to your list of desiderata. It did not at all surprise me that you want one of those Wine Funnels, which fact makes me doubly sorry that I was unable to hold the one I had. However, that one is gone, and 'it's no good crying over spilt milk'! Crying won't bring that funnel back any more than it will retrieve the spilt milk!

When I read your letter I said to myself 'Oh dear, where in the world am I to find another of those funnels'. BUT would you believe it I've heard of one already? I have been going to Droitwich three times a week for special treatment, under Dr. Severne MacKenna, for rheumatism, and last Saturday, whilst lying on the Doctor's surgical bed, having injections and electric shocks, I suddenly thought about that Wine Funnel, and I asked the Doctor whether he happened to know of one. By an amazing slice of luck he was able to give me the name and address of a friend of his who has one which he loaned to Dr. MacKenna to be photographed for illustration in his book on 'Worcester'. Whether or not this man will be prepared to part with this rare piece, remains to be seen, but I have at once written to ask whether I can buy it. It may be a few days before I can get a reply from him.

Dr. MacKenna told me what I know already, that these funnels are extremely rare. When I wrote you last I would have said that there was only one other apart

from mine known, but this one held by Dr. Mac's friend makes a third; and if Mr. Frank Stoner knows of one that makes a fourth. There certainly can't be many more of them.17 This particular one by-the-way, according to the doctor, has a very slight surface-chip.   *Cat. No.31.*

The Mug, in Dyson Perrins' Collection, painted Saint George and the Dragon, is the only piece with that decoration I know of at all. The fact that it is dated 1776[18] (which is very late for blue and white Worcester) rather suggests that this may have been decorated for a special order, in which case it would in all probability be the only one.[19] I will however, be on the qui vive for another.

Continued, after a series of interruptions, Tuesday 16th.

This morning's post brought a reply from Dr. MacKenna's friend who owns that Bristol-Worcester Wine Funnel. As you will have gathered from the cable which I sent you straight way this morning, he is willing to part with it at a price. I would not go so far as to say that the price is outrageous, but I think it is quite high enough, and I quite anticipated that it would be a bit less. That one which I had a week ago I sold for £50, and although I expected another might run a bit more I didn't expect a difference of £30 in the price. The fact of the matter is that where these very scarce bits are concerned, it is very difficult to place a value on them. One owner may have an altogether different idea about it from another. Anyway I've asked this chap to hold it for a few days to enable me to get your decision.

It is my profound hope that before 1951, we shall have turned these socialist-cum-communist blighters out of The House of Commons, and put in their place a strong anti-socialist government, with Churchill or Eden at its head. General opinion is that we cannot hope for a working majority for the Conservatives, but that there may also be a fair number of Liberals who, tho' not quite of our thinking, are at any rate with us in their hatred of socialism. There appears to be a likelihood of our present Gov't coming out in October next, and a General Election in November.

Before bringing this epistle to a close I've just been looking through your letter again, and note your next trip is to be to Atlantic City to attend a 'Title Convention', at end of September. What precisely is a 'Title' Convention? It appears to be an excellent excuse for you to go gallivanting, this time about three thousand miles across the U.S.A., to New Jersey, and at other times to attractive spots many miles from Seattle! I have some recollection of your having attended a Title Convention at Chicago, which included inter alia attendance at Football matches, Theatres, and Orchestral Concerts – hence those 'serious doubts' of mine to which you refer! Let us hope that Atlantic City will be devoid of all such distractions, thus enabling you to devote your full time to the agenda of the Convention!

One other matter of business I have just remembered. About 14 days ago my friend 'Blank' wrote to offer me what he says is a very unusual Worcester teapot. I had better quote from his letter. I see it is dated 10th August. He says: 'Would you be interested in a very rare Teapot and Cover, of Dr. Wall period? The decoration is as follows:– It is decorated with oval and circular panels of Chinese Figure subjects in landscapes with buildings in the foreground and in the distance. The whole of the ground colour dark blue enriched with fine gilding and further relieved with sprigs of flowers gilt and foliage. This teapot and cover is perfect with the exception that the flower-knob to cover has been off at some time or other.'

His letter goes on to say that he has never seen this decoration before nor can he find it illustrated any-where. Price is £75.0.0.

17 See page 39.
18 See Appendix B. D29.
19 Four of these mugs are known.

Letter No.20   20th August 1949

Further to my letter of the 15 inst. I now have the photograph of unusual Worcester Teapot which was referred to therein, and have pleasure in enclosing a print herewith. I certainly have not met with this decoration before, on a dark blue ground. I was with Dr. MacKenna this morning, and he tells me he hasn't seen it before, as far as he can recall.

I venture to hope that you will agree with me that this piece is very well worthy a place in your Collection. That it is unique there seems little room for doubt. I have made an exhaustive search through hundreds of Worcester illustrations without finding anything like it. The nearest is on Plate 59, No.294, in the Frank Lloyd Catalogue, with panels of exotic birds. In view of its rarity the price asked for this piece is, I think extremely reasonable at £75.0.0. *Cat. No.128.*

I am now in communication with another American Collector, whose name, strangely enough begins with 'K', to wit Mr. Sigmund J. Katz,[20] of Covington, La., who has, so I understand a wonderful Collection of Chelsea Porcelain. 'K' would appear to be my lucky letter!

20 The Katz Collection is now in the Museum of Fine Arts, Boston, USA.

Letter No.21   23rd August 1949

Yes. 'It's that man again'! It was very kind of you in your recent letter to say how pleased you are at finding a letter from Tewkesbury when you get home. I fear, however, that you will grow tired of my letters if I write quite as often as has been the case the past week or so!

I am quite excited to find that you are now seeking another of my pieces in the Dyson-Perrins Collection. What I mean by 'my pieces' are those which I have had the pleasure of finding for Mr. Perrins. That oval bowl is a real gem, and although I know it is not quite unique, it is the only one I can remember having had in my possession.

I think it must have been just before the war, or in the early days of the war, that Mr. Perrins appeared suddenly to wake up to the importance of Bristol-Worcester, or as we then termed it Lowdin's. Anyhow

one day when I was at his house, he and I had a talk about the products of this more-or-less unknown factory and he expressed his wish to add some specimens to his collection. That was good enough for me to get on the warpath for soft-paste Bristol. I went to Bristol and stayed there for a couple of nights, spending the time poking around all the little back-street dealers to see what I could find. Bristol, as you probably know, is a very old City and at that time it had a slummy quarter (& to some extent still has) in which were numerous Wardrobe Dealers and Marine Store Dealers – little poky shops filled with all the rubbish imaginable, worn out boots and shoes, second hand clothes, old lace curtains, little bits of china and glass (mostly cracked and broken). On the whole my effort was worthwhile, though my 'Lowdin' finds were very few.

Now you 10 or 12 years later are following in Mr. D.P's footsteps and quite rightly as a Worcester Collector, taking an interest in these early pieces which were the forerunners of Worcester Porcelain.

As soon as I can spend a day away (or two), I think I'll make another trip to Bristol, although alas, with not quite the same hope of success because around 1942–43, that arch-fiend Hitler made a most destructive air-raid on Bristol and completely wiped out a very big portion of the ancient quarter of the City, including much of what was its slum area.

Letter No.22   8th September 1949

I attended a Country House sale on Sept. 7th. Most delightful surroundings to a very convenient house of Mid-Victorian period. I bought nothing at the sale, but enjoyed the afternoon with a dealer friend sitting on chairs on the lawn in a lovely flower garden which adjoined an orchard of apple-trees, well filled with choice fruit just ready for picking. There was some china there, but not really up to my standard and only worth buying at prices considerably less than those which were realised yesterday. It was all of the 1830–40 vintage, in which collectors are beginning to take some amount of interest. Hitherto I have more or less confined my dealings to the products of the 18th century, but know that we are halfway through the 20th century, I suppose we'll have to take a lot more notice of the first half of the 19th century – but to my mind it was a horrid period aesthetically!

Letter No.23   29th September 1949

I think I'll plunge away into the business matters and leave the chatty bits to the last! Here are descriptions of some of the fresh pieces I brought back with me, and which I think may be of interest to you.

A Worcester Punch Bowl. Diameter 9 inches. Dr. Wall. Circa 1760. In exceptionally fine and brilliant condition. Painted in enamel colours & slight gilding, on white ground – inside, in centre, a group of 4 Chinese figures, with long tobacco-pipes and fans, and with a narrow border in rouge-de-fer – on the outside other Chinese figures, 2 seated at a table and others singly & in groups, in various attitudes and with Trees and a Bush, on branches of which is perched a Monkey *with a human face.* The last feature is a rarity. Price £45.0.0. *Cat. No.82.*

A Worcester Porcelain Bowl. Diameter 4⅛ inches. Height 2⅝ inches. Early period, circa 1755–60. This is one of the most interesting little bits I've picked up for a long time. Painted in colours in what can best be described as a Desert Scene, with Mountains in background; in the foreground are a pair of Doves, perched on a sheaf of arrows under which is a bow, following on round the side of the bowl there are successively a flowering bush, a bird in flight, next a vase-like object from which are growing three tiny trees, and then a curious palm-like tree which is festooned with flowers and foliage which obviously do not belong to it. The whole decoration is clearly of Chinese origin. I can find no record, nor illustrations like it in any of my books.[21] Quite perfect. Price £12.10.0. *Cat. No.56.*

A Worcester Porcelain cylindrical Mug. Height 4¾ inches. Decorated with Hancock transfer-prints. On one side 'May-Day', after Francis Hayman, and on the other 'The Milkmaids'. Both subjects are illustrated in Cyril Cook's book 'Life & Work of Robert Hancock, Item No. 68 & 73'. Mint perfect. Price £20.0.0. *Cat. No.185.*

Now for the Chatty part of letter!

In a local paper the other day I noticed a paragraph in which it was stated that an enormous influx of visitors to this Country from abroad, is expected in 1951. This reminded me of your impending visit in that year, and to which I am looking forward so pleasurably and eagerly. I trust you will not deem it an impertinence on my part, to impress upon you the advisability of making your London hotel reservations as far in advance as possible, especially if you wish to secure accommodation at Grosvenor House, as in a recent letter you suggested.

This brings me to another matter, of special interest to you, as a Collector of Worcester Porcelain. Although no public announcement has yet been made, I have it on good authority that the Worcester Royal Porcelain Company, are planning special celebrations to mark the Bi-Centenary of Dr. Wall and of their Company. In the months of May, June and July 1951, at their London Headquarters in Mayfair, is to be organised the finest and most extensive exhibition of Worcester Porcelain which has ever before been displayed under one roof. The aim is to show every known decoration in Worcester from its inception to the present day (1751–1951). It will include all periods – Bristol-Worcester, Dr. Wall, Flight, Chamberlain, Grainger, Kerr & Binns & so-on. Probably the bulk of Mr. Dyson Perrins' private Collection, as also the contents of the Worcester Works Museum will be shown, plus specimens loaned from the various private collections throughout the Country. I gather that the Company is asking a few of the leading members of the English Ceramic Circle, to assist in an honorary and advisory capacity, in the organisation of this very important event. I assume that this will be one more addition to your list of 'MUSTS'![22]

Devaluation of our pound, though not wholly unexpected, came upon us somewhat suddenly, and is everywhere here the subject of conversation. We are all feeling rather blue about it, and unsettled too, not quite realising yet what will be the outcome. I cannot but think that inevitably prices will rise still higher, though that may not come just immediately. It definitely means that we shall have to tighten our belts still more, and exist on less food than ever! As doubtless you will have seen in your newspapers the whole question is now being debated in the House of Commons, and the vote will be taken tonight on the Government's Motion of Confidence. Last night Winston Churchill made one of his brilliant speeches, speaking for 80 minutes in which he hit out at the Government and gave them something of the trouncing they so richly deserve. If as one hopes, the Government is defeated we shall have an immediate general election. As might be expected they were overwhelmingly defeated in the House of Lords, by 93 to 24, but such a vote in the Commons is unlikely.

[21] The 'Valentine' pattern.
[22] This Exhibition was held at 30 Curzon Street, London W1, from 7th May to 28th September 1951, and comprised 855 pieces.

Letter No.24   14th November 1949

My trip to Town was one hectic rush, but one outstanding event which will long be remembered was my visit to the home of Mr. & Mrs. H. Rissik Marshall, at Hampstead, who so kindly invited me to see their collection. Mrs. Marshall collects old English Glass, and her husband, as is so well known, collects Worcester. The latter is so vast that one could only bring away a general impression of a wonderfully displayed collection, comprising almost every known style and decoration of the whole period of Dr. Wall, many pieces extremely rare and fine. I was there for just over four hours and except for a brief break for tea, was looking at and handling Worcester all the time.[23]

My stay in London was extended, one of the reasons for doing so was that I had very much wanted to attend the Sotheby Sale on 21st. October, if only for the excitement of seeing that pair of unrecorded Figures sold. On that very morning, however, I had a letter from Dr. MacKenna in which, inter alia, he told me that a week previously he had seen in Cambridge, a pair of Bristol-Worcester bowls [24] (Stieglitz Plate IV, No.11) which he knew I had been trying to find for you. That opportunity was too good to be missed, so instead of going to Sotheby's I set off on the sixty miles run to Cambridge in my car, only to find that the dealer there who did have that pair of Bowls had sold them only three days before, to a private collector. That was a dreadful disappointment. The dealer in question is an old friend of mine, and he has promised to see whether his customer would be prepared to part with one, if not the pair, but he holds out very little hope. Had they been sold to another dealer I could probably have got them, but with rare pieces such as those Bowls, it is scarcely to be expected that any keen private collector, having found them would want to part with them again. He might possibly be prepared to part with one of them, and of that I still hold a faint hope.

The run down to Cambridge was not altogether wasted,

as I bought several nice bits there, mostly Chelsea though. One piece my be of interest to you:

An early Worcester Finger Bowl, painted in underglaze blue on white, with a Chinese river scene, figure of a man fishing from a boat, a curious Chinese bird perched on rocks, and Chinese flowering trees. It bears the T.F. Monogram mark, discussed by Hobson on pages 42–45. I know you do not normally buy blue and white, but this may well be deemed an exception. Price £12.0.0. *Cat No.200.*

You are to be congratulated on your recent finds in New York, all of which I am interested to note. Referring to item (a) ill'td in Hobson Plate 24, fig 1, you may know already, or if not will be interested to know that the names of the 'Three Immortals' pictured thereon are 'Ho Hsien Ku' representing Happiness or Contentment, 'Chaing Quokuo-Lao' = Learning and Literature, and 'Lu Hsing or Shou Lao', the God of Longevity. That information was passed on to me years ago by the late C.H. Tipping,[25] who had a remarkable collection of Worcester decorated with Chinese figures, and who made it his business to trace the origins of the figures. A very interesting study if one has the time and the patience to pursue it

[23] The H. Rissik Marshall Collection of Worcester is now housed in one gallery of the Ashmolean Museum at Oxford.

[24] *Cat. No.6.*

[25] See letter No.5.

Letter No.25 12th January 1950

I am so anxious about this general election that I find it difficult to concentrate on business!! Forgive me please therefore if for the moment I've appeared to forget that this is really a business letter, and for having started it at the wrong end, as it were!

Yesterday I had news of a very rare decoration in Dr. Wall Worcester being available, and at once took steps to secure an option on same. I did not get full details until this morning and immediately dispatched the following cable to you:

'An exceptionally rare pair of Worcester plates mazarine blue cornucopia borders exotic birds flowers foliage. Only other pair known in Marshall collection. Borders match Hope Edwardes except colour. 175 pounds.' *Cat. No.102.*

Each is in brilliant condition, and one is faintly marked with a script W in gold, which is in itself unusual. There is a pair in Mr. H. Rissik Marshall's collection which, until this pair came to light, had been considered the only pair known.

Another piece which I think should appeal to you, bought since my last letter, is a Saucer-dish, $7\frac{1}{4}$ inches in diameter, of precisely same decoration as the fine Worcester Service which I sold to the Borough of Cheltenham for presentation to H.R.H. The Princess Elizabeth and The Duke of Edinburgh, on occasion of the Royal Wedding. This is illustrated in Drane Catalogue, No.793. Mint perfect. £25.0.0. *Cat. No.143.*

The first point now arising from your letter of Nov 21, is in reference to that pair of Bristol-Worcester oval bowls which 'by the skin of my teeth' I just missed at Cambridge. I have had further correspondence with my friend there in regard to these bowls, and he has definitely promised to let me know if he is able to get his customer to part with them, either one or both bowls; but, unfortunately his customer is away from home and is not expected back for some months. That would happen, of course! There is just the small satisfaction of knowing that it is not impossible that we may get a chance yet.

Continued Friday morn. 13.1.1950

Referring to your letter No. 3, dated 21 December, in which you enclosed cheque to value $200.00 covering the MacHarg Fable Plate, *Cat. No.136,* and for which many thanks. In this too I am glad to know that it is to go into your Collection. When I bought it I had you in mind, but it very nearly went to someone else! One of my Worcester Collectors called in the same day, and before I had sent the cable off to you. Coming into my office he at once spotted that Fable plate and asked about it. Invariably this man when he likes a piece, says he wants 48 hours to think about it, and he is still thinking about this one! But he has lost it!

It is very encouraging to us to know that we have so many well-wishers in your Country. You have repeatedly voiced hopes which coincide precisely with my own. Mr. W.T. Wells, of Los Angeles, as also other of my U.S.A. correspondents, has in different words expressed the same hopes. In our *Daily Telegraph* a day or two ago, I read that never before has so much interest in the British General Election, been manifested in the U.S.A.

Despite the old saw 'Faint heart never won fair lady', I cannot feel very optimistic over the result, much as I want to see a resounding victory for the Conservative Party. The defeat of Labour in New Zealand, Australia and Jamaica, is bound to have some effect on our own election, and that is all to the good. Also to our advantage is the fact that as a party, the Conservatives are far better organised for this election than in 1945.

Letter No.26 23rd January 1950

A recent purchase of mine is a pair of Tea Cups and Saucers from Mr. MacHarg's Collection, the saucers bearing his labels. These are very charming and in every respect are of the Lord Henry Thynne pattern except that instead of clusters of fruit at the sides, they have bouquets of flowers. In the centre of each saucer, and inside each of the cups, is a circular panel painted with landscapes and with gold-lined turquoise blue husk border. These little landscapes are generally attributed to the painter J.H. O'Neale, the fable-painter. Whether or no he was the artist, they are certainly worthy of him. The four pieces, all perfect, price £30.0.0. *Cat. No.144.*

P.S. 1951 is coming nearer.

Letter No.27 31st January 1950

Thank you very much for your letter of the 24th inst to hand yesterday morning. This must not be a long letter because early tomorrow morning I have to start off in my car for London and have much to do first!

You will be pleased, I think, with Dr. MacKenna's new book,[26] and will recognise some of the illustrations of pieces in your own collection. Read especially the Dr's remarks on Bristol-Worcester, page 15, and his scathing comments about 'a popular omnibus book on English China'. You will no doubt quickly tumble to the book this refers to! The Dr., and the author of the latter book, hate each other like poison, and they are constantly 'crossing swords'. It's a great pity, because each of them has made great contributions to ceramic knowledge.

Your recent purchase of three books from Quaritch puts you well ahead of me on those for I don't think I have either of them. As the Bible tells us 'Of making many books there is no end'!, but I have to put a stop somewhere on the buying of books, much as I would like to get them all.

[26] *Worcester Porcelain*, Leigh-on-Sea, 1950.

Letter No.28 8th February 1950

For five days last week I was away on one of my stunts searching for nice goods, and was part of the time in London. Amongst the goods I brought back are two items which I think will interest you, for both of them are on your list of 'desiderata':

A very nice specimen bowl, diameter $6\frac{1}{4}$ inches, with pencilled decoration – a Chinese garden, with a Chinaman, holding in his left hand an open parasol and with a bird on his slightly extended right hand, a square stool supporting a vase of flowers, a pheasant in flight, also trees and fences. Inside border also pencilled. Black on white. Quite perfect. Price £35.0.0. *Cat. No.173.*

A pair of Tea-bowls and Saucers, painted in colours, with Hop Trellis decoration identically same as in Plate LXVIII in Hobson. The saucers marked with open crescent in blue. All four pieces in brilliant condition. Price: £35.0.0. *Cat. No.111.*

I did have three of these, but Mr. H.R. Marshall who, like you, has been on the look-out for a very long time for this particular version of the Hop Trellis, has asked me to keep one cup and saucer back for him. He tells me that this is the true Hop Trellis which was copied direct by Worcester from a Sèvres Decoration.

On the whole things are going pretty well for our party, but though there are many encouraging signs, I don't feel very optimistic as to the result of the Election.[27] Mr. Winston Churchill is receiving great ovations everywhere he goes, and has already given some magnificent speeches far and away ahead of his first broadcast. On the other hand Aneurin Bevan (the man who described the Conservatives as 'lower than vermin') and Mr. Herbert Morrison, have been howled down and found it difficult to get a hearing, in many instances from the socialist supporters.

How I wish Mrs. Klepser and you could only pop in occasionally to see my fine stock of Worcester. It is seldom that it numbers less than 100 to 150 pieces of Wall period, and it is, of course constantly changing.

[27] The General Election of February 1950, resulted in a narrow victory for the Labour Party.

Letter No.29 16th February 1950

I hope you will not feel that I am writing too frequently and thereby worrying you. Here I am writing before you've had time to reply to my last letter; but, when something specially good comes along, and which I think is 'your cup of tea' (an old Devonshire expression) I like to let you know about it without delay. That is the case now and is the reason for my bothering you again so soon.

The piece concerned is a small dish, size 6 inches by $5\frac{1}{2}$ inches, moulded in relief with what is usually known as 'The Blind Earl's' pattern. Painted in colours in the centre with a cluster of fruits, flowers and foliage, and with border of cornucopiae in claret ground, relieved by lightly tooled gold foliage. It is really in every respect the 'Hope Edwardes' pattern, but with fruit decoration instead of flowers. It is a little gem. In superb and brilliant condition throughout. Price £90. *Cat. No.96.*

Letter No.30 Friday 10th March 1950

I am enclosing herewith some photographs which may be of interest to you, all of which are in my stock, and most of which are recent acquisitions:

A Teabowl and Saucer. Dr. Wall. Circa 1765. Very rare decoration, after Kakiemon, and in some ways similar to the well known Quail (or Partridge) pattern. Painted in colours & gilding. With a border of Rouge de Fer foliage, relieved at intervals by a small gilt flower. In centre a Red and Gold Dragon is descending from, a group of grey-blue & yellow clouds, to attack two land-crabs. On either side of the two crabs is a flowering plant. Teabowl and saucer in mint state and brilliant condition throughout. Price £40.0.0. *Cat No.63.*

A very attractive Creamjug. Height $4\frac{5}{8}$ inches. Finely painted with exotic birds standing in landscapes, on either side with floral sprays in front. The bird painting probably by Giles. Gilt dentil edge at top. Handle lined in gilt, and two gilded bands around footrim. The sparrow beak spout relieved by gilding. No cover – unfortunately, but a very delightful bit. Price £20.0.0. *Cat. No.76.*

A Plate. Diameter $9\frac{1}{2}$ inches. With escalloped rim with gold dentil-edging, and fluted border. The centre painted in brilliant colours with two large exotic birds in landscape, a smaller bird perched on a tree, and other birds in flight. A nice clean piece in perfect condition. Price £25.0.0. *Cat. No.78.*

A Cup and Saucer, the body moulded in white relief, painted in colours and gilding with 'Parrot pecking Fruit'. Mark on each, in underglaze blue, Crossed-swords and numeral 9. If you would allow me to do so I would like to include this Cup and Saucer, in your next shipment, without charge as compensation for having sent you such a poor specimen last time. *Cat. No.84.*

Letter No.31   1st April 1950

On the subject of the Parrot Cup and Saucer, please do not bother about getting the other one returned to me in exchange, but kindly accept this better example by way of compensating yourself for my having sent you that poor specimen in the first place. The latter is the only piece I have ever sent you, which I have not felt pride in selling you, and which I have not felt worthy of a place in your Collection. After it had gone I was worried about it and wished I had not sent it; and, I made up my mind then that as soon as I could find a better and brighter specimen, I would ask you to accept same.

I have seen again the man who sold that pair of Oval Bristol-Worcester Bowls (Stieglitz Plate IV, fig 11) which you will remember I missed by the 'skin of my teeth' six months ago. He tells me that there is still a chance that he may be able to secure one of these for me. His client, to whom he sold them is still abroad. The matter will not be forgotten.

I enclose two photographs of recent additions to my stock which may be of interest to you; and of which descriptions follow:

A Bristol-Worcester Sauce Boat, length from tip of spout to back of handle 5¾ inches, moulded in white relief with reserved panels on either side, with Chinese figures, Vases & Trees in garden scene, in colours. One figure is of a small boy, with blue coat and yellow trousers, balancing himself precariously on the edge of a blue and red vase which leans at a dangerous angle. (One wonders how he does it!) On reverse side is figure of a Chinaman, in blue coat, yellow trousers, fishing with a curious basket suspended at end of rod. Price £15.0.0.
Cat. No.22.

A Bristol-Worcester Jar & Cover. This is a curious piece the like of which I have never come across before, and I am a little intrigued as to what is its object. It is not a mustard pot, because there is no slot in the cover for a spoon. I think it might be a pomade or ointment jar, possibly part of a service for use on a Toilet-table. It is 4¾ inches high and diameter widest point 3 inches. It is quite delicately painted in blue underglaze, with Chinese figures in a garden scene, with trees and flowering plants. On reverse side a Chinaman is sitting on a stool. There is a slight hair-crack on the bottom of the jar, and which may be a fire-crack. Anyway it is quite out of sight and too insignificant to justify refusal of so interesting and rare a piece on that account. Price £7.10.0.

This was in fact a dry mustard pot and cover from the mysterious class of porcelain, variously ascribed to William Reid's Liverpool factory or the Pomona factory. Twenty-five years later Mr Klepser presented this, as a gift, to a Californian collector.

Letter No.32   16th May 1950

On Easter Monday, I went to see a dealer friend of mine in Eastbourne, and bought from him a wonderful piece of Worcester, which I at once recognised as a piece I had seen, and much wanted to buy at the Eckstein Sale. I enclose a photograph of this very important piece. It is a Dish, 7¼ inches in diameter, with escalloped border. Painted with four panels of Exotic Birds and a central panel of flowers, the whole on a rich CLARET GROUND, relieved by lightly tooled gilding. The gilding and the decoration are not unlike the 'Lady Mary Wortley' Service, but the latter is of course on a blue scale and not this fine all-over Claret ground. The whole piece is in brilliant condition. This dish was almost certainly painted by James Giles. The rarity of this piece, and which I think adds immeasurably to its whole attractiveness, is the fact that it is an all-over Claret ground, and not just a cornucopia border as is the case with most of the Claret-Worcester one usually finds. (There's not very much of that to be had either). Price £130.0.0.
Cat. No.169.

It was a slice of luck my getting this from the dealer at Eastbourne. He is really a furniture dealer and he hasn't the market I have for fine porcelain. He bought it at the Eckstein Sale, March 1949, and has held it all that time. I think he was quite pleased for me to relieve him of it. I certainly was pleased! At the moment of writing the Dish is in the hands of *Apollo* magazine, for the making of colour blocks, but will be back here soon after you get this letter. The picture will appear first on the front cover of the August issue of *Apollo* magazine.

The only other piece amongst recent purchases which might interest you, is a Bristol-Worcester Mug. The decoration painted in underglaze blue on white is the same as the Finger Bowl which you bought from me not very long ago, and which you said you had been looking out for; viz a Chinese River scene in which are a man fishing from a boat, a fantastic bird on a rock, and a large flowering plant. Price £10.0.0.

Mr Klepser did not purchase this piece, but it is included here as an example of the prices prevailing at this time for early blue and white Worcester porcelain. This price, for a 'scratch cross' class mug painted with the 'Cormorant' pattern, seems extraordinarily low by comparison with prices of many coloured pieces, but it is no more than a reflection of the tastes and preferences of this period.

Letter No.33   28th June 1950

In your letter of May 14th, you have painted for me a delightful picture of the 'little park' close to your apartment with its 'Vista of water, snow covered mountains and City'. Would the snow-covered mountain be 'Mount Olympus' which according to an atlas I have here would appear to be a pretty high altitude and perhaps 40–50 miles East of Seattle? The Rocky Mountains would surely be too far away for you to see them from Seattle. I have always wanted to live on high ground but circumstances (otherwise 'Fate') have always ruled otherwise. When we married in 1908, we settled in Tiverton, North Devon, where I had my first business, and we lived on the premises, in centre of the town, which lies down in a basin, as it were, and surrounded by high hills – always a delight to look up to. In 1919, after the First World War, we sold the business and went to London to live – no delightful vistas there of hills and woodland scenery! In 1922, I became Managing Director of a Limited Company carrying on business as Jewellers, Silversmiths, Antique Dealers & Opticians in Guildford. There again we lived in the centre of a town, though on fairly high altitude. I had a delightful 18th century house there with oak-panelled rooms, and a long garden sloping down to the River Wey, with our own landing stage, a punt, a canoe and a skiff. In 1928, the Company decided on certain changes with which I did not agree and which led to my resignation. So back we went to London, where I established a business, specialising in Antique Silver and Old Sheffield Plate plus English Porcelain, at the back of Oxford Street and quite close to Selfridges. There we lived at Ilford, Essex (one of London's big suburbs) altitude about 200 ft. above sea-level. I found a good site on which to have our house built, on a corner overlooking Wanstead Park. We had only to cross the road to go into that lovely park, with its heron ponds, big boating and bathing lake, and woodland walks. Early in 1939 we settled here in Tewkesbury, in xvth Century premises. Again we are in the centre of a town not many feet above sea-level and in the near vicinity of three rivers; the Severn, Shakespeare's Avon and the Swilgate. Thus, although always hankering to live on high ground, I've never been allowed to. Instead I have to be content with looking at the Cotswold Hills, viewed from the back of this house, or the Malvern Hills of which there is one small peep from the front.

You speak of Music and Mrs. Klepser and you being great lovers of it. I too am a lover of good music. I qualify music with the word 'good' to distinguish it from the stuff called 'Jazz' and 'Swing' and other so-called music, so popular today, all of which is to me hateful and loathsome. I can sit very contentedly and listen to a good symphony orchestra, or to an organ recital in a big Church or Cathedral, but what over here is known as 'Cinema Organ' or 'Concert Organ' – no more like a church organ than chalk is to cheese – on which is usually played dance music and jigs and popular airs, I cannot stand at any price! Though a lover of music, unfortunately I am no musician.

It is high time now that I turned to business matters, and in that respect may I 'start the ball rolling' by saying how glad I am that you have decided to have that truly beautiful Claret-ground dish from the Eckstein Collection. I gave you the first offer of it, and its a good job I did, for since it was returned (only last week) from the blockmakers, some of my regular buyers of Worcester have 'called me over the coals' for letting it go out of this Country.

If you don't mind my saying so, I always like giving you the first offer of any fine and unusual piece I get, because quite apart from the fact that you have always been a

very good friend to me – which is something I appreciate more than words can tell – you are always very good in coming to quick decisions one way or the other, and that is most helpful to me.

I've nearly finished now. Did you ejaculate 'Thank Heaven'? A bit of news which excites and pleases me, and which perhaps you will be interested to hear, is that I have been honoured by instructions to send 4 Chelsea Plates to Buckingham Palace, for inspection by Her Majesty The Queen. The parcel went off on Monday, and I now await the result. It is very unfortunate that the very first time I have the opportunity of doing business with Her Majesty, she should have chosen 4 plates which are not in the best of condition, and of which frankly I am not proud, but as it was these particular pieces which were asked for there was nothing for it, but to send them. Hitherto, I have done business with Queen Mary, Princess Alice of Athlone, Princess Elizabeth and The Duchess of Gloucester, but never with our King and Queen. If this deal comes off . . . but I mustn't count my chickens before they are hatched.

There were other matters I wanted to talk to you about, I know, but for the moment they have escaped me. Oh yes, of course. I've just remembered one of them, and it's not a bit important. I don't know whether you regularly subscribe to *Apollo* magazine, monthly, but if you do, look-out for a brief article in the fairly near future, entitled:
'A CROW, CAWS CANDIDLY ON CERTAIN CERAMIC CONUNDRUMS'!
Article-writing in magazines is not really 'up my street' at all, tho' in 1922 or thereabouts I contributed one which was very nicely received by the trade, on the subject of Old Sheffield Plate, and the Late Mr. Frederick Bradbury, who was the greatest living authority on that subject, wrote to me complimenting me on my article and telling me it was quite the best short article he had seen! Have just discovered that this was in 1929 – not 1922. That is the only time I have ventured to air my opinions publicly, on any subject connected with the antique trade. Now, 21 years later I am tempted to burst into print once more. I have indicated to the Editor of *Apollo* my intention to condescend to offer him some of my 'pearls of wisdom' in the form of an article, under the above suggested title; and he has duly replied to the effect that *Apollo* will be highly honoured (as of course it should be) to publish same!

Letter No.34   31st July 1950

I enclose photographs of some pieces which I have recently acquired, descriptions as follows:

A Dish of early production circa 1755–60, and interesting. Length 10¼ inches by 7⅞ inches across. Moulded in the form of overlapping cabbage-leaves, the stalks as handles. Painted in colours with Chinese figures, on the extreme left a woman and a little boy standing by a stool, or log, in centre a man seated under a tree and playing a flageolet (or some queer wind-instrument), and on extreme right a woman seated fanning herself. Dish is perfect. Unmarked. Price £42.0.0. *Cat. No.44.*

A Chocolate Cup and Saucer of superb quality and with lavish & elaborate gilding. Painted in brilliant colours with panels of English flowers on white, remaining surface of a rich Royal Blue, relieved by above-mentioned gilding, two side handles of same blue, touched with gold. Cup is marked with a fretted square and saucer with open crescent, in blue underglaze. This is quite the finest chocolate cup and saucer I have seen for a very long time. Price £47.0.0. *Cat. No.137.*

Blind Earl Dish or Spoon-tray. Same size as the claret-bordered one you bought from me recently. The decoration of this one is unusual, and I don't believe I've met with it before, the butterfly and flowers of outstandingly brilliant colouring, the twig-handle, stalks and rosebuds in high relief are green, and the narrow scroll border, with, on each side a device which must represent the Rising Sun in splendour all painted in purple. The extreme tip of one rosebud is missing, otherwise all perfect. Price £35.0.0. *Cat No.49.*

In my last letter to you I mentioned having sent 4 Chelsea Plates to Buckingham Palace, for The Queen's inspection; and I am now pleased to say that Her Majesty decided to buy all four plates, and since then has bought another for which I received payment a couple of days ago. I begin to visualise 'The Royal Arms' over my shop front, and at the head of letter paper!!

This month of July has been a record month for sales of porcelain from my stock, and about 90% of the sales have been to collectors in this country. Releasing petrol from rationing, has of course contributed very largely to this fine result. An analysis taken quite roughly, puts Worcester (Dr. Wall) easily at the head of the sales, accounting for about 50%. Chelsea comes next with about 25%, and the remaining 25% shared amongst Longton Hall, Derby, Bristol, Plymouth, Nantgarw, Swansea etc. My worry now is how and from what sources can I replace all that Worcester!

We are all very worried about the international situation. Fearing what is to be the outcome from this Korean conflagration. Another world-wide war is surely unthinkably terrible and will mean the end of civilisation as we understand it. Yet everything is tending that way. The conception of the U.N.O. did appear to be the ideal method for keeping peace between the Nations, but thanks almost solely to Stalin and his detestable communism, it now seems doomed to failure. We feel very strongly over here that if Winston Churchill were at the head of the British Government instead of the weak and washy Atlee, whose broadcast we listened to last evening, the situation might now have been very different.

On 25th June 1950, North Korean forces invaded the Southern Korean Republic. Two days later, President Truman pledged military support for South Korea and the British Prime Minister, Atlee, called upon all the members of the United Nations to resist communist aggression.

In common with my fellow Quakers, the whole world over, I share the view firstly that force by lethal weapons is morally indefensible and a crime against the Laws and Will of God, and secondly that its absolute futility has been amply demonstrated. In 1914, the ambitions of the Kaiser threatened the peace of the world, so we have to go to war with him, regardless of the immeasurable sacrifice in human lives and misery, and in economic resources. We gained the Victory then, but at what a cost! Twenty-five years later, Nazi-ism rears its ugly head, so to war we go again and come out of it again, nominally victorious, but infinitely more impoverished. Where is the victory, and what its value, when arising from that second war is a further 'ism' – Marxism or Communism – threatening the world with a third, and still more terrible war?

Letter No.35   22nd September 1950

This letter to you is long overdue, but the delay is simply due to lack of time – to say nothing of physical strength – to tackle all the things which have to be done in connection with the business.

I sent a parcel off to you on 30th August containing Leaf Dish, Chocolate Cup and Saucer 'Blind Earl' Spoon-tray, and the pair of S.P. Bristol oval Bowls. *Cat. No.6.*[28] I'm sure you'll like the Bristol-Worcester Oval Bowls which we had to wait so long for, and by-the-way, comparing the painting on one, if not both of these, with that of the 'defiant' and 'coquettish' birds on your sauce-boat,[29] do you agree that they are manifestly by the same hand?

Many thanks for your cable of 10th inst:– 'Want pieces decorated with Watteau Musicians', *Cat. No.123.* This refers to Teacup, Coffee-cup & Saucer painted with figures, in the Watteau style, each with a musical instrument, enclosed in large gold reserves, and with exotic birds and insects in smaller reserves on a very clear blue scale ground – the decoration usually attributed to John Donaldson. The three pieces are in lovely condition as also is the spoon-tray which I bought with them. Dr. MacKenna, who is in Scotland on holiday, has asked me to reserve the spoon-tray for him. He is almost certain to have it, but should he not do so, would you be interested in it?

[28] See letter No.24.
[29] *Cat.No.25.*

In 1951, Mr and Mrs Klepser made a visit to England and met Mr Crow for the first time, once at the Bi-Centenary Exhibition of the Worcester Factory in London, and later on in Tewkesbury, when Mr Crow was in hospital. They did not meet again.

Letter No.36   7th July 1952

I am much interested in your comments upon the chances of the various candidates for nomination by the Republican Party, for the Presidential Election nearly four months hence. I certainly do hope that in the final event the Republican will be at the head of the poll. We all thought Senator Taft[30] was to be the President last time, and it was only by an extraordinary and quite unexpected fluke that Truman won the day.

Well now, I want to talk to you on something of far greater importance than such small matters as Political Campaigns and Presidential Elections! I'm glad to hear you have made a further purchase from John Perkins.[31] He is a good fellow and well deserves to succeed, as I am sure he is doing. My wife and I are very fond of him. On three occasions since he lost his father. W. Leslie Perkins (who was a great friend of mine), John has been down here to spend the week-end. I was in London last Wednesday and quite by chance ran into John Perkins, in King Street, St. James's. He told me he had sent off a pair of Worcester vases to you. *Cat. No.52.*

Frank Tilley, of Tilley & Co (Antiques) Ltd,[32] has recently had a nasty illness. I rather like him, have known him many years, so wrote him a letter to cheer him up when he was having to stay in bed. Incidentally I mentioned that I have for a very long time been trying to find a specimen from the 'Kew House' Service, and asking him to let me know if ever he heard of a piece in the market. In his reply, he wrote 'All I can say is ex-Kews-me.' His inference is, as I knew before, that one might as well 'cry for the moon' as to hope to find a piece from that service. It is known that Queen Mary has almost the whole service in her private collection. Anyhow if it is at all possible to find it, I'll do what I can to that end.

[30] Robert A. Taft, the conservative Senator from Ohio, was defeated by Dwight Eisenhower for the Republican nomination in 1952.

[31] John Perkins, proprietor of Albert Amor Ltd until his death in 1974.

[32] Frank Tilley, raconteur and wit, a specialist in early English pottery and porcelain and author of *Teapots and Tea.* Together with his wife Kathleen, he was the proprietor of a shop, just off Sloane Square and their kindness and help to collectors, however humble, is almost legendary.

Letter No.37   6th October 1952

I have something which I am sure will interest you! I bought it only a week ago and as soon as I saw it, said to myself K.C.K! It is an extremely unusual piece – I've never come across it before. A soft-paste Bristol or Bristol-Worcester Mustard Pot and Cover, delightfully painted in colours with Chinese Figures in a garden, with a Snake, rockwork and flowering plants. A boy, with a spear and standing behind a rock evidently trying to kill the snake. Overall height of the mustard pot and cover is $3\frac{3}{4}$ inches. In mint condition, with one small exception, and that is a little piece flaked off the surface at edge of cover and certainly insufficient to condemn so rare and so attractive a piece. Photograph is enclosed. Price £50.0.0. *Cat. No.9.*

Also enclosed is a photograph of a Teapot and Cover of exceptionally fine quality, and in brilliant mint condition throughout. Painted in colours and gilding, with exotic birds in the fan-shaped reserves and butterflies in circular reserves, on a bright powder blue ground relieved with gilded flowers. Price £115.0.0. *Cat. No.125.*

At the date of your letter it certainly did appear that the Republicans would surely carry everything before them and that Eisenhower's success was assured. Since then the scene has changed and the issue seems much in

doubt. Most days my *Daily Telegraph* gives pretty full reports of the activities of both sides, and as far as one can judge from them, I think it will be a neck-&-neck race between Eisenhower and Stevenson. When you write I shall be interested in your prophecy as to who will win.

The Conservative Party had returned to power when Churchill won the Election in October 1951 and in November 1952, Eisenhower won the Presidential Election for the Republicans, defeating the liberal Democrat Adlai Stevenson.

Letter No.38   20th November 1952

When the great news of your Republican Victory was announced I wanted, at once, to write sending you my hearty congratulations, but unfortunately then we were having a rather anxious time with my wife. On 26th October – her 72nd birthday she had a slight stroke and she had to be rushed off to hospital and for some days was really very ill. I am glad to say we have her home again now and that she has made an excellent recovery, but she will never be fit to take up her work of assisting me in the business as she has done hitherto. With all this upset and the consequent domestic upheaval I could not get my mind down to writing about the Election or for that matter anything else. Result is that my correspondence is 'like a cow's tail' – all behind!!

That is a wonderful S.P. Bristol Vase *(Cat. No.2)*, John Perkins is sending you. I saw it just after he bought it and he asked me whether he thought it would interest you and I did not hesitate to assure him that it was 'right up your street' and that I was quite certain you would want it. I've never seen, nor was I aware that anything like it was in existence.

Reverting to the Presidential Election, I think one of the factors which must have helped Eisenhower to victory was his promise to go to the Korean war front personally and to form his own opinion as to the position there. It seems likely that this brought him many votes.

Letter No.39   9th December 1952

In all probability this will be the last time I shall have the pleasure of offering you Antique Porcelain from Tewkesbury. For some past weeks my wife's health has been giving us cause for great anxiety. Rest seems to be the only answer and doctor is now keeping my wife to her bed where she is likely to stay for some time yet. The doctor has impressed upon me the urgency of getting my wife right away from the business at the earliest possible date and the desirability of her living where there are no stairs. This, with my own helpless state means only one thing, and that is retirement from the business. Ever since last May, my business has been in the market as a going concern and that is how I had hoped to dispose of it. That having failed my only course now is to close down by realising my stock, fixtures and fittings and let the premises for some other trade. This I shall do early in the New Year.

Taking my mind back to the year 1897 (Queen Victoria's Diamond Jubilee) when I left school, I started my business career by being apprenticed to a Watchmaker, Jeweller and Silversmith. For the first year I was paid one shilling a week, 2nd year half-a-crown a week, 3rd year five shillings a week and fourth year seven shillings and sixpence. In 1901 I got a job in the Country with a jeweller's shop in which there was an antiques department. That was in Dorchester, Dorset and I was paid £1.10.0. a week as a salesman. It was there I had my first experience with antiques. In 1908 my father set me up in business for myself as a Jeweller and Antiques Dealer and gradually I dropped right out of the modern side of the trade and confined my activities to antiques and dealt in antique watches, clocks, jewellery, silver, old Sheffield Plate and China. The latter has always held my greatest interest and finally I turned from all other antiques and became the specialist I am today.

May I take this opportunity to try to express my grateful thanks to you for the constant business you have done with me and for all your many kindnesses over the past ten or dozen years. Your support has been and is most sincerely appreciated by me.

Letter No.40   9th April 1953

A recent letter from my friend John Perkins tells me that in a letter he had from you, you kindly referred to me and mentioned that you had not heard from me for some time. I am sorry for that, but for many weeks past my affairs have been more or less upside down. My Galleries were finally closed for business on the 26th of February; and next day a representative of the very old-established firm of Auctioneers, Messrs. Bruton, Knowles & Co. of Gloucester, were here all day, going through the remains of my stock, noting down my descriptions for catalogue of sale, finally packing it and taking it away. The sale has not yet taken place, but will be very soon.

Although my business has been closed, that does not mean that I have been idle and living a life of ease in the meantime. On the contrary we have been more busily occupied than ever, if that is possible! Firstly there has been the very difficult task of finding a house in the district in which we want to live. That has entailed many journeys in my car to Hertfordshire, a hundred miles away to inspect various houses. At long last I'm glad to say we have found one which greatly pleases us, and which my son and I are in the process of buying. He and his family will be living with us. It is in Welwyn Garden City, and we hope to be leaving Tewkesbury in about a month.

I have a few bits which I think may appeal to you, especially the little bowl which I will describe first. I had you in mind when I bought it feeling pretty sure you would want it:

A very unusual Worcester Bowl. Diameter 4¾ inches. With escalloped rim and painted inside with a scroll border in red and gold. The outside with the most attractive pattern with two Quails, one sitting and the other running, pencilled in sepia on the opposite side of bowl is a rock (or it may be a tree trunk). Between the latter and the two Quails are flowering plants painted in brilliant colours. Date circa 1755. This is undoubtedly a rare piece. Price £57.10.0.   *Cat. No.166.*

A Worcester Teapot and Cover. Of fairly conventional shape. The special feature of this is that it is transfer-printed, engraved by Robert Hancock, with subjects, all of which are unrecorded. On the front a Harlequin scene from the Comedie Italien; on the reverse side, a group of sheep with a cottage in the background; and on the cover two new versions of the Parrot pecking Fruit. Mr. Cyril Cook whose book on 'The Life and Work of Robert Hancock' you most probably have, has not seen either of these subjects before, and he intends using this teapot as one of the illustrations in a new book on Robert Hancock, which he hopes to publish very shortly.[33] Date, circa 1756–57. Price £45.0.0.   *Cat. No.177.*

A Worcester Bowl. 4⅞ inches in diameter. Painted in blue under the glaze on a white ground, in the rare decoration sometimes referred to as 'The Strutting Birds' – Two quail-like birds strutting across a landscape, and with Oriental Trees. Date, Circa 1755. Price £35.0.0. *Cat. No.207.*

[33] Cyril Cook: Supplement to *The Life and Work of Robert Hancock*, London 1955.

In May 1953, Mr and Mrs Crow moved to Welwyn Garden City, where they occupied two large downstairs rooms in their son's family house. In one of these rooms, Mr Crow had his china cabinets, and from this time on his business was conducted from this room.

Letter No.41   26th August 1953

A very kind letter from you dated 17th April is on my desk still awaiting acknowledgement. In the meantime our removal from Tewkesbury to Welwyn Garden City has been accomplished. In the process it has seemed that our whole world has been turned upside down, and the whole job of turning out at Tewkesbury and settling in here has been like one long nightmare spread over no less than three months. It's all over now and the least said of it the better! At least we are fairly straight and I feel we shall be happy here.

Except for half a dozen pieces, the whole of my Tewkesbury stock was disposed of, some of it privately and the remainder by public auction, and I've no cause to complain of the financial result. Subsequently I sold the lease to the premises with some of the fixtures and fittings to a firm who are now carrying on business there as Watchmakers and Jewellers.

We did quite seriously consider my retirement from the business altogether but tho' in my 71st year and physically handicapped by the loss of leg-power my brain is just as active as ever, and in myself I feel as fit as a fiddle, so why should I retire? What is more to the point is that I don't want to retire. Buying and selling antique English porcelain has become part and parcel of my existence, and is of absorbing interest to me. In another 30 years or so, I'll be quite prepared to consider the question!

Now you know! I am carrying on dealing quietly on much the same lines as hitherto, but with this difference. From now on it will be my aim to confine my stock and my dealing to the rare and more exclusive pieces. It means that instead of having upwards of a thousand pieces in my stock to look after and keep clean and displayed in a dozen or more cabinets, I don't intend to be bothered with more than a hundred pieces at any one time, or maybe considerably fewer, but every piece will be worth having and quite out of the ordinary rut. In a private room here I have a couple of nice china cabinets and I don't intend to have more. This is not an open shop, but is a private house, in a residential quarter right away from the trading centre, and apart from export and postal trade, I can only do business by prior appointment.

One of the difficult problems in this trade is that of price, and it has always been a worry to me. In the case of, say, a bicycle, a motor car, or of any modern product one knows that there is a definite standard of price, for a certain standard of quality, and when buying one knows that the price is neither more nor less than that standard; and, no matter who he is the dealer, or middleman has his definite standard of profit. That, however, does not and never has appertained to the trade in antiques, and one cannot see how it could. All the same it does seem a haphazard way of doing business. The only fair way to my mind is to take the rough with the smooth. If one buys cheaply, one should sell cheaply, and if one buys dearly then one should sell as reasonably as one can.

Please forgive an old man's soliloquies upon a problem which if it be argued over from now till Kingdom come will never be solved! As a matter of fact it is a problem which of late is troubling me more than it has done hitherto because of my present aim to deal in only the rare bits. In trying to achieve that aim, all the time I am up against this price question. Owners of the rare bits if they know they are rare, promptly ask mad prices, and I've been putting my foot down quite firmly and have said NO.

Before turning from your letter to other matters, I do want to say how very much my wife and I appreciate and how sincerely we thank you for the very kind way in which you have expressed your good wishes for our happiness here in Welwyn Garden City. To that I would add my personal thanks for the generous and kindly terms in which you tell me that my letters have been a joy to Mrs. Klepser and to you. If that is so then you must be sure that I am the happier for having written them.

Now may I call your attention to a few pieces of Worcester, all quite recent purchases, and some of which at least will be of interest to you:

A Dessert Plate. Diameter 8¾ inches. Painted in brick-red with landscapes, including a windmill, figure of an old man, and buildings enclosed within 3 large mirror-shaped reserves, and with flowers and foliage in brick-red enclosed in vase- and other small shaped reserves, on a blue scale ground. No gilding. The whole of the scale pattern is remarkably clean and distinct. I must say quite candidly that I do not offer this piece for its aesthetic beauty. To me, at least it isn't at all beautiful. Gilding

would have improved it. Undoubtedly this is a Worcester rarity. Mark a crescent in underglaze blue. Circa 1770. Price £30.0.0. *Cat. No.156.*

A Bowl with a shaped rim. Diameter 6¼ inches. Pencilled in lilac, with a Chinese lake scene, Figures and a small house in the foreground; a Junk in full sail on the lake and mountains in the distance; trees and plants on the lakeside and birds in flight. Circa 1755. Mint state. Price £57.0.0. *Cat. No.174.*

Letter No.42   22nd September 1953

From what you tell me it's a wonderful trip you are planning. Will you go by plane or by sea? I've been looking it up in my atlas and if you go right down to the south of Brazil, beyond Rio de Janeiro, you will be covering considerably more mileage than you would on a trip to England. From what John (*Perkins*) tells me you don't reckon to be back home until well into the New Year. After this I guess you will be turning your nose up at anything so piffling as a Title Convention! Pooh!

For several years Mr Crow's health had been gradually deteriorating. His left leg had been amputated in 1951 and in February 1954, he lost his right leg. The letter that follows conveys some idea of his courage and spirit in these tragic circumstances.

Letter No.43   10th November 1954

My good friend John Perkins tells me that in a recent letter to him you very kindly made enquiries about me. This kind solicitude for me is, I assure you very much appreciated.

I wish I could say 'I'm as fit as a fiddle' but unfortunately that is far from true.

As you will remember when you and Mrs. Klepser so kindly came to see me in Tewkesbury in June 1951 I was in hospital for the amputation of my left leg. It was not very long before my right leg began to deteriorate and in October 1953 I was in hospital again for an operation which was designed to save this leg. This was, however, not successful and in February 1954 at the Middlesex Hospital I said 'Good-bye' to my right leg. Ever since then I've been confined to bed having undergone two more major operations in the meantime.

Thank heaven the surgeons have not yet decided to amputate my head and have allowed me to keep my two arms and hands intact! I have hopeful visions of being able to get out and about again in my self-propelled wheel chair in the near future, and to be driven out in my motor car.

These physical misfortunes with ten months lying idle in bed have very effectively brought my business to almost complete standstill; and what is worse have made big inroads on my slender capital financially. It behoves me therefore to get cracking again to recoup some of my losses. With this object in view I am enclosing some photographs of Dr. Wall Worcester in my stock at the moment, descriptions are as follows:

A Teabowl, Coffeecup and Saucer in an unusual version of the hop trellis pattern. Painted in colours and gilding with festoons of green leaves and red berries divided by gold scrolls. Circa 1765. Price £37.10.0. *Cat. No.108.*

A rare Finger Bowl and Stand with wavy edges lined in sepia. Transfer printed in sepia with three rare subjects engraved by Robert Hancock. These are illustrated by Cyril Cook in his 'Life and Work of Robert Hancock', Items 21 'Le Chalet des Palmes', 22 'Le Chalet Double' and 93 'River Scene'. Circa 1756/60. Price £30.0.0. *Cat. No.181.*

These pieces are in brilliant condition and I will hold them in reserve for you long enough for a cable to reach me. I shall be pleased to hear of any notable additions you have made to your collection since I have been laid up. I can very well imagine that yours must now be the finest Collection of Dr. Wall Worcester in the U.S.A.

Letter No.44   24th November 1954

Please accept my warmest thanks for your very kind and delightful letter of the 16th inst. which, needless to say, I am indeed pleased to receive.

I note you refer to the decoration of the hop trellis Teacup, Coffeecup and Saucer *(Cat. No.108)* as 'Mignonette' pattern. This somewhat intrigues me, for whilst I do know that this name has in recent years applied to this particular decoration, I always wonder why! It happens that this Old English garden flower is one of my favourites, with its delicious perfume, but there is nothing whatsoever in this particular Worcester decoration which reminds me of mignonette! Do you happen to know how it comes about that this name has been applied to this particular pattern?

Turning now to other topics in your letter, may I say at once that I greatly appreciate and that I deem it a high honour that you have asked me to write the Foreword to the Catalogue of your collection when it is exhibited at the Seattle Art Museum. I should much like to have a shot at this although it will entail a considerable amount of reference to my many books. Already, my good friend, Dr. F. Severne MacKenna has promised me assistance on any points on which I may be in doubt. I think I had better in the first place send you a rough draft for you to approve or otherwise, but I doubt whether I will be able to complete this much before the New Year because in my present physical state I soon get tired and my brain gets fuzzy!

I'm glad you have commissioned John (*Perkins*) to bid for you at the Lady Heilbron Sale[34] on 7th December. I do not of course know which are the lots you have earmarked but one can easily prophecy that prices will run high. Looking through the catalogue fairly makes my mouth water! If only I had the capital there are many lots I would like to buy myself, but alas that cannot be!

I envy you those two plates, Lots No. 84 and 85 *(Cat. Nos 147 and 148)*. I reckon them to be the most interesting and desirable pieces amongst the lots from Mr. Marshall's collection which was sold at Sotheby's on 27th Jan.[35] The monochrome decoration is rare. I saw all of it at Mr. Marshall's house some time ago.

P.S. I'm glad too that you secured that fine s.p. Bristol Vase, Lot 19. *Cat. No.1.*

[34] A small collection of fine quality Worcester, sold at Sotheby's on 7th December 1954.

[35] Mr Crow is refering to the Sotheby's sale of 27th January 1953 which contained 100 lots from the Rissik Marshall collection. These included many superb pieces and Mrs Klepser was able to make several significant purchases including the early vase, *Cat. No.1*, and the two Giles' plates, *Cat. Nos 147 & 148.*

Letter No.45   17th December 1954

The delay in this acknowledgement to your letter dated 30th November is due in some measure to the time I am spending in writing the 'Foreword' for your catalogue!

May I offer you my hearty congratulations upon your purchase at Sotheby's on the 7th inst.[36] The yellow scale cream jug, though very desirable was pretty hot at £420 (*Cat No.93*), but the last lot Claret ground Tea Bowl and Saucer was fantastic at £300!

Thankyou for your comments on the 'Mignonette' pattern which I have read with great interest. This decoration will be mentioned in my 'Foreword'. The latter is well under way but it is a bigger job than I had anticipated. However, I am very much enjoying it.

I mentioned that Dr. F.S. MacKenna has promised to read through my rough draft and now my old friend Mr. H.R. Marshall has kindly undertaken to do likewise.

My wife joins with me in wishing Mrs. Klepser and you a very merry Christmas and a happy and prosperous New Year.

[36] From the Lady Heilbron Collection.

Letter No. 46   1st March 1955

It is difficult to find words which express at all adequately my thanks for your kind letter of 25th February to hand this morning and my grateful appreciation of your very generous check you have sent as an honorarium for my Foreword to your catalogue. I do indeed thank Mrs. Klepser and you most sincerely.

I am very glad that the Foreword meets with your approval and that you are so manifestly pleased with it. I am sorry that it was so lengthy and can well understand that some abridgement may be necessary. If it would be of any assistance to you, I shall be only too pleased to read the printer's proofs and to make any corrections thereto. It is my experience that all printers are liable to make the most astonishing blunders! Thankyou also for so kindly saying that you will send me several copies of the catalogue when it comes off the press. There are quite a number of folk over here to whom I should much like to send it, including of course, Mr. & Mrs. Rissik Marshall, Dr. F. Severne MacKenna, Cyril Cook, George Savage,[37] Mr. C.W. Dyson Perrins and many members of The English Ceramic Circle who are old friends of mine.

I hear that at Sotheby's today, a Worcester Teapot, Lot No.103[38] *(Cat. No.37)* was 'knocked down' to John Perkins, and I presume this is the piece to which you refer in your 'P.S.' I note that Sotheby's say of this Teapot 'The only other recorded example in the V.&A. Museum'.

I have noted that you will not be interested in purchasing additional pieces of Worcester for the present. If, later on, you should start buying again perhaps you would let me know. In the meantime I will not worry you with any photographs, unless I should find something which is exceptionally fine and rare.

Alas, my own dealing days are nearly over! For purely physical reasons I shall never again be seen in Sotheby's or Christie's, or any other Auction Rooms. I hope however, to continue quietly, buying and selling bits here and there, if only as a matter of interest.

From memories of years gone by I can and do derive much enjoyment, and when I visualise the many truly fine pieces which have passed through my hands. Mr. Dyson Perrins has been a wonderful friend to me – the old gentleman now in his 92nd year, just 20 years my senior – wrote me a lovely letter which I shall always treasure, in which he thanked me for the interest I had taken in his Collection over so many years. I remember his delight when I first took him that magnificent set of three Vases, signed by Donaldson. He gave me £850 for them. Why today they would make more like £3,500 at Sotheby's.

Well I must not weary you with my chatter. Once more, I thank you with all my heart for your great kindness to me.

[37] George Savage, author of several books on antique porcelain.

[38] From the first portion of the sale of the Rev C.J. Sharp Collection.

The 'Exhibition Catalogue of the Klepser Collection of Early Worcester Porcelain', was published by the Seattle Art Museum in the Spring of 1955, with an introduction by T. Leonard Crow, of six pages. The catalogue consisted of 200 items and had 23 black and white illustrations. The Klepser Collection was exhibited at the Seattle Art Museum from 6th April until 3rd May 1955.

Letter No. 47   12th April 1955

Thank you very much for your kind letter, dated April 5th and which arrived on Good Friday the 8th inst. I would like to congratulate you on having accomplished so much in so little time, in organising your exhibition. I think it is marvellous that you have, despite such setbacks as illness, got all details settled, catalogues printed and everything in train before the opening date.

It is very gratifying to me, not only to know that my Foreword has met with your approval, but also that some of the members in your Ceramic Circle have enjoyed reading it. I am glad to know too that it has contributed to the success of your catalogue.

This afternoon John Perkins has read to me over the telephone, the very nice letter he received from you this

morning, telling us that a bunch of red carnations had duly been delivered to Mrs. Klepser and had arrived on the opening day of the exhibition. Also that some pieces from your collection had been televised. From this it is clear that the exhibition is creating quite a stir in public circles, which is by no means to be surprised at. That the museum authorities have displayed the collection in no less than eighteen large cabinets is a good indication as to its extent, and such a display of fine Worcester Porcelain could do no other than attract widespread attention, and draw thousands of people from all parts of the U.S.A. How I wish I could fly to Seattle to see it all for myself, but for me it is quite impossible now. Had this happened, say five years ago I would have seriously considered such a trip and perhaps would have persuaded John to accompany me!

Letter No.48   25th April 1955

I think you have made a splendid job of the catalogue. I am delighted with it. Your Preface is interesting and to the point. I thank you and Mrs. Klepser most sincerely for the kind reference to myself. I think you realise that, quite apart from the business aspect – and for which I am ever grateful – your collection and its formation has always been one of my personal interests and any contribution I may have made towards its success, and that of your Exhibition, has afforded me the utmost pleasure.

The illustrations are all very good, cleanly printed and well selected. It must have been considerably difficult to decide which pieces to illustrate and which not to. In fact the whole catalogue reflects great credit upon yourself and its producers. It appears you are exhibiting less than half your entire collection, which must run into about 500 items.[39] My nurse is waiting to put me to bed now. Fancy a 72-year old having to be put to bed by a nurse, as though he were in his infancy!

[39] Mr Crow greatly overestimated the size of the Klepser Collection at the time of the Exhibition. At around this period, however, Mr Klepser had disposed of a considerable portion of his blue and white wares.

Letter No.49   7th May 1955

My very best thanks to you for your kind letter dated 3rd May, received today; also for the package of fifteen more catalogues delivered here on the 5th inst. Folk to whom I have already sent the catalogues all express enthusiastic approval; and Mr. A.J.B. Kiddell[40] seems particularly pleased with it.

Finding specimens for your collection has been a great enjoyment to me over the past dozen or so years, and I recall my excitement whenever able to track down a piece from one of the named services. I note from your catalogue Preface that you still lack three of these – a state of affairs which I really must try again to remedy. The 'Kew' I think it quite hopeless to expect, because practically every known piece was bought by the late Queen Mary, and it is quite unlikely that her collection will ever be on the market. Of the 'Enniskillen' and the 'Sebright' services there must be some specimens somewhere. Anyway I am determined to make a big effort to find them. The British Antique Dealers' Ass'n publishes a 'House Journal' entitled BADA which is distributed exclusively amongst the Members of the Association. They number about 550 of the leading antique dealers in England, Wales, Scotland and Ireland. This journal has a few advertising pages which are headed 'GOODS WANTED' and I will insert an advert for pieces from these three services, and see whether any is forthcoming. It hadn't occurred to me until now that this might succeed where other means have failed.

My wife and I both chuckled when we read in your letter that you and your Title Officer were 'all ready to start for Walla Walla'! What a queer name that sounds. To me it savours of those places one reads about in the stories of 'The Wild West' in the late 19th Century!

[40] The late A.J.B. Kiddell of Sotheby's, President of the English Ceramic Circle and greatly respected for his wide knowledge of English pottery and porcelain.

Letter No.50   25th July 1955

I enclose photographs of two of my latest acquisitions of Worcester porcelain, viz; a Teacup and Saucer, and a Christening Mug.

The former is unquestionably rare. I have never seen this decoration hitherto and the only one I have ever seen is in Mr. C.W. Dyson Perrins' Collection. Careful search through the many pieces illustrated in Mr. Marshall's book[41] fails to reveal a specimen, from which it may be presumed that he hasn't one.

Painted in colours and gilding, with birds perched on branches, with purple wings and vari-coloured breasts, within a wide border of mottled green relieved with gilded floral sprays and gilded edges. Marked with crossed swords and numeral 9 in underglaze blue. Circa 1765–70. I would say outside decorated at Giles' Studio, though not by the 'ruffled-bird painter' because these birds are by no means ruffled. The rare feature is the mottled green ground which is so seldom found. Price £52.10.0. *Cat. No.152.*

[41] *Coloured Worcester Porcelain of the First Period*, Newport 1954.

Letter No.51   19th August 1955

When John Perkins advertised that Bristol-Worcester Cream Boat, in *The Antique Collector* I at once phoned him to tell him that this is one of the pieces that you have been looking for for a very long time, and I'm delighted now to hear from John that you have bought it. Unless I am mistaken, I should say that it is identically the same in its moulding and colouring as the one which turned up in Sotheby's about 5 years ago and which was marked 'Wigornia'. I can now cross this item off my list of 'Mr. Klepser Wants'. *Cat. No.21.*

Letter No.52   16th September 1955

Though seemingly insignificant, the small soft-paste Bristol Wine Cup, of which I enclose a photograph, is very charming, apart from its interest as a piece of early date. It is photographed in exactly its actual size. Barely

2 inches high. Fluted body. Painted in colours with Chinese flowering plants, and with border around the top which I believe matches the borders on that pair of Oval Bowls which you bought from me years ago.

In years gone by I have had at different times perhaps a half dozen of these little cups but never with a saucer. Price £15.0.0. *Cat. No.35.*

Letter No.53   21st October 1955

I am enclosing a photograph of a Worcester Bowl which I have just bought believing it a rarity. Mr. Marshall confirms this and says he considers it to be 'extremely rare'. Back in 1940 he bought a 2-handled cup & saucer with this decoration, for £6.0.0. – fancy that! Description is as follows: A Worcester porcelain Bowl. Period of Dr. Wall, with fluted body. Diameter 6½ inches. Circa 1765–70. Painted in colours and gilding with an unusual version of the trellis pattern, in red and green; and with a scale pattern border outlined in black on a bright turquoise blue and lined with gold. In brilliant condition. Price, £57.10.0. *Cat. No.106.*

Through you inviting me to write the introduction to your catalogue, I am becoming quite an author on Ceramics! The Editor of 'BADA' – a small magazine which circulates exclusively and privately amongst the Members of the British Antique Dealer's Asso'n – has invited me to contribute an article for publication in that magazine, leaving the choice of subject to me. It has been duly completed and submitted to the Editor, who wrote saying it has made him laugh, and that he will publish it in full. The article is written in semi-humorous vein though with serious intent. My title is 'Candid Comments on Certain Ceramic Cognomens'! It commences with: 'If I were Pope of Rome, I would excommunicate all antique dealers and others, who still persist in mis-describing Tea Bowls as handleless cups . . .'

Letter No.54   13th April 1956

Doubtless you duly received my cable a week ago which was as follows:

'Klepser, Main 6133, Seattle. Through my advertisements have bought pair Enniskillen plates brilliant condition one hundred and fifty pounds May I send? Letter will follow kind regards   Crow.'

I was quite surprised when a man living in a suburb of London telephoned me and said that he had seen my advertisement in 'The Connoisseur' last December for a piece from the Worcester 'Enniskillen' Service. He went on to say that he had three plates he wished to dispose of. I first had the plates on approval, and I at once realised that, though similar in some respects, they are not as the plates illustrated by Hobson, (Pl. LV. Fig. 2), nor as the saucer-dish described, but not illustrated in the Drane Catalogue No.782.

Before actually buying the plates I consulted my good friend Frank Tilley, whose judgement on all ceramic matters is very sound, and in his opinion these three plates are definitely of the 'Enniskillen' pattern. He says Robert Drane's description is quite incorrect and that the Enniskillen Service was painted with Fruit and Insects only, without any Flowers. I then followed my rule 'When in doubt where Worcester porcelain is concerned ask Mr. H.R. Marshall!'. I telephoned him and he very kindly came to see these plates. As soon as he saw them he said that they were the true Enniskillen decoration and precisely matching a plate in his collection, which he considers to be from the Enniskillen Service.

They are 8½ inches in diameter. Both plates in the pair I am offering you are quite perfect – one of them shows slight 'fritting' on the back, which is of course as it left the kiln originally. All include a large butterfly measuring approximately 3½ inches in length, from one wing tip to the other tip, and two beetles. London decorated by Giles. Date circa 1760–65. Price for the pair £150. *Cat. No.160.*

Letter No.55   19th April 1956

It is kind of you to enquire about my last operation. It pulled me down a bit at the time but I've forgotten about that now!

Through writing the introduction to your Exhibition Catalogue I've got quite into the way of writing articles on Ceramic subjects. All my spare time in the last couple of months has been given over to the composition of an article the title of which is 'Quaker Pioneers in The English Ceramic Industry'. I am hoping this will be accepted for publication in one of the Quaker periodicals. It is quite surprising to find how many Quakers were concerned in the early days of English porcelain and pottery. Thomas Fryc, who was the first to make English porcelain, viz Bow in 1743–44, was a Quaker. William Cookworthy, the first to produce hard-paste in this country was a Quaker, as also were Richard Champion of Bristol, and William Stephens the Plymouth and Bristol decorator. Benjamin Lund was a Quaker, who is virtually the founder of the Worcester Co. Likewise Richard Holdship of Worcester. So one can go on naming Quakers, one after another who were eminent in the English Ceramic field. If and when my article is in print I'll send you a copy.[42]

[42] This article was published in BADA, the quarterly journal of The British Antique Dealers' Association Ltd., July 1956.

Letter No.56   20th April 1956

I have bought a pair of 8½ inch Worcester plates, with very unusual decoration, and at a most reasonable cost compared with the average high prices of today. A photograph of one of the pair is enclosed.

They are painted in gold monochrome, with a formal flower in the centre, surrounded by leaves which extend to the escalloped rim, on an all-over ground of dark blue. The effect of this is very striking. Both plates perfect. Price £50.0.0. the pair.   *Cat. No.133.*

It is illustrated, plate 24, fig. 538, in 'Coloured Worcester, First Period' by H.R. Marshall. The latter tells me that these plates of mine are only the third specimens of this decoration he has come across, since he

bought his plate, about 15 years ago from the Wallace-Elliot Collection.

I venture to hope that this pair of plates will interest you.

Letter No.57   14th September 1956

I am sorry that I have nothing of sufficient importance to offer you at the moment, but one never knows what may come to light – perhaps a very nice piece of scale blue! Whatever it may be I hope it is something I can offer at pre-inflation price. The very high prices now ruling in this Country, for quite ordinary goods are gradually killing my trade. Same applies also to other sections of the antique trade. A set of 8 Hepplewhite chairs which a dozen years ago were valued at £120 was sold last week for a thousand guineas. The normal every day collector can't afford these fantastic prices.

Reprint from The Antique Collector, June 1957.

'In February 1958 Mr. T. Leonard Crow of Ceramic House, Welwyn Garden City, will enter on his Golden Jubilee Year of business as an antique dealer on his own account (1908–58). He left school in 1897 in his fourteenth year, and was apprenticed to the trade of restoring inter alia old clocks, watches, silver and jewellery. In 1901, after a breakdown due to working long hours in unhealthy conditions, he became a salesman to a jeweller and antique dealer in Dorset. There he became friendly with the late Frederick Bradbury and the late W.E. Hurcomb, who both enthused him with a love for antiques.

In the course of his long career, Mr. Crow has become a Liveryman and Freeman of the City of London; was President of the Guildford Chamber of Trade, 1926–7; is a life honorary member of the Glasgow Art Gallery and Museums Association; served for ten years on the Council of The National Association of Goldsmiths, Inc.; and has recently completed another ten years on the council of B.A.D.A. Ltd. Though entering his seventy-fifth year, Mr. Crow's services as a specialist in antique porcelain are gladly at the disposal of his many friends in the world of collecting and dealing.'

Letter No.58   12th August 1957

Looking back over my files I find that my last letter to you was dated October 1956, so it's high time to write to you again. In the meantime I trust that all is well with Mrs. Klepser and your good self.

Ten days ago I had a great treat, when my son took me in the car to Luton Hoo to see the Lady Ludlow Collection of Worcester and Chelsea. When you were over here in 1951, you may have seen it, though I'm not sure whether it has been open to the public as long as that. The Worcester is not as extensive as I had thought, though it makes up for quantity by superb quality. I don't know when I have seen such fine pieces of yellow and yellow scale ground in one collection before. The pink scale too is magnificent. The curator of the Luton Hoo Museum, kindly conducted me round himself, and has promised to come to see me here for a chat.

Since you and I last corresponded the Ceramic World has lost Dr. F. Severne MacKenna,[43] the sale of whose collection at Sotheby's was a great surprise to the whole trade. I attended the sale as a matter of interest and bought a few pieces. It is the only auction sale I have been to in the past six years, owing to physical handicaps. A great deal of the MacKenna Collection was bought from me at prices vastly less and indeed out of all proportion to those realised at the sale. Here is one example:– a yellow-ground sauceboat which I sold to Dr. M., in 1943 for £7.10.0, was bought by Mr. Weinberg[44] for £290. I call that sheer madness.

[43] Dr. MacKenna had ceased collecting porcelain, and his collection was sold at Sothebys on 12th March 1957. He remained however in good health and now lives in the north of Scotland.

[44] Proprietor at that time of the Antique Porcelain Company of London and New York.

Letter No.59   16th February 1959

I find that there is still some confusion in the minds of Collectors and dealers, in the use of the terms 'Lund's Bristol' and 'Bristol-Worcester'. Some folk say that the two are synonymous, and that they mean one and the same thing. That in my humble opinion is quite wrong. I consider that a piece can only be described as 'Lund's Bristol' when there is no room for doubting that it was produced at the Bristol Factory under the proprietorship of Benjamin Lund and his partners and prior to 1752 when the factory was taken over by Worcester.

The term 'Bristol-Worcester' implies a doubt as to whether a piece was produced in Bristol or whether in Worcester, in its very early days. Looking at the photograph of the Bowl[45] I have sent you, one would say going by the delicacy of the moulding and of the decoration, that it is Lund's Bristol; BUT turn the bowl upside down and look only at the base, it is at once seen that there is a shrinkage or recession in the glaze which is almost invariably found on first period Worcester, but *not* on Lund's Bristol.

So, who can say whether a piece was made in Bristol or in Worcester when it has features which are identifiable by each factory? These are the pieces which I think should be rightly termed 'Bristol-Worcester'. I rather like sometimes to ponder over such little problems as this, but I hope my lecture has not wearied you!

For all I know to the contrary, you may be away from home at one of those 'Pesky' Title Conventions! (That adjective is yours not mine!) Wherever you may be I hope Mrs. Klepser and your good self are very well and happy.

[45] Mr Crow sent a photograph and description of this bowl but Mr Klepser did not purchase it.

Letter No.60   28th February 1959

Thank you so much for your very kind and interesting letter, dated 24th inst. and received yesterday. You say I 'must be something of a mind reader'! As, however I cannot claim to have any such mystic powers, I had better explain that it was our mutual friend John who told me several weeks ago that you are confining your purchase now to Lund's Bristol.

There is an enormous lot of sheer nonsense about what is called silvershape, in relation to porcelain. Some years ago I discussed this problem with Tom Lumley (of Thomas Lumley Ltd., Dealers in antique silver). Tom is admitted to be one of our leading authorities on antique silver. Apart from his business he and his wife collect antique English Porcelain as a hobby. So Tom Lumley has a very sound knowledge of Silver; and is by no means ignorant on the subject of Porcelain. When we discussed this he completely agreed with me that fully 75% of the pieces of porcelain illustrated in books and described as 'silver shape' bear no more relation to known pieces of 18th century silver (or earlier) than have the legs of my table! It is agreed that Sprimont was a silversmith before he made Chelsea porcelain and that he did in fact produce a few pieces of Chelsea which in general shape bore some resemblance to pieces of his silver. This is made clear in a paper read by the late Dr. Bellamy Gardener to the English Ceramic Circle (*Transactions* Vol. 2, No. 6) in which a comparatively few pieces of Chelsea were copied from Sprimont's silver. As far as I am aware this is the only documentary evidence we have of any English Porcelain of the 18th century producing pieces of silver-shape; yet nearly every author of books on ceramics continues to talk of silver-shapes as glibly as though such things grew on trees!

Your trip through Japan and around the rim of the Pacific to New Zealand sounds wonderful. It seems to me that by now, one way and another in all your trips you have nearly conquered the whole World; and very soon you will be thinking of flying to the Moon! If you find any first period Worcester there perhaps you will let me know! I am simply delighted to know that there is a prospect of your coming to see us in the fairly near future.

Letter No.61   5th April 1960

Enclosed herewith is a photograph of a First-period Worcester porcelain Dessert Plate, with a rare decoration. Description is as follows: Diameter 8¼ inches. With escalloped and fluted border, with gilt dentil rim. Painted in colours with exotic birds, perched on the ground in a landscape setting, with misty trees in the background.

The painting on this plate is exceptionally good; and the misty effect in the trees in background is typical of Fidele Duvivier's hand. In fact the whole decoration might conceivably be his work.

A very similar plate is illustrated in H.R. Marshall's book, see Plate 42, Fig. 873. Date, circa 1760. Price £80., including insurance etc. This plate is in brilliant and perfect condition throughout; an outstanding feature is its exceptional fine quality.[46]

If I may send this to you, perhaps you would kindly cable me to that effect.

I shall be interested to hear your opinion of my article 'Good-bye Doctor Wall' a copy of which is enclosed. Before sending this for publication in *The Antique Collector*, I sent the typescript to Mr. H.R. Marshall, asking him to read it and to make any amendment to it he may think desirable. Only five days before his death, Mr. Marshall returned the typescript with a covering note in which he thought the whole article was excellent, and that he would not alter it in any way whatever. Since then Mrs. Marshall has told me that her late husband was delighted with my article; and she has very kindly sent a copy of it to each of the Members of The English Ceramic Circle.

You will, I am sure, be sorry to know that my Dear Wife has passed away. She died suddenly, but very peacefully, on the 10th March, in her 80th year.

[46] Mr Klepser did not purchase this plate.

Letter No.62   11th May 1960

I hope my letter dated 5th April, and a photograph of the plate reached you, but as I have not heard from you, I have concluded that you are away from home and perhaps attending another of those 'pesky Title Conventions'!

However that may be, and wherever Mrs. Klepser and your are, I hope you are both well and happy.

I am holding that Worcester Plate until I hear from you and in the meantime have not shown it to anyone else. It is so exceptionally attractive, that I feel it ought to be in your Collection.

Doubtless you have read my article 'Good-bye Doctor Wall' in the February issue of *The Antique Collector* but you may not have heard that one of the sequels to it is that Sothebys have decided to omit the name of Dr. Wall from all their catalogue descriptions. Naturally I am very pleased by this result.

Trusting to hear from you ere long, and with kindest remembrances to you both.

Letter No.63   28th June 1960

Thank you so much for your very kind letter of June 21st. I was aware that you have been concentrating on Lund's Bristol porcelain but I did not realise that you had given up collecting First Period Worcester. My impression was that you were still open to buy exceptionally interesting pieces of Worcester, and when I bought this very fine Dessert Plate I said to myself 'Mr. Klepser will like that' and that is why I sent you a photograph of it! It may well be that my memory is at fault. It has been functioning 77 years, and is failing somewhat now. Please accept my sincere apology for troubling you with this matter when you are so busily occupied with Title Insurance Affairs.

I am glad to hear that you have noticed my advertisements, from time to time in the Collector's Magazines. Yes, I still carry on business in a small way, though it is not a tithe of my trade in Tewkesbury, but I don't want to retire altogether. Doing business provides me with an interest in life, and without it I should be like a proverbial 'fish out of water'.

You say you doubt if you will get away before late this fall, which presumably means October or thereabouts. Is there any likelihood of your visiting Great Britain this time? In that case I hope you will include Welwyn Garden City in your itinerary. Your last visit was in 1951, when you stayed at Stratford-on-Avon.

With kindest regards and warmest good wishes to you both.

Leonard Crow died peacefully on 6th December 1960, aged 77.

Selected Bibliography

Books

Barrett, Franklin A.: *Worcester Porcelain and Lund's Bristol* (2nd ed.). London 1966

Branyan, Lawrence, Neal French and John Sandon: *Worcester Blue and White Porcelain, 1751–1790*. London 1981

Coke, Gerald: *In Search of James Giles*. Wingham 1983

Cook, Cyril: *The Life and Work of Robert Hancock*. London 1948

Cook, Cyril: Supplement to *The Life and Work of Robert Hancock*. London 1955

Dixon, J.L.: *English Porcelain of the Eighteenth Century*. London 1953

Fisher, Stanley: *English Blue and White Porcelain of the Eighteenth Century*. London 1947

Gabszewicz, Anton and Geoffrey Freeman: *Bow Porcelain*. London 1982

Godden, Geoffrey A.: *Caughley and Worcester Porcelains, 1775–1800*. London 1969

Hobson, R.L.: *Worcester Porcelain*. London 1910

Hobson, R.L.: *Catalogue of the Frank Lloyd Collection of Worcester Porcelain of the Wall Period, British Museum*. London 1923 (Referred to in catalogue as *op.cit.*)

Honey, W.B.: *Old English Porcelain* (2nd ed.). London 1948

MacKenna, F. Severne: *Worcester Porcelain*. Leigh-on-Sea 1950

Rissik Marshall, H.: *Coloured Worcester Porcelain of the First Period*. Newport 1954

Sandon, Henry: *Worcester Porcelain*. London 1969

Savage, George: *Eighteenth Century English Porcelain*. London 1950

Soil de Moriamé and Delplace: *Porcelaine de Tournay*. 1937

Spero, Simon: *The Price Guide to Eighteenth Century English Porcelain*. Woodbridge 1970 (Referred to in catalogue as *op. cit.*)

Tilley, Frank: *Teapots and Tea*. Newport 1957

Watney, Bernard: *English Blue and White Porcelain of the Eighteenth Century*. London 1963

Selected Catalogues and Articles

Amor Ltd, Albert: Exhibition Catalogues
Worcester Porcelain 1751–1784. 1973
Dr. John Wall 1708–1776. 1976
James Giles, China Painter 1718–1780. 1977
The Golden Age. 1980
Worcester Porcelain; The First Decade 1751–1761. 1981
The Elegant Porcelain of James Giles. 1983

Capell, G.W.: 'Rare Porcelain Decorated by Robert Hancock'. *Connoisseur*, November 1962

Clarke, S.M.: 'Marks on Overglaze-Decorated First Period Worcester Porcelain'. A Statistical Study, 1973
'Notes on "Wigornia" Type Creamboats'. *The American Ceramic Circle Bulletin*, No.3, 1980

Cooke, Nigel: 'Dated Blue and White Worcester Porcelain 1751–1780'. *The Antique Collectors' Club Magazine*, October, 1984

Emerson, J.: *The Collectors: Early European Ceramics and Silver*. Exhibition Catalogue 1978

English Ceramic Circle: Exhibition Catalogues 1948 and 1977

Handley, Joseph: 'Robert Hancock and G.P. Panini'. *English Ceramic Circle Transactions*, Volume 11, Part 2, 1982

Klaber & Klaber: *Oriental Influences on European Porcelain*. Exhibition Catalogue 1978

Mallet, J.V.G.: 'A Problematical Group of Eighteenth Century Porcelain'. *English Ceramic Circle Transactions*, Volume 9, Part 1, 1970

Manchester City Art Gallery: *Transfer Printed Worcester Porcelain*. Exhibition Catalogue 1966

Rissik Marshall, H.: 'Notes on the Origins of Worcester Decoration'. *English Ceramic Circle Transactions*, Volume 4, Part 3, 1956

Seattle Art Museum: *Catalogue of the Klepser Collection of Worcester Porcelain*, Seattle 1955

Spero, Simon: 'Lund's Bristol and Early Worcester Porcelain'. *The Antique Dealer and Collectors' Guide*, June 1977

Tait, Hugh: 'James Rogers'. *Connoisseur*, April 1963

Watney, Bernard and Robert Charlston: 'Petitions for Patents'. *English Ceramic Circle Transactions*, Volume 6, Part 2, 1966

Glossary

Atelier	A studio or workshop.
Banded Hedge	A decorative subject associated with porcelain decorated in the Kakiemon style, depicting a hedgerow usually accompanied by a squirrel and flying birds.
Bleu Céleste	Clear sky-blue, sometimes used as a ground colour.
Bleu de Roi	A rich enamel blue first developed at Vincennes and later used at Sèvres.
Bombé	Convex. A term principally used in connection with furniture.
Bough Pot	A pierced pot or vase for containing sprays of flowering shrubs.
Bouquet	An assortment of flowers arranged in a bunch.
Caillouté	From caillou, pebble. A decorative motif of meshed oval forms devised at Sèvres in about 1752.
Camaïeu	Painting executed in one colour only.
Cartouche	A term normally used loosely to describe an oval frame decorated with scrollwork.
Caudle Cup	A covered cup with either one or two handles for drinking caudle, a warm gruel.
Chinoiserie	European decoration inspired by oriental sources, especially Chinese.
Ciselé	Gilding "tooled" into decorative patterns.
Clobbering	Overpainting in enamels on previously decorated porcelain.
Coffee Can	A straight-sided cylindrical cup, normally about 2½ inches high and shaped like a mug.
Delftware	Tin-glazed earthenware made at Delft in Holland.
Diaper	Literally an ornamental diamond or lozenge pattern.
Dry Blue	A brilliant tone of overglaze blue, normally used in monochrome.
Dry Mustard Pot	For containing dry unprepared mustard.
Earthenware	The English term for pottery that is not vitrified, i.e. all pottery except stoneware.
Eggshell	A type of porcelain so thin as to resemble an eggshell.
Faïence	Tin-glazed earthenware, especially that made in France, Germany and Scandinavia.
Famille Verte	The category of Chinese decoration with a brilliant green enamel as the predominant colour, mainly dating from the K'ang Hsi dynasty (1662–1772).
Festoon	Garland of flowers, leaves or drapery hanging in a natural curve and suspended from the two ends.
Finial	The terminal ornament on such objects as teapots, coffeepots and vases.
Fire Crack	Damage sustained at the time of manufacture.
Garniture de Cheminée	A set of three, five or seven porcelain vases to decorate the mantelshelf of the chimney-piece.
Ho-ho Bird	A phoenix incorporated into several Kakiemon designs.
Hop-trellis pattern	A pattern of trelliswork entwined with hop-vines, originally devised at Sèvres and later adapted at Worcester.
Imari	Japanese porcelain made at Arita from the beginning of the eighteenth century onwards and shipped from the nearby port of Imari.

Kakiemon	A Japanese potter associated with a distinctive style of decoration much imitated in Europe.
Kylin	A Chinese monster, halfway between a lion and a dog.
Matt	Having a dull finish; not glossy.
Mon	A circular 'badge' enclosing a stylised flower or insect.
Monochrome	Decoration in one colour.
Oeil-de-perdrix	Literally, partridge eye. A pattern developed at Vincennes and Sèvres in either enamel colours or gilding.
Ogee	A shape or handle formed in a double curve as in the letter S.
Ozier or Osier	A willow twig used in basketry.
Palette	A group of colours peculiar to an artist or a factory.
Pencil	A very fine brush.
Polychrome	Decoration in two or more colours.
Pounce Pot	A pot with a perforated cover for sprinkling pounce, a fine powder of gum sandarac. Sometimes part of an inkstand.
Prunus	A white plum blossom.
Quatrefoil	A shape having four equal lobes or foils.
S-scroll	A decorative pattern basically in the form of the letter S.
Saucer Dish	A shallow dish of saucer shape, usually a component of a tea service.
Scale Ground	A ground pattern composed of overlapping scales, either in underglaze blue or in overglaze enamels.
Scalloped	Having a continuous series of segments of a circle, resembling the edge of a scallop shell.
Sparrow-beak	A pouring lip resembling the pointed beak of a sparrow. Associated particularly with creamjugs.
Spoon Tray	A narrow tray used to contain a hot or wet teaspoon when not in use. A component part of many tea services.
Strap-handle	A loop handle which is flat like a narrow strap.
Sucrier	The French term for a sugar bowl.
Teacaddy	A covered container for dry tea, for use on the tea-table in conjunction with a teapot and a kettle.
Throwing	The process of shaping ceramic ware on a rotating potter's wheel.
Thumb rest	A flat area at the top of a handle, usually found on sauceboats and creamboats.
Tin glaze	A glaze whitened and opacified by the addition of tin oxide.
Underglaze	Decoration applied to the unglazed ceramic body.
Waster	A broken or defective pot cast aside upon a waster-heap at some stage during the process of manufacture.

General Index

Index of Patterns